	System	Element
Flexibility matrix	$[a]$	$[\alpha]$
*ij*th element	a_{ij}	α_{ij}
Stiffness matrix	$[k]$	$[\kappa]$
*ij*th element	k_{ij}	κ_{ij}
Force vector	$\{F\}$	$\{P\}$
Displacement vector	$\{u\}$	$\{\delta\}$

MATRIX COMPUTER ANALYSIS OF STRUCTURES

Moshe F. Rubinstein

Associate Professor of Engineering
University of California, Los Angeles

Prentice-Hall, Inc., Englewood Cliffs, N.J.

PRENTICE-HALL INTERNATIONAL, INC., *London*
PRENTICE-HALL OF AUSTRALIA, PTY. LTD., *Sydney*
PRENTICE-HALL OF CANADA, LTD., *Toronto*
PRENTICE-HALL OF INDIA (PRIVATE) LTD., *New Delhi*
PRENTICE-HALL OF JAPAN, INC., *Tokyo*

Current Printing (last digit):
10   9   8   7   6   5   4   3

Library of Congress Catalog Card Number 66-24985
Printed in the United States of America
56548C

PRENTICE-HALL INTERNATIONAL SERIES
IN ENGINEERING OF THE PHYSICAL SCIENCES

PRENTICE-HALL, INC.
PRENTICE-HALL INTERNATIONAL, INC., UNITED KINGDOM AND EIRE
PRENTICE-HALL OF CANADA, LTD., CANADA

PRENTICE-HALL SERIES IN
ENGINEERING OF THE PHYSICAL SCIENCES

James B. Reswick and Warren M. Rohsenow, *editors*

To My Parents

לֹהוֹרי שרה ושלמה רובינשטיין

PREFACE

This book was developed in teaching courses in structural analysis during the past five years. Most of the material in the book has been used in a yearly course ("Use of Computers in Structural Engineering") for practicing engineers offered by the University of California Engineering Extension. The material, except for Chapters 1, 4, and 5, has also been used in a one-semester graduate course in advanced structural analysis. Portions of the first nine chapters and parts of Chapter 11 have been used in a senior one-semester course in structural analysis.

The book has two main objectives:

1. The Practicing Structural Engineer

   To acquaint the practicing structural engineer with the fundamental concepts of digital computers and enable him to develop, through independent study, working knowledge of modern matrix methods in structures so that he can exploit the capabilities of the computer

2. The Student

   To provide a textbook in modern methods of structural analysis for a one-semester course

To accomplish these two objectives, the book assumes no prior knowledge of computers or matrix algebra and develops all the necessary fundamentals in the theory of structures.

A brief survey of the book's content follows:

Chapter 1 introduces the fundamental concepts of digital computers which should prove sufficient background for the reader to embark on a program of independent study of an automatic programming language.

Chapters 2 and 3 introduce important modern concepts and characteristics of structures and show the need for matrix notation and matrix algebra.

Chapter 4 develops the fundamental tools of matrix algebra used in subsequent chapters, and gives examples relating to structural analysis and computer programs to manipulate matrices in structural analysis.

Chapter 5 discusses the solution of linear equations, which is one of the most important parts of structural analysis and of numerical analysis in general.

Chapter 6 deals with energy concepts from the modern point of view of matrix methods.

Chapter 7 develops transformations which serve to synthesize the characteristics of a system, as well as force and displacement transformations in general.

Chapters 8 and 9 give a complete parallel development of the *flexibility* and *stiffness* methods, including some special topics, such as an efficient method and associated computer program for synthesizing the stiffness matrix of a structure.

Chapters 10 and 11 develop methods for dealing with large systems. Chapter 10 is devoted to analysis by substructures and by recursion; Chapter 11, to analysis by iteration (including a computer program).

Chapter 12 extends and applies the tools developed earlier to the analysis of plates and shells.

The material presented is equally suited to courses in modern structural analysis in departments of civil, mechanical, aeronautical, or aerospace engineering.

As a text the book can be used for a one-semester course in structural analysis at the lower graduate level. For classes with a background in computers and in matrix algebra, Chapters 1, 4 and 5 may be treated lightly or reviewed. Chapters 1 to 9 inclusive, and possibly Chapter 11, can be used for a one-semester course in structural analysis at the high junior or senior level.

The practicing engineer who has no background in computers or matrices will find the book useful for independent study. He is advised to follow the book in sequence, verify the solution of all illustrated problems, and solve the problems when suggested in the text. Answers to problems are included at the end of the book.

The first nine chapters of the book may serve to develop a background for *Dynamics of Structures* by Walter C. Hurty and Moshe F. Rubinstein, Prentice-Hall 1964. A number of sections, such as Sections 5.9, 5.10, 7.9 and the introduction in Section 9.3, were included with this purpose in mind. The notation in the two books is identical.

The author wishes to express his appreciation: To Professor Walter C. Hurty, Head Structures Division Department of Engineering at UCLA who, through the years, has made the most significant contribution to the author's education in the fields of structures and dynamics. To Professor F. R. Shanley, Department of Engineering at UCLA for many fruitful discussions. To Mr. John C. Dillon, Dr. Sam Houston and Mrs. Betty Leventhal of Engineering Extension. To the participants in "Use of Computers in Structural Engineering" and to the many students in the course "Advanced Analysis of Structures," who solved problems, pointed out errors, and made suggestions to improve the presentation. To the Reports Group of the Department of Engineering under the supervision of Estelle E. Dorsey. To Edith Corsario and Rita Almon for secretarial services.

Finally, this book could not have been completed without the help and ever present encouragement of my wife, Zafrira, and the cooperation of my daughters, Iris and Dorit, who gave up many hours of play and helped in their own way.

Moshe F. Rubinstein

CONTENTS

CHAPTER 1

COMPUTERS:
FUNDAMENTAL CONCEPTS

1.1. INTRODUCTION

This chapter introduces fundamental concepts in digital computers. Starting with a hypothetical simple computer model, we discuss the basic components of a modern digital computer and its method of operating, as well as aspects of automatic programming. The presentation stresses organization of information which will subsequently be used in later chapters dealing with matrix methods in structures.

Before proceeding with our discussion of digital computers let us point out the difference between the two basic types of computers: analog and digital.

In the analog computer data is represented by a continuous variable, such as voltage (or current), which is read from a dial, or by the length of a line which is read from a graduated scale. The accuracy in the analog computer is limited by the accuracy of the measuring instruments employed to assess the value of the continuous variable. A slide rule is a simple example of an analog computer in which numbers are represented by their corresponding logarithms on a continuous scale, and the accuracy depends on the ability to measure the length of a line. In the digital computer, on the other hand, all data are represented in a discrete form by a sequence of digits. For instance, the number $\frac{1}{9}$ will be represented in the digital computer by a discrete finite number of digits $11111\ldots$ in which the decimal point is known to precede the first digit. The accuracy depends on the number of discrete digits employed to represent a number. Theoretically an infinite number of digits are required to represent the value of $\frac{1}{9}$.

Although an analog computer is very useful in the solution of many

1

specific engineering problems involving differential equations[1,2], the digital computer has the advantage of much greater flexibility for multipurpose use and is more accurate[3,4].†

1.2. A SIMPLE COMPUTER MODEL

Let us begin our story of a simple computer model by introducing our heroes: a boss and his secretary. The boss runs a computer service business with the assistance of his secretary. The computer is housed in a single room and consists of the following components (see Figure 1.1):

1. A wall with wooden compartments
2. A wall on which is inscribed a code of operations and their meaning‡
3. A typewriter
4. A calculator
5. A dial for setting integer numbers from 0000 to 9999

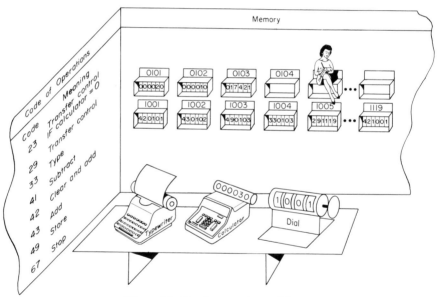

Figure 1.1. Simple computer model.

Each compartment in Figure 1.1 is connected to the wall and has a fixed *address* or *location* in the form of four digits above it. For instance, the address 1119 locates the compartment at the lower right corner of the wall very much as a house is located by its address. The inside back wall of

---

† Superscript numerals refer to material cited at the end of the book.

‡ These codes are actually used with Intercom-1000 on the Bendix G-15 computer. But any other codes could be used for our purposes.

each compartment is a blackboard surface divided by vertical lines into six equal spaces. One digit can be written in each space with a total of six digits per compartment.

The secretary is equipped with a secretarial pad, a pencil, and a piece of chalk. Before assuming her responsibility in the computer room, the secretary was trained for one full day. The boss found her acceptable because she had the following desirable qualifications: No previous experience, not inquisitive, willing to follow instructions with perfect accuracy, like a robot, without ever questioning their wisdom, having good eyesight.

Let us follow our secretary as she enters the computer room in Figure 1.1 at 8:00 A.M. As soon as she enters she walks over to the desk, picks up her pad, pencil, and chalk, and looks at the dial where she sees the digits 1001. The dial always tells the secretary where to go (to which address) for her next instruction. Consequently, she goes to the compartment with the *address* 1001 (the compartment at the lower left of the wall), looks inside it and records in her pad the digits 420101 which she sees. She is now ready to execute the first computer instruction which has the form: 420101.

First Computer Instruction 420101

In interpreting an instruction she has been trained to identify the first two of the six digits as an operation code and the remaining four as an address of a compartment. From the wall with the code of operations she finds the digits 42 to mean *clear and add*. With this information available she looks again at the digits 420101 and proceeds to execute the following operation: She *clears* the calculator to zero *and adds* to it the number which she finds in the compartment with the address 0101 which is specified by the last four digits of the instruction. This number is 000020, consequently the calculator will read 000020. The first instruction has been completed. She walks over to the dial and advances it by one number to read 1002. She always advances the dial by one number after the completion of an instruction unless she is specifically instructed to do otherwise.

Second Computer Instruction 430102

As indicated earlier, the dial tells her where to go for her next instruction. Hence she goes to address 1002 and reads the six digits 430102 which she finds at this address. Again the first two digits are an operation code and the last four represent an address of a compartment that contains the number she will operate on. Following this interpretation, she walks over to the calculator and adds (43 ≡ add) the number that she finds in compartment 0102. This number is 000010 and therefore, after the execution of this instruction, the calculator reads 000030. She now walks back to the dial and advances it by one number to read 1003.

Third Computer Instruction 490103

Next she goes to address 1003 and reads the digits 490103. This she interprets as: store (49 ≡ store) the number that you have in the calculator in the address specified by the last four digits of this instruction, that is, 0103. She promptly copies the number 000030 from the calculator and records it with chalk in compartment 0103 after erasing the digits 017421 which are currently shown there. Then she sets the dial to 1004. Note that this is the first time she erased the inside of a compartment. This is always implied in the instruction *store* which instructs to replace the existing six digits with six new ones.

Fourth Computer Instruction 330103

With the dial set at 1004 she proceeds to this address and reads the instruction 330103 which she executes as follows: She types (33 ≡ type) the number which she reads in address 0103. Since in executing the third instruction she stored there the number 000030, this is the number she reads there now and subsequently types. The dial is set to 1005.

Fifth Computer Instruction 291119

The next instruction at location 1005 reads 291119. This is executed as follows: She goes to the dial, which controls the sequence of operations by specifying the address of the next instruction, and sets it to 1119. Hence the instruction 291119 is interpreted as follows: Transfer the control of operations (29 ≡ transfer control) to the address specified by the last four digits 1119. This is the one case then, when she is specifically instructed to set the dial to a particular number instead of advancing it by one as she always does. With the dial set at 1119 she proceeds to location 1119 to read her next instruction.

Sixth Computer Instruction 421001

In compartment 1119 she reads 421001. She accurately interprets this instruction as: clear the calculator to zero and add to it (42 ≡ clear and add) the number which is presently stored in compartment 1001. Following the execution of this instruction the calculator reads 420101. The dial is advanced to 1120 and the secretary goes to this address to read her next instruction.

In executing the sixth instruction, 421001, the digits stored in location 1001 were treated as a number (four hundred and twenty thousand one hundred and one), whereas the first thing this morning after reading the number 1001 on the dial, the secretary walked over to this very same compartment and interpreted the very same six digits 420101 as an instruction (see First Computer Instruction). Is anything wrong with this? Absolutely not! The information within a compartment is always in the form of six digits, referred to as a *machine word*. Whether these digits are to be interpreted as a number (data) or a meaningful instruction depends on how they are being used by the boss (the *programer*) who used a piece of chalk (*input media*) to write a sequence of coded instructions (*program*) and data on the back wall of the compartments (*storage or memory*). As will be shown later there may be a good reason for using a machine word both as a meaningful instruction and a number.

Before proceeding to analyze what has been accomplished by our computer so far, let us relate what the boss had in mind when he prepared and stored two programs in our computer. In the first program he wanted to add the numbers 10 and 20, store the result in location 0103, and type it on the typewriter. To accomplish this he wrote a *program* which consists of a sequence of coded instructions and stored it in locations 1001 to 1004 inclusive. The data he stored in locations 0101 and 0102. He then set the dial to 1001 and proceeded to write a second program. The details of this program are not given but the boss decided to store its first instruction in location 1119. To be sure that the secretary will proceed to 1119 after she completes the execution of the first program, he placed in location 1005 the instruction to transfer control to 1119. We now compare the plans of our boss with what has been accomplished by the computer and find complete agreement. The number 30 which is the sum of 10 and 20 appears in location 0103 and on the typewriter; the computer has just finished executing the first instruction of the second program and is proceeding to the location 1120 for its next instruction.

1.3. BASIC COMPONENTS OF A DIGITAL COMPUTER

Now let us relate some terms used in connection with a modern electronic digital computer to the components of our model.

The wall with the wooden compartments is the computer *memory* where information (instructions and data) is retained as long as it is not erased. The calculator used by the secretary is the *arithmetic unit* of the computer. The chalk used by our boss to enter the information into the computer is the *input media*. The typewriter used by the secretary to type out the information which is stored in the computer memory is the *output media*. The secretary assisted by the dial and the operations code inscribed on the wall acted as the computer *control* unit. The control unit reads and stores information, interprets instructions, and causes all operations to be performed in the proper sequence.

Figure 1.2 shows the analogy between the components of our simple computer model and the terms describing the basic components of a digital computer. The arrows in the diagram show the direction in which information (numbers, instructions) flows. We shall discuss the components of the

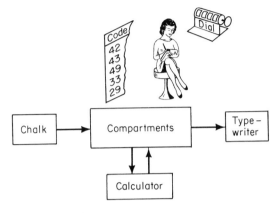

(a) Components of our simple computer model

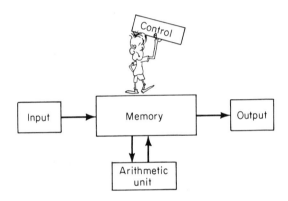

(b) Components of a digital computer

Figure 1.2.

"real" digital computer in later sections, but before we do so let us get a better understanding of the concepts introduced in Section 1.2 and develop some new ones by following the computer of Figure 1.1 as it executes a program designed to add N numbers.

1.4. A PROGRAM TO ADD N NUMBERS

A program to add N numbers is shown in Table 1.1. The program is assigned to locations 0200 to 0214 inclusive, as shown in the left-hand column of Table 1.1. The program instructions on the right-hand column of Table 1.1 are headed by OPADDR to remind us that the first two digits of an instruction signify an OPeration code and the last four represent an ADDRess.

TABLE 1.1

PROGRAM TO ADD N NUMBERS

Address		OPADDR
0200		424000
0201		495000
→0202		425000
0203		431001
0204		495000
0205	C ⌈	426000
0206	O	414001
⌐0207	U N	230213
0208	T E ⌊	496000
0209	R ⌈	420203
0210	A M	434001
0211	D D O D.	490203
└0212	R ⌊	290202
→0213		335000
0214		670000

To be more explicit let us use the computer of Figure 1.1 and the programs of Table 1.1 to add 700 numbers ($N = 700$). The data (the 700 numbers) will be stored in locations 1001 to 1700 inclusive, as shown in Table 1.2.

TABLE 1.2

DATA FOR PROGRAM OF TABLE 1.1

Address	Data
1001	000075
1002	000010
1003	000024
.	.
.	.
.	.
1700	002050

While writing the program of Table 1.1 the programer selected the address 5000 as the location where the answer (sum of the 700 numbers) will be stored. He also selected location 6000 to store in it the number 000700 so the computer can be told how many numbers it is expected to add. He also found it necessary to store 000000 and 000001 in the computer. The reason for this will become apparent later. He selected locations 4000 and 4001 for 000000 and 000001 respectively. The last four pieces of information are designated, for ease of reference, as auxiliary information and summarized in Table 1.3 for future reference.

TABLE 1.3
AUXILIARY INFORMATION

Address	Information
4000	000000
4001	000001
5000	Answer
6000	000700

We now input the program of Table 1.1 into the computer (locations 0200 to 0214 inclusive), then input the data of Tables 1.2 and 1.3 into the locations designated. Note that no information is placed in location 5000 which is designated for the answer. With the program and data in the computer we now set the dial to 0200 (location of first instruction), and start executing the program (*computing*). The operations are interpreted from the code of operations in Figure 1.1, and after each instruction the dial is advanced by one unless instructed otherwise. The program is executed as follows:

Clearing the Calculator and Location 5000

Instruction in 0200: 424000   The calculator is cleared and the number 000000 which is in location 4000 is added to it.

Instruction in 0201: 495000   The number 000000 currently in the calculator is stored in 5000, replacing any of six digits that are currently there.

Adding the First Number

Instruction in 0202: 425000   The calculator is cleared and the number 000000 in location 5000 is added to it.

Instruction in 0203: 431001   The number 000075 in 1001 is added to the calculator.

Instruction in 0204: 495000   The number 000075 currently in the calculator is stored in 5000.

At this point location 5000 has the number 000075 which is the first number to be added.

The next four instructions constitute a counter which is designed by the programer to tell the computer how many more numbers must be added, and when to stop.

The Counter

Instruction in 0205: 426000   The calculator is cleared and the number 000700 in 6000 is added to it.

Instruction in 0206: 414001   The number 000001 in 4001 is subtracted from the calculator (the calculator now reads 000699).

Instruction in 0207: 230213   This instruction is a conditional transfer of control and permits the computer to make a decision based on the results of the preceding computations. The interpretation is as follows. If the calculator reads 000000 (zero), transfer control to 0213 (the address specified by the last four digits of the instruction) and proceed to execute the instruction in 0213. If the calculator does not read zero, advance the dial by one and proceed to the next instruction (in 0208). Since the calculator reads currently 000699 (see last instruction), the computer proceeds to 0208.

We note here, however, that the calculator now reads 000699, because only one number has been added, but will read 000000 after all 700 numbers are added. At that time the computer will proceed to 0213 and type the answer which will be at 5000, then go to 0214 and stop.

Instruction in 0208: 496000   The number 000699 currently in the calculator is stored in 6000 replacing the number 000700 currently there.

So far only the number 000075 in 1001 has been added; therefore, we must go back and add the next number which is in 1002, then the next one in 1003, and so on, until we add the last one which is stored in 1700 (see Table 1.2). To avoid writing the instruction of addition 700 times, each time specifying a different address, we use the next four instructions to modify the address portion (last four digits) of the instruction in 0203 and cause the control to transfer back to 0202, so that, when the instruction in 0203 is executed, the number added to the sum will be read from location 1002. This will be repeated until all 700 numbers are added. Here is how this is accomplished :

Address Modification

Instruction in 0209: 420203   The calculator is cleared to 000000 and the number 431001 in 0203 (see Table 1.1) is added. Note that earlier 431001 was treated as a meaningful instruction; now it is used as a number.

Instruction in 0210: 434001   The number 000001 in 4001 (see Table 1.3) is added to the calculator. The calculator now reads 431002.

Instruction in 0211: 490203   The number 431002 currently in the calculator is stored in 0203, replacing the digits 431001 which are currently there (see Table 1.1).

Instruction in 0212: 290202   Control is transferred to 0202; that is, the dial is set to 0202 so that the computer goes there for its next instruction. From here the program is executed again as described earlier.

The instructions in locations 0202 to 0212 inclusive, are called a *loop* because they are performed repeatedly many times, proceeding in a loop from 0202 to 0212 and back to 0202. So far, we have completed one cycle of the loop. Before proceeding with a second cycle from 0202 to 0212 inclusive, we note that at this stage the inside of locations 0203, 5000, and 6000 appears as in Figure 1.3.

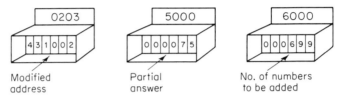

Figure 1.3. Locations 0203, 5000 and 6000 after executing one cycle of the loop 0202 to 0212 incl.

We suggest that the reader follow the computer as the second and third cycles are executed. After each of these cycles locations 0203, 5000, and 6000 appear as shown in Table 1.4. (Verify.)

TABLE 1.4

Location	After Second Cycle	After Third Cycle
0203	431003	431004
5000	000085	000109
6000	000698	000697

Suggested Exercise:† Do problem 1.

1.5. FLOW CHART

When a program involves a large number of operations, it is convenient first to draw a diagram describing the flow of the various blocks of operation in the proper sequence. Such a diagram is called a *flow chart*. The flow chart for the program of Table 1.1 which was discussed in Section 1.4 is shown in Figure 1.4. Each block of operations, such as modifying an address, is shown in a rectangular box. The diamond-shaped box represents a decision. In our program this represents the instruction in location 0207, but it also contains adjustment of the counter which is stored in 6000, because the decision in 0207 depends on the value in 6000.

Each block of operations in the flow chart can in turn be broken into other flow charts describing the operations in more detail. For ease of

---

† Suggested problems are at the end of the chapter.

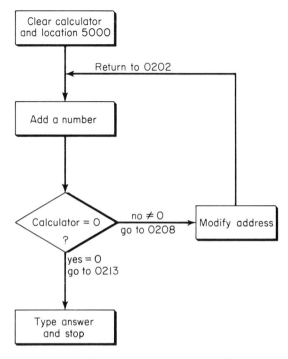

Figure 1.4. Flow chart for the program of Table 1.1.

reference we identified in the flow chart of Figure 1.4 some of the locations in the program of Table 1.1.

1.6. MEMORY (STORAGE) IN THE "REAL" COMPUTER

Actually we have been discussing a real computer all along. Ours, however, was a simple model. Now we describe some basic components of the more sophisticated modern digital computer, beginning with the computer memory in this section.

Serial Access Memory

The function of a computer memory is to store data and instructions, referred to as *machine words*, in properly addressed positions, so that they can be retrieved when necessary. In our simple computer model, a machine word consisted of a sequence of six decimal digits, and it was stored in a properly addressed compartment. Let us now see how a machine word and an address appear in a modern digital computer. Figure 1.5 shows two types of computer memories. The drum is about 6 in. in diameter and about 8 in. long; the disk is about 6 in. in diameter.† Both are mounted on shafts which rotate when the computer is in operation (approximate speed, 2000 rpm). The disk and drum are coated with a magnetic surface which is divided into channels (see Figure 1.5). Each channel consists of a serial sequence of positions which are identified by *addresses*. Each such position corresponds to one compartment in our simple computer model and consists of a sequence of minute magnetic surfaces occupying the width of a channel. Each of these minute surfaces can be polarized (magnetized) or depolarized independently so that a machine word can appear as shown in Figure 1.6(a) in which the black square indicates polarization. Since each square can assume one of two states, we can choose the digits 1 and 0 to represent polarization and no polarization of a square respectively. The machine word of Figure 1.6(a) appears then symbolically as shown in

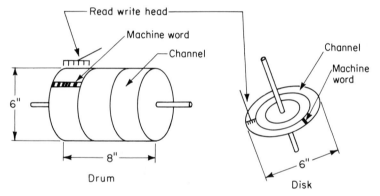

Figure 1.5.

Figure 1.6.(b). Any machine word in the computer appears in the form of a sequence of the digits 0, 1, of the binary number system.‡ Each of these digits is called a *bit* (contraction of *bi*nary dig*it*) and represents the most fundamental unit of information, 0 = No and 1 = Yes, in responding to a question. The number of bits in a common length machine word is 36. A machine word is stored (written) or retrieved (read) from the drum or disk through the use of a *read-write head*§ shown in Figure 1.5. One such head is positioned above each channel and can polarize or depolarize (write) each bit in any machine word in the channel as this machine word passes underneath it while the disk or drum is rotating. It can also detect

† These dimensions vary for different computers.
‡ See Section 1.8 for a discussion of the binary number system.
§ Also referred to as read-in and read-out head.

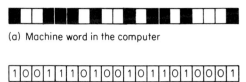

(a) Machine word in the computer

| 1 | 0 | 0 | 1 | 1 | 1 | 0 | 1 | 0 | 0 | 1 | 0 | 1 | 1 | 0 | 1 | 0 | 0 | 0 | 1 |

(b) Symbolic representation of a machine word

Figure 1.6.

(read) the state of polarization of the bits in any machine word. The writing and reading by the read-write head is aided by the input-output media which we shall discuss later.

We observe that the information is read or written on the drum or disk-type memories in a sequential or a serial fashion. The read-write head must wait for the drum or disk to rotate until the particular location (address) is directly beneath it so its content can be processed. Because of this the disk and drum are referred to as *serial access memories*.

Random Access Memory

A different type of memory called *magnetic core memory* is shown in Figure 1.7. This memory consists of a matrix of doughnut-shaped core elements of ferromagnetic material. Each core has two energizing coils x and y. The signals are such that one coil x or y is not sufficient to energize a core element. Only when a signal enters simultaneously through x and y will the corresponding core be energized. For instance, the upper left core element in Figure 1.7 will be energized by a signal from $x = 1$ and $y = 3$ simultaneously. The coordinates x, y establish the location (address) of each bit. Information is read from the core elements through a sensing wire. The core memory has the advantage of being free of any rotating element and being capable of storing and reading information at any location in memory with equal speed for all practical purposes.† It is therefore called a *random access memory*. A machine word in this type of memory also consists of a sequence of binary bits.

As in our simple model a machine word can be interpreted as an instruction or a number. The first portion of the instruction (for instance, the first 8 bits) serves as an operation code and the remainder specifies an address. It is easy to see how an operation code can be specified by a predetermined sequence of bits. If only two bit positions are available for operation codes, then the following four (2^2) distinguishable codes are possible: 00, 10, 01, 11. With three bit positions $2^3 = 8$ distinguishable

---

† The speed depends on the speed of signal travel and the location of the machine word being processed.

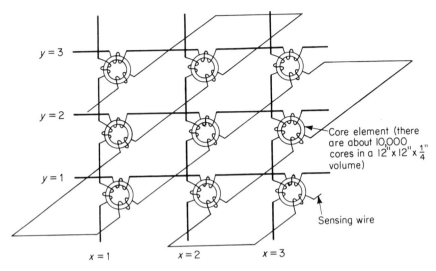

Figure 1.7. Magnetic core memory.

codes are possible, and using eight bits, 2^8 distinctly distinguishable codes are possible. But how about the address portion of an instruction, or how about a machine word representing a number (data)—what does it signify when in the form of a sequence of zeros and ones, and how does the computer compute with numbers in this form. We shall discuss these matters later but first let us describe briefly input-output media.

Suggested Exercise: Do problem 2.

1.7. INPUT–OUTPUT MEDIA

The principal types of input–output media in a modern digital computer are

1. A typewriter
2. Punched cards
3. Punched tape
4. Magnetic tape

It is not difficult to visualize how depressing a key on a typewriter can cause a circuit to be activated and consequently cause a 1 bit to be stored in the computer by the read–write head or by the xy coils in the core-type memory.

Similarly, mechanical fingers scanning a punched card will cause "one" bits to be stored when holes are detected. No holes will store "zero" bits.

Punched tapes may also be scanned mechanically or may be used with a photoelectric device. The tape moves next to a light source, and when a hole is present in the tape, the light goes through and activates a circuit causing a 1 bit to be stored. No hole will store a 0 bit.

Magnetic tape is the most compact storage media and as an input–output media can be read faster than the other three mentioned earlier. Detection of a polarized spot will cause a 1 bit to be stored, and no polarized spot causes a zero bit to be stored.

The reasoning used to describe the foregoing devices as input media can be used to describe them as output media; that is, detection of a polarized spot (a 1 bit) in memory will activate a circuit causing a typewriter key to be depressed or a hole to be punched in a card or tape, or a spot to be polarized on magnetic tape.

1.8. COMPUTER LANGUAGE: LANGUAGE OF ZEROS AND ONES

In any written language there are about 60 to 100 different characters. In the modern digital computer, the fundamental characters are the bits 0 and 1. These are combined to form distinguishable codes signifying various operations and control commands which are part of the *computer language*. They may also be used to represent the digits $0, 1, \ldots, 9$, or any number for that matter. To see how this is done let us briefly discuss number systems.

The most familiar of all number systems is the decimal system. Here is how we use this system (or convention) to interpret the number 252.2. The value represented by each digit is interpreted according to its position relative to the decimal point, so that

$$252.2 = 2 \times 10^2 + 5 \times 10^1 + 2 \times 10^0 + 2 \times 10^{-1}$$

in which 10 is called the *base* or *radix* of the system. For convenience, the foregoing interpretation can be written in a table as

...	10^4	10^3	10^2	10^1	10^0	10^{-1}	10^{-2}	10^{-3}	...
			2	5	2	2			

in which each decimal digit of the second row is multiplied by the value above it. Any other number can be evaluated by placing it in the second row of the table with the decimal point positioned as indicated. In the decimal system the base is 10 and there are ten digits $9, 8, 7, \ldots, 1, 0$. The highest digit 9 is the first integer number smaller than the base 10.

We can devise an *octal* system with base 8 and eight digits $7, 6, \ldots 1, 0$ (again the highest digit is the first integer number smaller than the base).

By analogy to the decimal system we can assess the value of octal numbers from the following table:

...	8^4	8^3	8^2	8^1	8^0	8^{-1}	8^{-2}	...

For instance, the number $252.2_{\boxed{8}}$ (the number in the box designates the number system) in the octal system has the value

$$252.2_{\boxed{8}} = 2 \times 8^2 + 5 \times 8^1 + 2 \times 8^0 + 2 \times 8^{-1} = 170.25_{\boxed{10}}$$

Using only the two digits 0 and 1 in a number system, then by analogy the base must be 2 and the number system is referred to as the *binary system*. Binary numbers are evaluated from the following table:

...	2^3	2^2	2^1	2^0	2^{-1}	2^{-2}	...

In general for a number system with base B the integers used are $(B - 1)$, $(B - 2), \ldots, 1, 0$ and the numbers are evaluated from the following table

...	B^3	B^2	B^1	B^0	B^{-1}	B^{-2}	...

in which any value B^n in the top row is the value of the digit 1 associated with the corresponding position relative to the decimal in the second row. Table 1.5 summarizes the information relevant to number systems.

TABLE 1.5

NUMBER SYSTEMS

System	Base	Digits	Values of the Digit 1 Associated with Position								
Decimal	10	$9, 8, 7, \ldots, 1, 0$	...	10^3	10^2	10^1	10^0	10^{-1}	10^{-2}	...	
Octal	8	$7, \ldots, 1, 0$	...	8^3	8^2	8^1	8^0	8^{-1}	8^{-2}	...	
Binary	2	$1, 0$	...	2^3	2^2	2^1	2^0	2^{-1}	2^{-2}	...	
B	B	$(B - 1), \ldots, 1, 0$	...	B^3	B^2	B^1	B^0	B^{-1}	B^{-2}	...	

Suggested Exercises: Do problems 3 and 4.

1.9. CONVERSION OF DECIMAL TO BINARY NUMBERS

We shall now show how to convert decimal numbers to binary numbers which is the language of the computer. The reverse (binary to decimal) can be accomplished from Table 1.5.

Let us start with the decimal number 25. To convert it to its binary equivalent we divide it by the base 2 repeatedly as follows: The number 25 is divided by 2—the result 12 and a remainder of 1 are recorded beneath it:

$$2 \underline{|25} \quad \text{remainder}$$
$$12 \qquad 1$$

Next the result 12 is divided by 2 and the result 6 and remainder 0 are recorded beneath it:

$$2 \underline{|25} \quad \text{remainder}$$
$$2 \underline{|12} \qquad 1$$
$$6 \qquad 0$$

This process is continued until finally 1 is divided by 2 to yield 0 and a remainder 1 which are recorded in the last row.

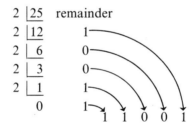

The binary equivalent of 25 is the column of remainder digits read from the bottom up or rotated 90° to the right as shown. Hence,

$$25_{\boxed{10}} = 11001_{\boxed{2}}$$

A similar procedure is followed in converting from decimal to octal. For instance,

$$8 \underline{|25} \quad \text{remainder}$$
$$8 \underline{|\ 3} \qquad 1$$
$$0 \qquad 3 \qquad 3\ 1_{\boxed{8}} = 25_{\boxed{10}}$$

The same procedure is followed in converting octal to binary numbers, etc.

Suggested Exercises: Do problems 5, 6 and 7.

Binary Coded Decimal Numbers

An alternate way to represent decimal numbers by binary digits is to convert each decimal digit independently into its binary equivalent using four bits as shown in Table 1.6.

TABLE 1.6
BINARY CODED DECIMAL DIGITS

Decimal Digit	Binary Equivalent
0	0000
1	0001
2	0010
3	0011
4	0100
5	0101
6	0110
7	0111
8	1000
9	1001

A decimal number that is translated (or coded) by this procedure is called a *Binary Coded Decimal* number (bcd number). For instance, the decimal numbers 25 and 11 are coded as

$$25_{10} = 0010 \quad 0101$$
$$11_{10} = 0001 \quad 0001$$

Note that this conversion is entirely different from that discussed earlier; it is simpler in the sense that everything required for conversion is given by Table 1.6.

Now that we know how operations and numbers can be translated into the computer language of zeros and ones, we can conceive of devices that can effect such translation. What remains to be shown is how the computer computes in its own language of zeros and ones.

Suggested Exercise: Do problem 8.

1.10. HOW DOES A COMPUTER COMPUTE

Since numbers in the computer are in binary form, we expect the computations to be performed in the binary system. The fundamental rules for adding binary digits are shown in Table 1.7. For convenience we identify the results of these four operations by a *sum digit* and a *carry digit* as indicated in the table. The rules of Table 1.7 can be applied to add the following binary numbers:

$$
\begin{array}{rrr}
1011101 & 1111 & 11010111 \\
+110110 & +111 & +10011111 \\
\hline
10010011 & 10110 & 101110110
\end{array}
$$

TABLE 1.7

RULES FOR ADDING BINARY DIGITS

		Case		
	I	II	III	IV
$a =$	0	0	1	1
$+$	$+$	$+$	$+$	$+$
$b =$	0	1	0	1
Carry digit ⟶ ⬛⬛	00	01	01	10
Sum digit ⟶				

We suggest that the reader verify these results by converting all the numbers to their decimal equivalents.

It can be shown that the operations of multiplication, division, extracting roots, etc., can be reduced to the most fundamental operations of addition given by Table 1.7. If this is so, then if the computer can perform the operations of Table 1.7, it can perform multiplication, division, extraction of roots, etc. We shall now describe a device called a *half adder* which is part of the computer arithmetic unit (calculator) and can execute the operations of Table 1.7. The half adder is extended in the computer to perform a complete addition of numbers.

Figure 1.8 shows diagrammatically a half adder. The digits ⓐ and ⓑ to be added (see Table 1.7) are entered in the form of signals from the left and the answer is recorded in the form of signals on the right. The direction of signal flow is indicated by the arrows. A signal will come though ⓐ in Figure 1.8 only when a polarized spot is detected where ⓐ is stored, signifying the digit 1 for ⓐ. Similarly for ⓑ. The locations of the sum digit and carry digit will be polarized, signifying the storage of the digit 1, only when a signal gets there, otherwise a zero is stored. The components that

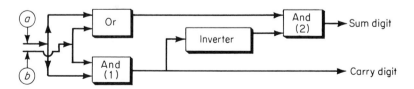

Figure 1.8. Half adder.

will effect this information transfer consist of two *and boxes*, an *or box*, and an *inverter box*.

An *and box* is a device which has two inputs and one output and will output a signal if, and only if, signals enter through the two inputs simultaneously. A simple example of an *and box* is shown in Figure 1.9(a). In the circuit of this figure a switch closes when an input signal excites it. Consequently two input signals entering simultaneously will close the circuit and cause an output signal represented by the light on.

An *or box* is a device which has two inputs and one output, and will submit a signal if at least one signal enters the box. [See Figure 1.9(b).] An *inverter box* has one input and one output. It will transmit *no signal* when a signal enters and will transmit a signal when no signal enters the box. An *inverter box* circuit is shown in Figure 1.9(c) in which the entry of a signal causes the switch to open. When no input signal enters, the switch is closed.

In early computer models *OR*, *AND*, and *INVERTER* boxes were constructed with electromagnetic relays. These were later replaced by vacuum tubes and then by transistors.

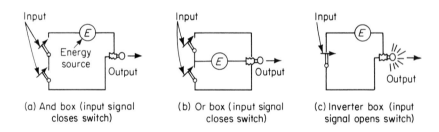

(a) And box (input signal closes switch)

(b) Or box (input signal closes switch)

(c) Inverter box (input signal opens switch)

Figure 1.9. Circuits for <u>and</u>, <u>or</u> and <u>inverter</u> boxes.

Let us follow the half adder diagram of Figure 1.8 as it executes case (4) of Table 1.7. Since in this case $a = 1$ and $b = 1$, two signals enter *and box* (1) and the *or box*; consequently, each of these boxes outputs a signal. From *and box* (1) the signal enters the inverter box and at the same time enters the carry digit position to store 1. *And box* (2) receives a signal from the *or box* but no signal from the *inverter box*; consequently, it transmits no signal so that a 0 is stored in the sum digit position. This agrees with case (4) of Table 1.7. (Verify the other cases.)

Suggested Exercises: Do problems 9 and 10.

1.11. COMPUTER CONTROL

The control of a computer has the functions of causing information to be stored in memory or retrieved from it, and causing a program to be interpreted and executed in a proper sequence.

In our simple model of Section 1.2, the secretary aided by a wall chart and a dial constituted a control unit. In the modern digital computer the control contains a command register where operations are interpreted (analogous to the wall chart in Figure 1.1) and a command counter which controls the sequence of operations (corresponding to the dial in Figure 1.1). To channel information in the computer, and in and out of the computer, the control makes use of *and, or,* and *inverter* boxes described earlier.

1.12. TYPES OF DIGITAL COMPUTERS AND THEIR KEY FEATURES

There are many types of digital computers; some are special-purpose computers designed to solve specific problems; others are general-purpose computers capable of solving a great variety of problems. The general-purpose computers are not all the same; they may vary in the number of fundamental operations they perform, their speed of operations,† storage capacity, input-output media, and of course, cost. In the light of our discussion in this chapter so far, we can state that no matter how many complex functions a digital computer can perform, these functions are combinations of the fundamental operations of detecting, transferring, and manipulating information in the form of bits.

1.13. PROGRAMMING

Programming a computer in machine language (its language of zeros and ones) consists of writing a sequential set of instructions specifying addresses where machine words (data, instructions, and answers) will be stored. All these are in binary forms in the computer. The task of programming in machine language can become very involved although it is very efficient in exploiting the capabilities of the computer[5, 6, 7, 8]. In recent years much has been done to make the task of programming simpler so that communication with the computer will be more direct insofar as the user is concerned. This brings us to *automatic programming* which provides an automatic translation from "almost" the English language, and the language of mathematics to computer language.

---

† Some computers can add 2.5 million numbers in 1 second!

Automatic Programming

The program of Table 1.1 is an example of a program written in a machine language (the language of our simple computer model). In writing this program we had to specify locations for the program, the data, and the answer, and to consider each step of the operations. All this is simplified when automatic programming is used. Automatic programming involves the use of a *compiler* program (which is a computer program) that translates a simple language of programming to machine language and automatically assigns locations to the program, the data, and the answers. The use of a compiler causes a less efficient utilization of the computer but this sacrifice is outweighed, most of the time, by the benefits of the simple programming language. An example of an automatic programming language is the IBM FORTRAN[9, 10] (short for FORmula TRANslator). This language is remote from the computer language and is very close to the English language and the language of mathematics. For instance, the words

$$\text{DO} \qquad \text{READ} \qquad \text{PUNCH} \qquad \text{PRINT}$$

instruct the computer to do, read, punch, and print; and the equation

$$X = A + B - C * D/E$$

instructs the computer to execute the operations† on the right of the equal sign and assign the result to the variable X on the left. To get a better appreciation of this language let us apply it to the program of Section 1.4 and follow all the steps in its development.

1.14. FORTRAN PROGRAM TO ADD N NUMBERS

The program of Table 1.1 is written in FORTRAN in Table 1.8. Each line of Table 1.8 is called a Fortran statement. Using punched cards as input media one statement is punched per card. Cards are punched by depressing keys on the keyboard of the punching equipment with the keys corresponding to the symbols (letters, numbers, etc.) which appear in the Fortran statements. The statement number preceding each statement is optional. A statement number is required only for those statements which are referred to by other statements of the program, as we shall see later. After the program is written, the programer checks it for any errors in the programming language, such as spelling, omission of commas, parentheses, equal signs, etc. Then the deck of Fortran cards is checked automatically by the computer (*precompiled*) to detect any further errors insofar as the

---

† The asterisk (*) and slash (/) designate multiplication and division respectively.

TABLE 1.8

FORTRAN PROGRAM TO ADD N NUMBERS†

Statement Number	Fortran Statement
1	SUM = 0.0
2	READ N
┌3	DO 4 I = 1, N
└→4	READ $A(I)$
┌5	DO 6 J = 1, N
└→6	SUM = SUM + $A(J)$
7	PRINT SUM

Fortran language is concerned. When errors are detected, special typed signals will indicate their nature so that they can be corrected.

After the Fortran program, also referred to as *source program*, has been precompiled and no errors detected, it is placed in the computer for translation into the computer language (*compilation*). The compilation produces a new deck of punched cards which represents the source program in machine language. The program in machine language is referred to as the *object program*.

At this point all data are punched on cards and arranged in the order called for by the program. (In the program of Table 1.8 N appears first and is followed by the 700 numbers to be added.) The data cards are placed behind the object program cards and the entire deck of cards is placed in the computer. When the start button is depressed the computer proceeds as follows: First the object program is stored in the computer memory, then it begins to execute the program. Note that the data have not yet been stored in the computer memory and will be stored only when the program is being executed and the word READ is encountered. Let us follow the computer as it executes the program of Table 1.8 with the value of $N = 700$ and the data as given by Table 1.2 (ignore the addresses specified in this table), using the concept of the compartments of Section 1.2.

Program Execution

Statement 1: The computer assigns the value zero to the inside of a compartment which it named (identified by an address) SUM.

Statement 2: The computer reads the first number (700) in the data cards and assigns it to a compartment with address N. The data card with the number 700 has now been processed through the input media and the card with the next piece of data (75) is ready to be read.

Statement 3: DO 4 I = 1, N The computer assigns I the value of 1 and

---

† The program should also specify the form of the data and answer (how many significant figures, floating point or fixed point) and also the number of $A(I)$ terms. These details are eliminated for the sake of clarity.

executes all the following statements down to and including Statement 4. Then *I* is assigned the value 2 and the process repeated, until finally Statement 4 has been executed the number of times specified by the number in address *N* (which is 700 after Statement 2 has been executed). At this point the computer proceeds to Statement 5. Statements 3 and 4 are called a *do loop*. This is indicated for our own reference by the line to the left of these statement numbers. As a result of executing this do loop, the computer stores in the compartments with addresses A(1), A(2),..., A(700) the data from the data cards, (see Figure 1.10), so that the number 75 is in A(1), 10 is in A(2), 24 is in A(3), and finally 2050 is in A(700). (See Table 1.2 for data.)

Statements 5 and 6 form another do loop. First the computer sets $J = 1$, then goes to Statement 6 which will now be SUM = SUM + A(1) and proceeds to execute the instruction on the right of the equal sign as follows: It goes to compartment SUM and reads the number inside it; next it goes to compartment A(1) and reads its content—then it adds these two numbers. (The present content of these compartments is shown in Figure 1.10.) Next it stores the result in the compartment specified on the left of the equal sign;† that is, it stores 75 in SUM replacing the 0.0.

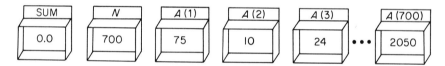

Figure 1.10. Content of memory compartments after the do loop of statements 3 & 4 is completed.

The do loop has now been satisfied for $J = 1$. Now the computer sets $J = 2$ and returns to Statement 6 which now reads

$$SUM = SUM + A(2)$$

Proceeding as before, the computer will add 75 and 10 and store the result of 85 in SUM, replacing its former content (75). Then *J* is set equal to 3, and so on, until finally $J = 700$ (the value of *N*) at which point SUM contains the sum of the first 699 data numbers and Statement 6 appears as

$$SUM = SUM + A(700)$$

After this is executed, SUM contains the desired sum of all 700 numbers. The computer proceeds to Statement 7.

---

† Note that the equal sign (=) in Fortran does not have the conventional meaning.

Statement 7: The computer prints the content of SUM which, of course, is the desired answer.

A More Efficient Fortran Program to Add N Numbers

The program of Table 1.8 requires 700 data storage compartments, one for each piece of data. We observe, however, that after a number has been added to the sum, it is not needed any more. Also we are adding one number at a time. This suggests the more efficient program of Table 1.9 which will save a lot of computer memory space. In this program there is a single compartment with address A for all the data. There is also a single do loop (3 to 5 inclusive). When the do loop is executed for $I = 1$ the computer reads first the data card with the number 75 and stores it in the compartment with address A, then executes Statement 5. Now I is set equal to 2 and when the computer encounters Statement 4 it reads the next data card (which has the number 10) and stores it in A replacing the 75. Now Statement 5 is executed and causes the value of 85 to be stored in SUM. This is repeated until the do loop (3 to 5) is executed 700 (the value of N) times. We suggest that the reader follow the execution of this program by picking five numbers, for instance (storing 5 in N), and drawing compartments for SUM N and A.

TABLE 1.9
MORE EFFICIENT PROGRAM TO ADD N NUMBERS

Statement Number	Fortran Statement
1	SUM = 0.0
2	READ N
3	DO 5 I = 1, N
4	READ A
5	SUM = SUM + A
6	PRINT SUM

1.15. FORTRAN SYMBOLS IN STRUCTURAL ANALYSIS

The conceptual model of computer memory (compartments) can be used together with the Fortran language to designate, store, and process information relative to structural analysis which will be discussed in subsequent chapters. For instance, in static or dynamic analysis of a building frame (Figure 1.11)

$$STF \ (I, J, K)$$

$$COF \ (I, J, K)$$

$$FEM \ (I, J, K)$$

can designate stiffness, carry-over factor, and fixed end moment of a member end at joint (I, J) where I is the column number and J is the floor number. K identifies which particular member's end, at the joint, is being considered by setting $K = 1, 2, 3, 4$, respectively, for the end framing into a joint from the right, from above, from the left, or from the bottom (see Figure 1.11). In the computer program STF (I, J, K) is interpreted as the address of the compartment in which the value of the stiffness at (I, J, K) is stored.

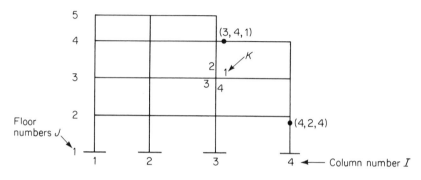

Figure 1.11.

A number of Fortran programs for structural analysis are discussed in Chapters 4, 9, and 11.

1.16. CONCLUDING REMARKS

The purpose of this chapter was to introduce the fundamental concepts and key features in digital computers. In so doing we did not consider the great amount of detail and complexity required to design these sophisticated machines. Familiarity with the fundamental concepts, however, should be sufficient background for the reader to embark on a program of study of an automatic programming language[9, 10] so that he will be able to exploit the vast capabilities of the digital computer.

PROBLEMS

Problem 1: It is required to add only the first three numbers in Table 1.2, type the result, and stop the computer. What change(s) must be introduced in Tables 1.1 and 1.3 if any. Follow the execution of the program until the computer is stopped by the program.

Problem 2: Prove that the number of distinguishable codes which can be constructed with n bit positions is 2^n.

Problem 3: Write the following numbers in the decimal system:

$$125.5_{[8]}$$

$$130_{[8]}$$

$$100.101_{[2]}$$

$$1011_{[2]}$$

$$100.1_{[8]}$$

Problem 4: What must be added to each of the following numbers to justify the equal sign?

$$11 = 1011 \qquad 1011 = 521$$

$$100 = 1000000 \qquad 13 = 11$$

$$1111 = 17$$

Problem 5: Convert the following decimal numbers to their binary equivalents.

$$47$$
$$64$$
$$14$$
$$125$$
$$3690$$

Problem 6: Convert the numbers in Problem 5 to their octal equivalents.

Problem 7: Convert the following numbers in the octal system to their binary equivalents

$$47$$
$$64$$
$$14$$
$$125$$
$$3670$$

Problem 8: Convert the decimal numbers 167, 893, 245, to their bcd equivalents.

Problem 9: Execute the following operations with the binary numbers given and check your results by converting the numbers to their decimal equivalents.

$$\begin{array}{cccc} 11111 & 1001 & 1111 & 10101 \\ +11111 & +1100 & -1011 & -10010 \end{array}$$

Problem 10: To convert a noninteger decimal number to its binary equivalent we multiply it by the base 2 repeatedly as follows:

Consider the number $0.625_{[10]}$. To convert it to its binary equivalent we multiply it by 2 and record the result 1.25 in two parts: the leading digit 1 to the left of the decimal and the remaining portion .25 to the right of the decimal as shown

$$\begin{array}{ll} \text{Leading digit} & 0.625 \\ \downarrow & \underline{\times 2} \\ 1 & .25 \end{array}$$

Next the portion to the right of the decimal, .25, is multiplied by 2 and the result is again recorded in two separate parts of a leading digit 0 and the remaining portion .50 to the right of the decimal

$$
\begin{array}{ll}
\text{Leading digit} & 0.625 \\
\downarrow & \underline{\times 2} \\
1 & .25 \\
& \underline{\times 2} \\
0 & .50
\end{array}
$$

This process is continued until finally the part to the right of the decimal is zero. In the present example this is accomplished when .50 is multiplied by 2:

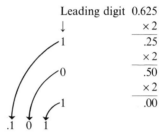

$$
\begin{array}{ll}
\text{Leading digit} & 0.625 \\
\downarrow & \underline{\times 2} \\
1 & .25 \\
& \underline{\times 2} \\
0 & .50 \\
& \underline{\times 2} \\
1 & .00
\end{array}
$$

.1 0 1

The binary equivalent of 0.625_{10} is the column of leading binary digits read from the top down and preceded by a decimal point

$$0.625_{10} = 0.101_{2}$$

Using the foregoing procedure and the procedure for converting integer decimal numbers to their binary equivalents convert the following decimal numbers to their binary equivalents.

0.125	29.1875
0.875	763.203125
0.703125	0.95625
13.375	0.515625

CHAPTER 2

STRUCTURES:
FUNDAMENTAL CONCEPTS

2.1. INTRODUCTION

This book uses *structure* to describe a system which has the function of transmitting loads. A structure may consist of a single element, such as a beam, for instance, or it may consist of an assembly of connected elements. The elements may be tension rods, compression bars, beams, shear panels, plates, etc. This classification is based on the element's mode of load transfer, but a classification based on the shape of the element is also possible.

We are concerned with both the system and its elements, and one of our prime objectives is to synthesize the system's characteristics from the characteristics of the elements. The characteristics of the system enable us to predict its behavior. Thus, for instance, we can find the set of forces which, when applied to the system, will cause it to assume a prescribed deflected configuration; or the reverse, we can find the deflected configuration that will result from applying a prescribed set of forces. In these analyses we shall also generate the internal forces at any point within the system. But let us not get ahead of ourselves; let us stick to fundamental concepts as the title of our present chapter suggests. These concepts are primarily concerned with measurements of forces and displacements which are always involved when we deal with structures.

2.2. FORCE AND DISPLACEMENT MEASUREMENTS

There are a number of ways of measuring a force applied to a structure or its displacement at some point in a specified direction. For instance, a hydraulic jack can be used to apply a force, and a dial on the jack can indicate its magnitude. Similarly, torques can be applied and measured by equipment designed for this purpose. Displacement can be measured by a tape or a ruler, and rotation by a protractor.

From here on, we use the word *force* to include torques and moments (couples), and *displacement* to include rotations. A *measurement* of force or displacement describes their magnitude. To establish where on the structure, and in which direction, a measurement is taken, we shall use a *coordinate system*. The coordinate system will identify our measurements. A *coordinate system* for measuring forces and displacements (velocities and accelerations can also be included) is shown in Figure 2.1. This system consists of eight coordinates which are identified by eight numbered arrows shown at specific points on the structure (at the four joints of the frame).

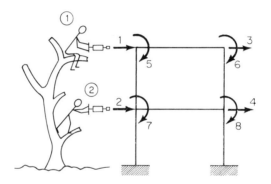

Figure 2.1. Coordinate system.

The number of coordinates in Figure 2.1 is arbitrary. We can remove some of the coordinates, or add others at points between the joints, or in the vertical direction at each joint. It is not necessary to have arrows point vertically or horizontally; any direction in which a measurement is desired will do. For our purposes let us require measurements at the eight coordinates shown in Figure 2.1 and consider the frame to be constructed of beams and columns which can deform and change shape.

Force Vector

Let us assign one man to each coordinate in Figure 2.1. Each man can apply a force or produce a displacement in the direction of his coordinate or opposite to it, and can report its magnitude. When the men report their force measurements, we record them in a column between brackets as follows:

$$\begin{Bmatrix} F_1 \\ F_2 \\ F_3 \\ \vdots \\ F_8 \end{Bmatrix}$$

The first element of the column, F_1, indicates the magnitude of the force at coordinate 1. F_2 indicates the force at coordinate 2, etc. Hence, the subscript serves to designate the coordinate number which in turn identifies a point on the structure and a direction of an arrow in Figure 2.1. We note, however, that the subscript also corresponds in number to a position (an address) in the column of forces. Consequently if the men report the forces in their stations in sequential order, starting with coordinate 1, and call out the numbers: 3^k, 16^k, -5^k, 7^k, $0'^k$, $16'^k$, $19'^k$, $-2'^k$, we record them in a column as follows:

$$\begin{Bmatrix} 3^k \\ 16^k \\ -5^k \\ 7^k \\ 0'^k \\ 16'^k \\ 19'^k \\ -2'^k \end{Bmatrix}$$

Such a column of forces is referred to as a *force vector* and represents an ordered array of force measurements, in which a position in the array identifies a particular coordinate. A negative sign indicates that the measurement is in a direction opposite to the arrow in the coordinate system. For instance, the third element in our column, $F_3 = -5^k$, signifies that a force of 5 kips acting to the left is applied at the upper right corner of the frame.

Displacement Vector

Similarly when the men in Figure 2.1 report the displacement measurements, $u_i(i = 1, 2, \ldots, 8)$, at their coordinates, we record them in a *displacement vector*.

$$\left\{ \begin{array}{c} u_1 \\ u_2 \\ u_3 \\ \vdots \\ u_8 \end{array} \right\}$$

The displacement vector represents an ordered array of displacement measurements with position and sign having the same significance as in the force vector.

Column Matrix

The force and displacement vectors can be written more compactly as $\{F\}$ and $\{u\}$ respectively. In this form, the letters F and u, which designate force and displacement respectively, can represent any number of measurements, depending on the number of coordinates in the coordinate system. A vector, such as $\{F\}$ or $\{u\}$, representing n measurements is also known as *a column matrix*, or *a matrix of order $n \times 1$* (read: n by one), in which the first number indicates the number of rows and the second number indicates the number of columns in the matrix.

2.3. GENERALIZED OR INDEPENDENT MEASUREMENTS

Independent Forces

In Figure 2.1 each man is free to apply any force he pleases at his particular coordinate. For instance, suppose the man at coordinate 1 decides to change his force from 3^k to 9^k, while all the other men insist on keeping their forces unchanged. As the man at 1 proceeds with the change, the other seven men will keep the forces at their coordinates unchanged. The displacements will change at all the coordinates, but at the moment we are not concerned with these measurements. The man at 1 can make F_1 any other value with F_i ($i = 2, 3, \ldots, 8$) unaltered. Hence we see that the value of F_1 is *independent* of all other F's. A similar argument will show that the value of any F is independent of all other F's or the forces F_i ($i = 1, 2, \ldots, 8$) are *independent*.

Independent Displacements

So far we discussed the force measurements in Figure 2.1 and indicated under what condition they will be independent. Now let us discuss the displacements. A set of n displacement measurements will be independent if each can be assigned an arbitrary value independent of all others. For instance, in Figure 2.1 we can assign u_i ($i = 1, 2, \ldots, 7$) some specific values and hold these values while we keep assigning different values to u_8. In the process, the forces at all the coordinates will keep changing, however, we are not concerned with their values when we focus our attention on the displacements.

To summarize, we say that a system of n measurements is independent if each measurement can be varied arbitrarily and independently. Independent measurements are also referred to as *generalized measurements.*†

Degrees of Freedom

The number of independent displacement measurements that serve to describe all possible displacement configurations of a structure is known as the number of its *degrees of freedom*. It is apparent then that any elastic structure has an infinite number of degrees of freedom. If, however, we content ourselves with a limited description of a deformed configuration, by selecting a finite number of coordinates as in Figure 2.1, then this finite

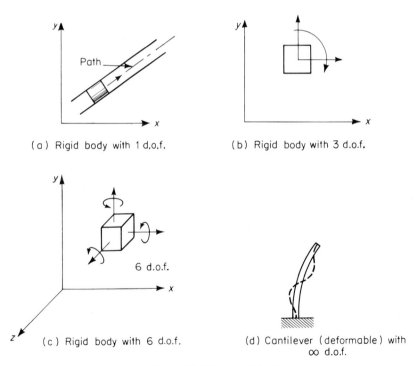

(a) Rigid body with 1 d.o.f.

(b) Rigid body with 3 d.o.f.

6 d.o.f.

(c) Rigid body with 6 d.o.f.

(d) Cantilever (deformable) with ∞ d.o.f.

Figure 2.2. Degrees of freedom.

---

† In this book, we are concerned with forces and displacements, but the definitions of measurements and independent measurements apply also to temperature, pressure, volume, etc., which are scalars and have no direction.

number of displacement measurements will describe all possible configurations to our satisfaction, but the shape of the structure between coordinates will not be known. For instance, in Figure 2.1, we can produce an infinite number of displacement configurations of the members (by assigning men to new stations) while the displacements at the eight coordinates shown remain unchanged.

A rigid body in which no point can be displaced relative to any other point has a finite number of degrees of freedom. For instance, in Figure 2.2(a), the rigid body constrained to move along a path in the plane of the paper has 1 d.o.f. The rigid body in Figure 2.2(b), free to move in a plane, has 3 d.o.f.; and the rigid body in space, Figure 2.2(c), has 6 d.o.f. Figure 2.2(d) shows a cantilever beam (deformable material) which has, of course, an infinite number of d.o.f.

2.4. CONSTRAINED OR DEPENDENT MEASUREMENTS

A set of measurements is *dependent* when each measurement cannot be varied arbitrarily and independently of the other measurements in the set. A dependent set of measurements is said to be *constrained*. We use the word *measurement* here, because it is possible to have a system of coordinates in which the force measurements are independent while the displacements are dependent, and vice versa. The relationship among constrained measurements is expressed by equations which are called *equations of constraint*.

Constrained Displacements

Let us return to Figure 2.1 and see under what conditions the displacement measurements will be constrained. Suppose the axial stiffness of the members is so great that no change in their length can be detected, however large the axial forces. In this case, we cannot arbitrarily and independently assign eight displacements because as long as the man at 1, for example, keeps his displacement, the man at 3 will find it impossible to produce a different displacement at his coordinate. The same holds true for coordinates 2 and 4. These displacement constraints can be expressed by the following equations of constraint:

$$u_1 - u_3 = 0, \quad \text{or} \quad u_1 = u_3$$

$$u_2 - u_4 = 0, \quad \text{or} \quad u_2 = u_4$$

The number of independent displacements is now only six, in which only one of the coordinates 1 or 3, and only one of the coordinates 2 or 4 is present.

If, however, we focus our attention on the forces that can be applied at the eight coordinates of Figure 2.1, we find them to be independent, because the men at 1, 2, 3, and 4, as well as at the other coordinates, are free to apply independently any force they please.

Constrained Forces

To give an example of a reverse situation in which the forces are dependent and the displacements are independent let us refer to Figure 2.3. Four coordinates are shown for the beam in Figure 2.3(a). The four men assigned to these coordinates in Figure 2.3(b) are given the following instructions: They can produce displacements or apply forces at their respective coordinates, provided that the beam does not undergo any acceleration. This means that no net force can act on the beam at any time, or else an acceleration will result as a consequence of Newton's second law of motion

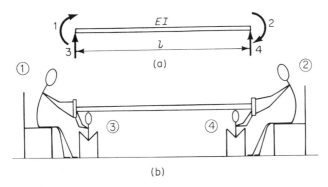

Figure 2.3. Dependent force measurements.

(force equals the product of the mass and acceleration). In Figure 2.3 this implies that the force at 3 will always be equal and opposite to the force at 4, and the sum of the moments on the beam will always be zero. These are, of course, the two conditions of static equilibrium for the beam (the third condition, that is, no net force to the right, is implied by our figure which makes no provision for applying forces in this direction). The two conditions of equilibrium can be written as (consider moments taken about the right end of the beam)

$$F_1 + F_2 + F_3 l = 0, \quad \text{or} \quad F_1 = -F_2 - F_3 l$$

and

$$F_3 + F_4 = 0, \quad \text{or} \quad F_3 = -F_4$$

These equations constrain our freedom of assigning force measurements at the four coordinates, and they may be thought of as equations of constraint on the force measurements. Because of these constraints no more than two force measurements can be assigned arbitrarily (see Problem 1), with the other two determined from the equations of constraint which are, of course, in this case the equations of equilibrium.

The four displacement measurements in the present case are independent, however, and can be assigned arbitrary values.

In general, in a system with m measurements and r equations of constraint amongst them, there are $m - r$ independent measurements. All m measurements can be expressed in terms of the $m - r$ independent ones.

Suggested Exercise: Do problem 1.

2.5. n-DIMENSIONAL SPACE

It is interesting to relate the concepts developed so far to more familiar ones. We know from geometry that two independent measurements can be assigned to a point in two-dimensional space (a plane), and three to a point in three-dimensional space. The eight coordinates of the frame in Figure 2.1 can be assigned eight independent measurements although the frame is in the plane of the paper. Mathematically, however, the forces and displacements at the eight coordinates of Figure 2.1 have the same significance as the coordinates of a point in two- or three-dimensional space; that is, the concept of independence is the same for all these coordinates. It is therefore customary to refer to problems in which n independent measurements are present as problems in *n-dimensional space* or in n space. The vectors of ordered measurements in n space are referred to as *vectors in n space*. We note here again that the measurements need not have direction. They can be scalars, such as temperature, pressure, and volume, etc. For instance a vector in 5-dimensional space may represent the temperature, $T(t_1)$, the pressure, $P(t_1)$, the displacement, $u(t_1)$, the velocity, $v(t_1)$, and the acceleration, $a(t_1)$, all measured at time t_1, for a point mass in a system.

$$\begin{Bmatrix} T(t_1) \\ P(t_1) \\ u(t_1) \\ v(t_1) \\ a(t_1) \end{Bmatrix}$$

2.6. BEHAVIOR OF STRUCTURES

In considering the force-displacement relationships of a structure we distinguish the following modes of behavior: elastic, inelastic, linear, nonlinear.

Elastic and Inelastic Behavior. A structure is elastic or inelastic depending upon its response to the application of loads.† If after the loads are removed from a structure it returns to the configuration it had before the loads were applied, then the structure behaves elastically. On the other hand, if upon removal of the loads the structure does not return to its initial configuration, its behavior is inelastic. Elastic or inelastic behavior is characteristic of the material used to form the structure.

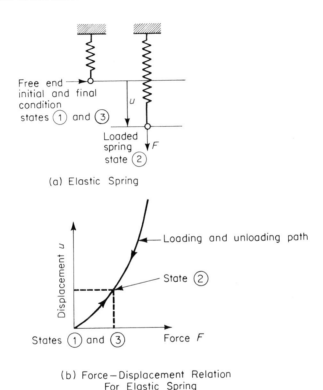

(a) Elastic Spring

(b) Force–Displacement Relation
For Elastic Spring

Figure 2.4. Elastic spring.

An example of elastic behavior is shown in Figure 2.4. The elastic spring follows the same force-displacement curve in loading and unloading and always returns to its initial unloaded position (state 1) when the load is removed (state 3).

To demonstrate a case of inelastic behavior we refer to Figure 2.5. The spring of Figure 2.5 behaves elastically up to a point which is designated on its force displacement curve as the *proportional limit*. Beyond this

---

† The term *load* is used here in the same sense as an applied force.

point the spring is inelastic, and when loaded to state 2 it experiences a displacement u which is not completely recovered after the load is removed at state 3. The permanent displacement at state 3 is designated by u^*. The behavior of the spring in Figure 2.5 is typical of many structural materials[11].

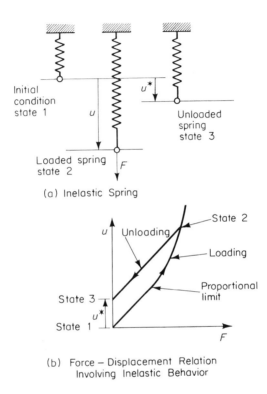

(a) Inelastic Spring

(b) Force – Displacement Relation
Involving Inelastic Behavior

Figure 2.5. Inelastic spring.

Linear and Nonlinear Behavior. A structure behaves as a linear or nonlinear system, depending on whether its force displacement relation is linear or nonlinear.

We consider first a simple spring as a linear structure with its force displacement relation written as

$$u = \frac{1}{k}F \tag{2.1}$$

in which F and u are, respectively, the force and displacement at the free end of the spring, and k is the spring stiffness constant. Equation (2.1) is a linear equation, and mathematically it implies that the displacement due to a number of loads acting simultaneously on the spring can be obtained by adding the displacements due to each load applied separately. This is the *principle of superposition* which applies to all linear systems, structural, electrical, and others.

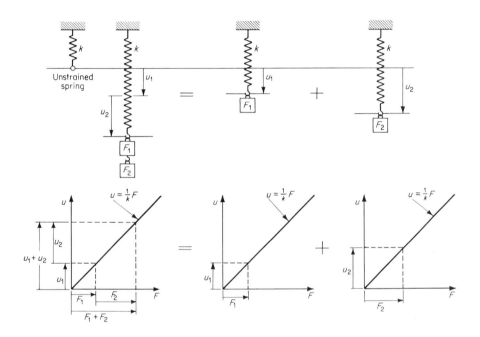

Figure 2.6. Principle of superposition (linear springs).

The principle of superposition is demonstrated in Figure 2.6. On the left of the equal sign, the spring is loaded first with F_1 causing displacement u_1, then F_2 is added causing displacement u_2. On the right, two springs identical to the one on the left are loaded with F_1 and F_2 separately causing displacements u_1 and u_2 respectively. The important point here is that the *loading history* is not relevant to the effect of a particular force. For instance, force F_2 will always cause the same displacement u_2, no matter how much load was placed on the spring (and is still there) before it is applied.

When a structure is nonlinear, superposition does not apply, and the displacement due to a given load depends upon the total force that is presently acting on the structure, that is, the *loading history*. Figure 2.7 demonstrates why superposition does not apply to a nonlinear spring which has the nonlinear force displacement relation

$$u = \frac{1}{k}F^n \tag{2.2}$$

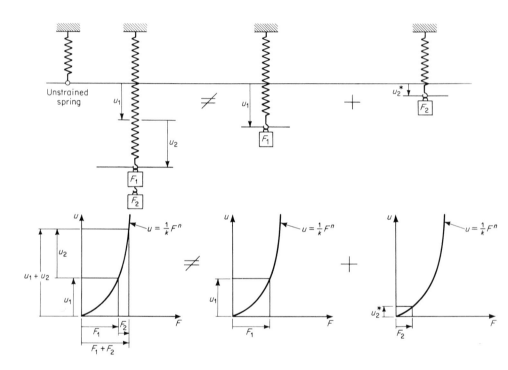

Figure 2.7. Superposition not applicable to nonlinear springs.

where $n \neq 1$ and k is a constant. On the left of the "not equal" sign ($\neq$) the spring is first loaded with F_1 causing displacement u_1, then F_2 is added causing u_2. On the right, two springs identical to the one on the left are loaded with F_1 and F_2 separately, causing displacements u_1 and u_2^* respectively. But $u_2 \neq u_2^*$ because the loading history is not the same in the two cases, and F_2 following F_1 causes a much larger displacement than when it is applied with no load preceding it.

Nonlinear behavior of a structure may be due to the inherent nonlinear stress–strain relationship of the material or due to the changes in the geometry (dimensions and configuration) caused by the loads. If the material has a linear stress-strain curve, then as long as the displacements caused by the loads are small compared to the dimensions of the structure (its geometry), the structure will behave linearly for all practical purposes (neglecting second-order effects in the computations). The structural theory dealing with such structures is referred to as the *small deflection theory*. As the displacements increase, greater inaccuracies in the computation are caused by the linearity assumption and *large deflection theory* must be applied. (In this book we are concerned only with elastic and linear structures.)

2.7. SUPERPOSITION

To illustrate the power of the principle of superposition we shall use it to investigate the behavior of structures. We know from Section 2.6 that the effects of a given number of forces at the coordinates of a structure can be obtained by a superposition of the individual force measurements and their corresponding displacements. The same is true for displacements; that is, the forces required to produce a given set of displacement measurements at the coordinates of a structure can be obtained by a superposition of the separate displacement measurements and their corresponding forces. In each case, whether we focus our attention on the forces or on the displacements, both are present. We shall, however, distinguish between a superposition of forces and a superposition of displacements, depending on whether we apply the forces separately (one at a time) or the displacements separately. Let us consider a few examples in each case.

2.8. SUPERPOSITION OF FORCES

Example 1

Consider the cantilever beam of Figure 2.8(a) loaded with known forces F_1 and F_2 as shown. Suppose that we know how to compute the deflected configuration of a cantilever beam and all the internal stresses as caused by a single concentrated load. Then we can use this knowledge to find the deflected configuration and internal stresses in Figure 2.8 by a superposition of forces. In Figures 2.8(b, c), forces F_1 and F_2 are applied separately, and the sum of the displacements at any point in these figures gives the displacement at the corresponding point in Figure 2.8(a). Similarly, the sum of the stresses at any point in Figures 2.8(b, c) is equal to the stress at the corresponding point in Figure 2.8(a).

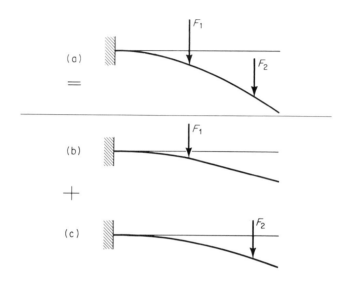

Figure 2.8.

Example 2

A second example of superposition of forces is shown in Figure 2.9. The beam is fixed at one end and simply supported at the other end. Figures 2.9(b, c, d) show how we superpose the applied forces F_1, F_2, and the reaction F_3 so that in each case we again deal with a cantilever beam and a single concentrated load. The displacements at the three coordinates in each figure are identified by a superscript (b), (c), or (d) corresponding to Figure 2.9(b), (c), and (d), respectively. In Figure 2.9(a), we know only F_1 and F_2 but not F_3. We can, therefore, find the displacements and stresses in Figures 2.9(b, c), but how about Figure 2.9(d)? Reexamination of Figure 2.9 will give us a clue. Since in superposing Figures 2.9(b, c, d) we must get Figure 2.9(a), the sum of the displacements at the tip of the cantilever in (b), (c), and (d) must add up to zero, or

$$u_3^{(b)} + u_3^{(c)} + u_3^{(d)} = 0$$

Since F_1 and F_2 are given there is nothing we can do about Figures 2.9(b, c). This means that F_3 in (d) must be chosen such that it will cause the tip of the cantilever to displace an amount equal in magnitude and opposite in direction to the sum of the corresponding displacements in Figures 2.9(b, c).

Since we know how to compute the displacements in Figures 2.9(b, c), we can use this information to work backwards (from displacement to force) and find the appropriate value of F_3.

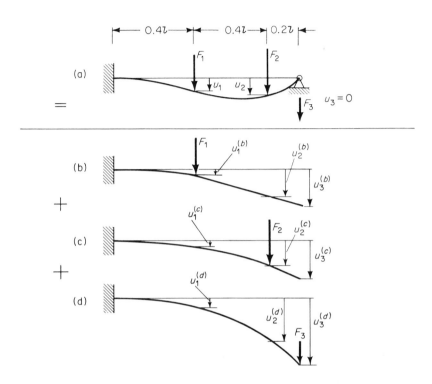

Figure 2.9.

Example 3

A third, more complex, example where superposition of forces can be applied is shown in Figure 2.10. The frame shown is loaded with F_1 and F_2 which are known. Again we know how to compute the stresses and displacements for a cantilever with a single concentrated force (which may, of course, be a couple). The reactions F_3, F_4, and F_5 are not known. The configurations to be superimposed are shown for F_1 and F_5; the reader may fill in the rest.

The reactions F_3, F_4, and F_5 will be established by satisfying three conditions of constraint on the displacements at coordinates 3, 4, and 5 which will result in three simultaneous equations in terms of F_3, F_4, and F_5.

With F_3, F_4, and F_5 established, the stresses and displacements on the frame are obtained by a superposition of the corresponding values in Figures 2.10(b, c, d, e, f).

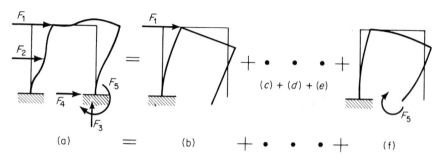

Figure 2.10.

Example 4

We proceed with a fourth example which we shall actually solve and use in later developments. The beam of Figure 2.3 is deformed as shown in Figure 2.11(a). The displacement vector $\{u\}$ is given by

$$
\begin{Bmatrix} 1 \\ 0 \\ 0 \\ 0 \end{Bmatrix}
$$

and the force vector $\{F\}$ is not known. Figures 2.11(b, c) show the superposition† of forces F_1 and F_3, applied separately, which will yield Figure 2.11(a) (F_2 and F_4 are dependent upon F_1 and F_3, see Section 2.4).

Considering only bending deformations, we can use the moment area method[12] to calculate u_1 and u_3 in Figures 2.11(b, c). In these figures, the forces F and displacements u are shown in the positive direction which is established by the coordinates shown in Figure 2.11(a), and the moment diagrams are drawn on the compression side of the member. For simplicity let the moment of inertia, I, along the beam be constant (prismatic member). From the moment area method[12], the displacements $u_1^{(b)}$ and $u_1^{(c)}$ in Figures 2.11(b, c), respectively, are given by the area of the corresponding moment diagrams divided by the flexural rigidity EI. Hence,

$$
u_1^{(b)} = \frac{F_1 l}{EI} \quad \text{and} \quad u_1^{(c)} = \frac{1}{2} \frac{F_3 l^2}{EI} \tag{2.3}
$$

---

† It is possible to superpose any two force measurements which are independent.

The displacements $u_3^{(b)}$ and $u_3^{(c)}$ are given by the static moment of the moment/EI diagrams in Figures 2.11(b, c), respectively, taken about the left end of the beam.

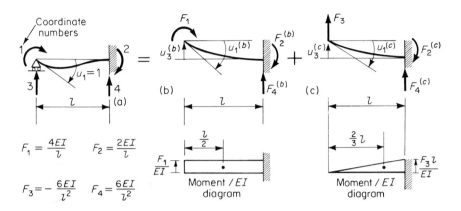

$$F_1 = \frac{4EI}{l} \qquad F_2 = \frac{2EI}{l}$$

$$F_3 = -\frac{6EI}{l^2} \qquad F_4 = \frac{6EI}{l^2}$$

$E =$ Modulus of elasticity
$I =$ Moment of inertia of cross section

Figure 2.11.

$$u_3^{(b)} = \left(\frac{F_1 l}{EI}\right)\left(\frac{l}{2}\right) \qquad \text{and} \qquad u_3^{(c)} = \left(\frac{1}{2}l\frac{F_3 l}{EI}\right)\left(\frac{2}{3}l\right) \tag{2.4}$$

To match the displacement configuration in Figure 2.11(a)

$$u_1^{(b)} + u_1^{(c)} = 1 \qquad \text{and} \qquad u_3^{(b)} + u_3^{(c)} = 0 \tag{2.5}$$

Substituting from Equations (2.3) and (2.4) into Equation (2.5) gives

$$F_1 + \frac{1}{2}F_3 l = \frac{EI}{l}$$

$$F_1 + \frac{2}{3}F_3 l = 0$$

The solution of these two simultaneous equations yields

$$F_1 = \frac{4EI}{l} \qquad \text{and} \qquad F_3 = \frac{-6EI}{l^2}$$

The minus sign means that F_3 acts opposite to the arrow shown for the coordinate 3 in Figure 2.11(a). Using the values of F_1 and F_3, we compute

$F_2^{(b)}$, $F_2^{(c)}$, $F_4^{(b)}$, and $F_4^{(c)}$ from equilibrium and superpose them to give

$$F_2 = F_2^{(b)} + F_2^{(c)} = -F_1 - F_3 l = \frac{2EI}{l}$$

$$F_4 = F_4^{(b)} + F_4^{(c)} = 0 - F_3 = \frac{6EI}{l^2}$$

F_2 and F_4 can also be solved directly from Figure 2.11(a) using the conditions of equilibrium, that is, $F_2 = -F_1 - F_3 l$, and $F_4 = -F_3$.

Summarizing our results, we have a unique force vector

$$\begin{Bmatrix} 4EI/l \\ 2EI/l \\ -6EI/l^2 \\ 6EI/l^2 \end{Bmatrix} \tag{2.6}$$

corresponding to the displacement vector

$$\begin{Bmatrix} 1 \\ 0 \\ 0 \\ 0 \end{Bmatrix} \tag{2.7}$$

at the coordinates of the prismatic beam in Figure 2.11.

The value of $F_1 = 4EI/l$ in Figure 2.11(a) and the ratio $F_2/F_1 = \frac{1}{2}$ are respectively the stiffness and carry-over factor used in the moment distribution method of structural analysis[47, 12, 13, 14].

Suggested Exercise: Do problem 2.

2.9. SUPERPOSITION OF DISPLACEMENTS

We now focus our attention on displacements at selected coordinates and produce them separately one at a time, then apply superposition to yield a final configuration. The stresses and displacements at any point on the structure in the final configuration will be equal to the sum of the corresponding values in the superposed configurations.

Example 1

Consider the beam of Figure 2.3 with the four coordinates as shown and apply a force vector $\{F\}$ to produce a displacement vector $\{u\}$ in which $u_1 \neq 0$, $u_2 \neq 0$, and $u_3 = u_4 = 0$. The resulting configuration is shown in Figure 2.12(a). In Figures 2.12(b, c), u_1 and u_2 are produced separately by force vectors whose elements are designated by superscripts (b) and (c), respectively. A superposition of Figures 2.12(b, c) will yield Figure 2.12(a). Let us use this procedure to compute force vector $\{F\}$ in Figure 2.12(a) in terms of u_1 and u_2.

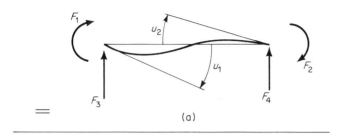

(a)

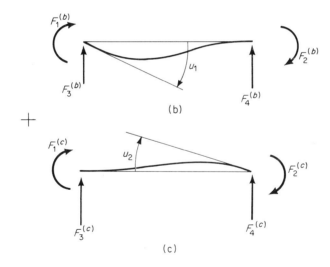

(b)

(c)

Figure 2.12.

When we examine Figure 2.12(b), we find it similar to Figure 2.11(a) except that $u_1 \neq 1$. Since superposition applies to our linear systems, the elements of the force vector in Figure 2.12(b) are different by a factor u_1 from those in Figure 2.11(a). The force vector in Figure 2.11(a) is given by the vector of Equation (2.6); hence, multiplying all its elements by u_1, we obtain for Figure 2.12(b)

$$F_1^{(b)} = (4EI/l)u_1$$
$$F_2^{(b)} = (2EI/l)u_1$$
$$F_3^{(b)} = -(6EI/l^2)u_1$$
$$F_4^{(b)} = (6EI/l^2)u_1$$

Figure 2.12(c) is also similar to Figure 2.11(a), except that the rotation is at coordinate 2. Hence, we obtain

$$F_1^{(c)} = (2EI/l)u_2$$
$$F_2^{(c)} = (4EI/l)u_2$$
$$F_3^{(c)} = -(6EI/l^2)u_2$$
$$F_4^{(c)} = (6EI/l^2)u_2$$

Adding the corresponding force and displacement measurements at the four coordinates of Figures 2.12(b, c) we obtain, for Figure 2.12(a),

$$F_1 = (4EI/l)u_1 + (2EI/l)u_2$$
$$F_2 = (2EI/l)u_1 + (4EI/l)u_2$$
$$F_3 = -(6EI/l^2)u_1 - (6EI/l^2)u_2$$
$$F_4 = (6EI/l^2)u_1 + (6EI/l^2)u_2$$

$$u_1 = u_1 + 0$$
$$u_2 = 0 + u_2$$
$$u_3 = 0 + 0$$
$$u_4 = 0 + 0$$

Again we note that F_3 and F_4 can be obtained directly from Figure 2.12(a) by using the conditions of equilibrium. We proceeded differently here for the sake of completeness.

Example 2

Let us try another example in which the fundamental information of Figure 2.11(a) is again used in a superposition of displacements. We wish to compute the force F_1 required to produce displacements $u_1 = 1$, and $u_3 = u_4 = 0$, provided that F_2 equals 0, as shown in Figure 2.13(a). The value of F_1 in Figure 2.13(a) is known in moment distribution as the *reduced stiffness* of the member[12]. In Figures 2.13(b, c), u_1 and u_2 are produced separately. Using the results for Figure 2.11(a), the forces at coordinates 1 and 2 are recorded in Figure 2.13(b). [The forces at coordinates 3 and 4 are not shown, their final values will be computed from Figure 2.13(a).] In Figure 2.13(c), u_2 is produced. The value of u_2 is not known at this stage, but the force at coordinate 2 must be equal and opposite to the corresponding force in Figure 2.13(b) so that the condition $F_2 = 0$, in Figure 2.13(a), will not be violated. Hence, a moment of magnitude $2EI/l$

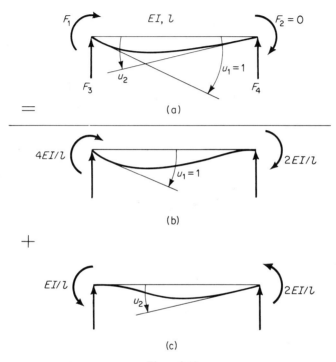

Figure 2.13.

is applied at coordinate 2 as shown, and from Figure 2.11(a) we know that half of this value must be applied at coordinate 1 as shown. We also know now from Figure 2.11 that $u_2 = -\frac{1}{2}$. Adding the force and displacement measurements at the four coordinates in Figures 2.13(b, c) we obtain for Figure 2.13(a)

$$
\begin{aligned}
F_1 &= 3EI/l & u_1 &= 1 \\
F_2 &= 0 & u_2 &= -\tfrac{1}{2} \\
F_3 &= -3EI/l^2 & u_3 &= 0 \\
F_4 &= 3EI/l^2 & u_4 &= 0.
\end{aligned}
\tag{2.8}
$$

in which the positive direction of the u's and F's is as shown by the co-ordinates in Figure 2.3.

Example 3

Another example of superposition of displacements using the fundamental information of Figure 2.11(a) is shown in Figures 2.14 and 2.15. The displacement vectors in Figures 2.14(a) and 2.15(a) are given, respectively, by

$$\begin{Bmatrix} 0 \\ 0 \\ u_3 \\ 0 \end{Bmatrix} \quad \text{and} \quad \begin{Bmatrix} 0 \\ 0 \\ 0 \\ u_4 \end{Bmatrix}$$

The corresponding force vectors $\{F\}$ are computed by superposition as shown. First the member is rotated as a rigid body an amount u_3/l and u_4/l in Figures 2.14(b) and 2.15(b), respectively. Then the rotation at coordinates 1 and 2 is set equal to zero by producing in (c) and (d) of Figures 2.14 and 2.15, rotations at 1 and 2 in a direction opposite to that in (b) of Figures 2.14 and 2.15 respectively. Figures 2.14(b) and 2.15(b) involve no forces at the coordinates, and the forces in (c) and (d) of Figures 2.14 and 2.15 are computed from Figure 2.11. The positive direction of the u's and F's is as shown by the coordinates in Figure 2.3. The results of the superposition yield F_1 and F_2 for Figures 2.14(a) and 2.15(a), with F_3, F_4 computed by applying the conditions of equilibrium. The force vector in Figure 2.14(a) is found to be

$$\begin{Bmatrix} F_1 \\ F_2 \\ F_3 \\ F_4 \end{Bmatrix} = \begin{Bmatrix} -(6EI/l^2)u_3 \\ -(6EI/l^2)u_3 \\ (12EI/l^3)u_3 \\ -(12EI/l^3)u_3 \end{Bmatrix} \tag{2.9}$$

The single equal sign in this equation implies that all corresponding elements in the two columns are equal. Similarly for Figure 2.15(a) we have

$$\begin{Bmatrix} F_1 \\ F_2 \\ F_3 \\ F_4 \end{Bmatrix} = \begin{Bmatrix} (6EI/l^2)u_4 \\ (6EI/l^2)u_4 \\ -(12EI/l^3)u_4 \\ (12EI/l^3)u_4 \end{Bmatrix} \tag{2.10}$$

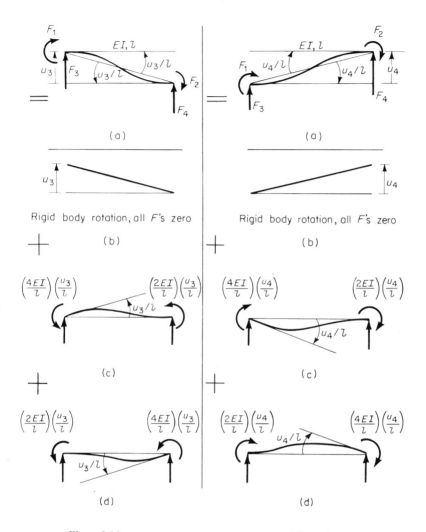

Figure 2.14.   Figure 2.15.

Example 4

As a fourth example, we consider the frame of Figure 2.16(a) with co-ordinates 1 and 2 undergoing displacements u_1, u_2, when acted upon by forces F_1, F_2. The frame members have lengths l_1 and l_2, and flexural rigidities EI_1 and EI_2. In Figures 2.16(b, c), displacements u_1, u_2 are applied separately. From superposition, we can compute F_1 and F_2 in Figure

2.16(a) by adding the corresponding values in Figures 2.16(b) and (c):

$$\begin{Bmatrix} F_1 \\ F_2 \end{Bmatrix} = \begin{Bmatrix} F_1^{(b)} \\ F_2^{(b)} \end{Bmatrix} + \begin{Bmatrix} F_1^{(c)} \\ F_2^{(c)} \end{Bmatrix} \tag{2.11}$$

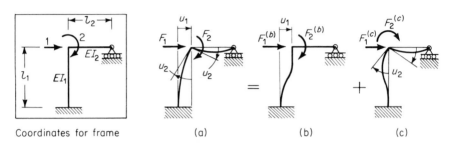

Coordinates for frame   (a)   (b)   (c)

Figure 2.16.

To compute the force vectors in Figures 2.16(b, c), we use the free body diagrams shown in Figures 2.17 and 2.18, respectively.

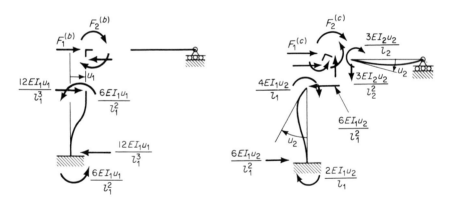

Figure 2.17. Free body diagrams for Fig. 2.16(b).

Figure 2.18. Free body diagram for Fig. 2.16(c).

In Figure 2.17, the results of Figure 2.15(a), Equation (2.10), were used to write the forces in the free body diagram of the column (note that u_4 in Figure 2.15(a) corresponds to u_1 in Figure 2.17). In Figure 2.18, the results of Figures 2.11(a) and 2.13(a) were used for the column and beam, respectively. Writing the equations of equilibrium at coordinates 1 and 2 in Figures 2.17 and 2.18 (the sum of horizontal forces is zero, and the sum of moments is zero for the free body of the corner) we have, from Figure 2.17,

$$F_1^{(b)} - 12EI_1u_1/l_1^3 = 0$$
$$F_2^{(b)} + 6EI_1u_1/l_1^2 = 0$$

and from Figure 2.18

$$F_1^{(c)} + 6EI_1u_2/l_1^2 = 0$$
$$F_2^{(c)} - 4EI_1u_2/l_1 - 3EI_2u_2/l_2 = 0$$

or

$$\begin{Bmatrix} F_1^{(b)} \\ F_2^{(b)} \end{Bmatrix} = \begin{Bmatrix} 12EI_1u_1/l_1^3 \\ -6EI_1u_1/l_1^2 \end{Bmatrix}$$

and

$$\begin{Bmatrix} F_1^{(c)} \\ F_2^{(c)} \end{Bmatrix} = \begin{Bmatrix} -6EI_1u_2/l_1^2 \\ 4EI_1u_2/l_1 + 3EI_2u_2/l_2 \end{Bmatrix}$$

Substituting these values in Equation (2.11) gives F_1 and F_2 in terms of u_1 and u_2

$$\begin{Bmatrix} F_1 \\ F_2 \end{Bmatrix} = \begin{Bmatrix} 12EI_1u_1/l_1^3 - 6EI_1u_2/l_1^2 \\ -6EI_1u_1/l_1^2 + 4EI_1u_2/l_1 + 3EI_2u_2/l_2 \end{Bmatrix}$$

2.10. METHODS OF STRUCTURAL ANALYSIS

The Force or Compatibility Method†

The superposition of forces in Figures 2.9, 2.10, and 2.11 is typical of the *Force* or *Compatibility Method* used to analyze indeterminate structures. The condition that the tip of the cantilever in Figures 2.9, for instance, must remain at its support is referred to as a condition of *displacement compatibility*. This condition is used to establish the value of F_3 in Figure 2.9. Similar conditions are used to compute F_3, F_4, and F_5 in Figure 2.10 or F_1 and F_2 in Figure 2.11. Compatibility conditions in general, are those conditions which insure that all parts (elements) of the structure will fit together and that no *boundary conditions*, such as points which are fixed against translation, or rotation, or both, will be violated when the final displaced configuration of the structure is obtained by superposition. The compatibility conditions can be expressed as equations of compatibility

† This method is called the *Flexibility Method* in this book and is treated in Ch. 8.

which constitute equations of constraint on the displacement measurements of the structure (for instance in Figure 2.9, $u_3 = 0$ and in Figure 2.10, $u_3 = u_4 = u_5 = 0$). The topics mentioned in this paragraph will be discussed in greater detail in a later chapter, and the comments here should be considered as a first exposure to them.

The Displacement or Equilibrium Method‡

The superposition of displacements in Figure 2.16 is typical of the *Displacement* or *Equilibrium Method* used to formulate and solve problems in structural analysis. Here the conditions of compatibility are always satisfied because no geometric constraints are removed from the structure as in the superposition of forces. However, we satisfy the conditions of equilibrium on free bodies involving the coordinates of interest. As indicated earlier in this chapter, the equations of equilibrium constitute equations of constraint on the forces in much the same way as the equations of compatibility constitute constraints on the displacements in the superposition of forces.

As is seen from this discussion there is an analogy between the superposition of forces and displacements. When forces are superposed, displacements are constrained to satisfy conditions of compatibility; when displacements are superposed, forces are constrained to satisfy the conditions of equilibrium. Again we emphasize that both forces and displacements are present and both conditions (compatibility and equilibrium) are satisfied in each case. The measurements which are applied one at a time in the process of superposition distinguish between superposition of forces and of displacements.

In the analysis of structures the choice between a procedure involving superposition of forces or displacements will depend on the particular problem considered, the ease of formulation, and the time required for the computations. The ease of formulation and computing time depend on how sophisticated and how complete our computer programs are and on the capabilities of the computer. We shall discuss these matters in later chapters and give reasons and guides for an appropriate choice of procedure, depending on the problem and the circumstances under which a solution must be obtained.

Suggested Exercises: Do problems 3, 4, 5, 6, 7, and 8.

PROBLEMS

Problem 1: Which of the four force coordinates in Figure 2.3(a) can be selected as independent?

‡ This method is called the *Stiffness Method* in this book and is treated in Ch. 9.

Problem 2: In the beam of Figure 2.9 set $EI = $ constant, $F_1 = 2^k$, and $F_2 = 4^k$. Compute F_3, u_1, and u_2.

$$u_1 = u_1^{(b)} + u_1^{(c)} + u_1^{(d)}$$

$$u_2 = u_2^{(b)} + u_2^{(c)} + u_2^{(d)}$$

Problem 3: Use the results of Section 2.9 in a superposition of displacements to express the forces F_i ($i = 1, 2, 3$) in terms of the displacements at the same coordinates.

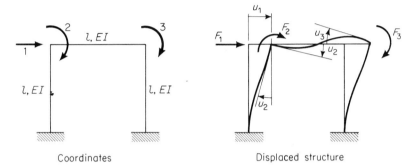

Coordinates   Displaced structure

Problem 4: Repeat problem 3 for the following structure.

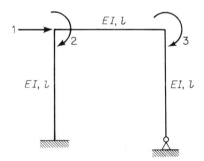

Problem 5: Repeat problem 3 for the following structure.

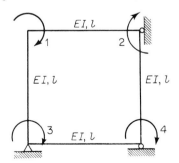

Problem 6: The stepped beam with fixed ends as shown has a force, F_2, applied at coordinate 2, and $F_1 = 0$. Compute the fixed end moments at the ends using the results of Section 2.9 in a superposition of displacements u_1 and u_2. For simplicity set $EI_1 = 2$, $EI_2 = 1$, $l_1 = l_2 = 1$.

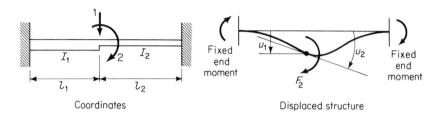

Coordinates   Displaced structure

Problem 7: Repeat problem 6 with $F_1 \neq 0$ and $F_2 = 0$.

Problem 8: In problem 6 replace the fixed end condition at the right end of the stepped beam by a roller. Compute the fixed end moment at the left end for $F_1 = 0$ and $F_2 \neq 0$.

CHAPTER 3

CHARACTERISTICS
OF STRUCTURES:
STIFFNESS AND FLEXIBILITY

3.1. INTRODUCTION

In Chapter 2 we discussed force displacement measurements, and how they can be related by superposition at coordinates of a structure. In this chapter we shall formalize the procedures of relating forces and displacements in a structure by using its *flexibility* and *stiffness coefficients*. These coefficients are characteristics of a structure and its coordinate system.

The *flexibility coefficients* characterize the behavior of the structure by specifying its displacement response to applied forces at the coordinates, and the *stiffness coefficients*—by specifying the forces required to produce given displacements at the coordinates. *The stiffness and flexibility coefficients depend on the force displacement properties of the structure and the coordinate system.*

In developing the concepts of stiffness and flexibility we shall motivate the need for matrix notation and matrix algebra.

3.2. STRUCTURES WITH A SINGLE COORDINATE

In the structures of Figure 3.1 a single coordinate is indicated for force and displacement measurements. The spring in Figure 3.1(a) can be characterized by a *flexibility coefficient, a,* which is defined as the displacement at coordinate 1 caused by a unit force at 1. Since the spring is linear, the displacement u due to a force F will be F times larger than a, or

$$u = aF \tag{3.1}$$

Equation (3.1) serves to transform information in terms of force to information in terms of displacement at coordinate 1. The transformation is effected by the flexibility coefficient, a, which not only transforms the magnitude but also the units of the measurements.†

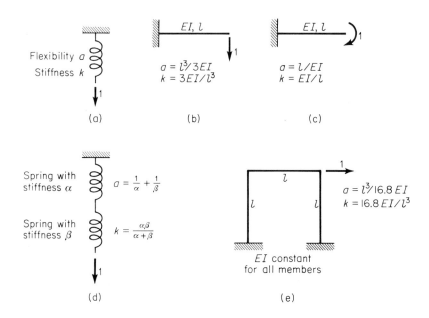

Figure 3.1. Structures with a single coordinate.

An alternate way to characterize the spring is through its *stiffness coefficient*, k, which is defined as the force required at coordinate 1 to produce a unit displacement at 1. The force F required to produce a displacement of u units is computed from

$$F = ku \tag{3.2}$$

This equation transforms displacement measurements to force measurements through the stiffness, k, which has the units of force/displacement.

Substituting Equation (3.2) into Equation (3.1), we conclude that

$$ak = 1 \tag{3.3}$$

Namely, the product of stiffness and flexibility coefficients for a structure with a single coordinate is one, or the stiffness and flexibility are the inverse of each other.

---

† The units of a are displacement/force.

Using the moment area method, see Figure 2.11(c) and Equation (2.4), we find for the beam of Figure 3.1(b)

$$a = \frac{l^3}{3EI} \quad \text{and} \quad k = \frac{3EI}{l^3}$$

Similarly for Figure 3.1(c) we have

$$a = \frac{l}{EI}, \quad k = EI/l$$

In Figure 3.1(d) the stiffness of each spring, considered separately, is given by α and β, respectively. To get the flexibility, a, for the system of the two springs connected as shown, we apply a unit force at 1 and compute the resulting displacement at 1. The springs with stiffnesses α and β will elongate amounts $1/\alpha$ and $1/\beta$, respectively, causing at 1 a total displacement of $1/\alpha + 1/\beta$ or

$$a = \frac{1}{\alpha} + \frac{1}{\beta}$$

To obtain the stiffness k in Figure 3.1(d), we can use Equation (3.3) and simply write $k = 1/a$; let us use this as a check, however, and generate k, independently, by computing the force required to produce a unit displacement at coordinate 1. The unknown force at 1, which is the desired stiffness k, propagates both springs and causes springs α and β to elongate $k(1/\alpha)$, and $k(1/\beta)$ respectively. The sum of these elongations must equal the displacement at 1, or

$$k\frac{1}{\alpha} + k\frac{1}{\beta} = 1,$$

and

$$k = \frac{1}{(1/\alpha) + (1/\beta)} = \frac{\alpha\beta}{\alpha + \beta}$$

This result checks with Equation (3.3), that is, $ak = 1$ for the two spring system of Figure 3.1(d).

The flexibility coefficient for the frame in Figure 3.1(e) is the displacement caused by a unit force at 1, and the stiffness coefficient is the force required to produce a unit displacement at 1. To compute the stiffness and flexibility in Figure 3.1(e) requires much more effort than in (b), (c), or (d) but they have the same significance, and Equations (3.1), (3.2), and (3.3) still apply.

3.3. STRUCTURES WITH TWO COORDINATES

We now extend the concepts of stiffness and flexibility to two coordinates.

Flexibility Matrix

Figure 3.2 shows a structure consisting of two connected springs with stiffnesses α and β and coordinates 1 and 2. Let us characterize the behavior of this structure so that we can easily transform any forces F_1 and F_2 to

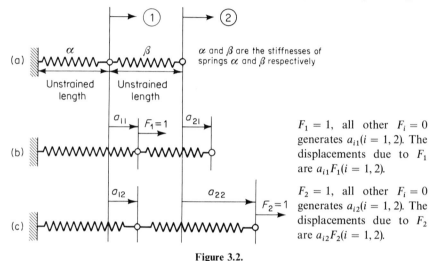

Figure 3.2.

the corresponding displacements u_1, u_2 at the coordinates. To do this, we apply a superposition of forces as follows:

First, we apply a unit force at 1 only, Figure 3.2(b), and designate the displacement at 1 and 2 as a_{11} and a_{21}, respectively. The first subscript designates the coordinate where the displacement is measured, the second subscript designates the coordinate where the unit force is applied. For instance, a_{21} is the displacement at 2 due to a unit force at 1 only.

Next we apply a unit force at 2, Figure 3.2(c), only and designate the displacements at 1 and 2 as a_{12} and a_{22}, respectively.

To find the displacements u_1 and u_2 due to forces F_1 and F_2 acting simultaneously we multiply the displacements in Figure 3.2(b, c) by F_1 and F_2, respectively, then add to give

$$u_1 = a_{11}F_1 + a_{12}F_2$$
$$u_2 = a_{21}F_1 + a_{22}F_2$$

(3.4)

The four displacement influence coefficients a_{ij} ($i = 1, 2; j = 1, 2$) in Equations (3.4) can be arranged in a square box, with their position in the box (address) identified by the subscripts i, j. The first subscript, i, identifies the row number and the second subscript, j, identifies the column number,

Column 1   Column 2

$$\begin{array}{c} \text{row 1} \\ \text{row 2} \end{array} \begin{bmatrix} a_{11} & a_{12} \\ a_{21} & a_{22} \end{bmatrix}$$

This box is the *flexibility matrix*† for the structure of Figure 3.2. We note that the elements of the first column of this matrix are generated by applying a unit force at 1 only, and the elements of the second columns—by applying a unit force at 2 only.

The flexibility matrix can be used to rewrite Equation (3.4) as a *matrix equation*

$$\begin{Bmatrix} u_1 \\ u_2 \end{Bmatrix} = \begin{bmatrix} a_{11} & a_{12} \\ a_{21} & a_{22} \end{bmatrix} \begin{Bmatrix} F_1 \\ F_2 \end{Bmatrix} \tag{3.5}$$

This equation indicates that u_1 is equal to the sum of the products of the elements of the first row of $[a]$ and the elements of vector $\{F\}$, and u_2 is equal to the sum of the products of row 2 of $[a]$ and $\{F\}$. Compare Equations (3.4) and (3.5). For the structure of Figure 3.2

$$\begin{bmatrix} a_{11} & a_{12} \\ a_{21} & a_{22} \end{bmatrix} = \begin{bmatrix} \dfrac{1}{\alpha} & \dfrac{1}{\alpha} \\ \dfrac{1}{\alpha} & \dfrac{1}{\alpha} + \dfrac{1}{\beta} \end{bmatrix} \tag{3.6}$$

In Equation (3.6) each element on the left-hand side is equal to the element in the corresponding position (row and column number) on the right-hand side.

Equation (3.5) is similar to Equation (3.1), and serves to transform information in terms of forces to information in terms of displacements at the coordinates through the use of the flexibility matrix of the structure.

Stiffness Matrix

We shall now characterize the structure of Figure 3.2 in an alternate way so that displacement information at the coordinates can be easily transformed into corresponding forces. To do this we apply a superposition of displacements as shown in Figure 3.3.

---

† A *matrix* in general is defined as a rectangular array of quantities arranged in rows and columns and will be discussed further in Chapter 4.

First we apply a unit displacement at 1 only, Figure 3.3(b), and designate the required forces at 1 and 2 as k_{11} and k_{21}, respectively. The first subscript is the coordinate where the force is measured, and the second subscript is the coordinate where the unit displacement is applied. Similarly in Figure 3.3(c), forces k_{12} and k_{22} are required to cause a unit displacement at 2 only.

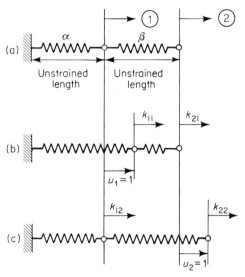

$u_1 = 1$, all other $u_i = 0$ generates $k_{i1}(i = 1, 2)$. The forces required to cause displacement u_1 are $k_{i1}u_1(i = 1, 2)$.

$u_2 = 1$, all other $u_i = 0$ generates $k_{i2}(i = 1, 2)$. The forces required to cause displacement u_2 are $k_{i2}u_2(i = 1, 2)$.

Figure 3.3.

The forces required to produce displacements u_1 and u_2 simultaneously are obtained by a superposition of Figures 3.3(b) and (c) [after all forces in (b) and (c) are multiplied by u_1 and u_2, respectively], to yield

$$F_1 = k_{11}u_1 + k_{12}u_2$$
$$F_2 = k_{21}u_1 + k_{22}u_2$$
(3.7)

The four stiffness influence coefficients k_{ij} in Equation (3.7) can be arranged in a *stiffness matrix*, and Equation (3.7) can be written as the following matrix equation:

$$\begin{Bmatrix} F_1 \\ F_2 \end{Bmatrix} = \begin{bmatrix} k_{11} & k_{12} \\ k_{21} & k_{22} \end{bmatrix} \begin{Bmatrix} u_1 \\ u_2 \end{Bmatrix}$$
(3.8)

The stiffness matrix has the following values for the structure of Figure 3.3

$$\begin{bmatrix} k_{11} & k_{12} \\ k_{21} & k_{22} \end{bmatrix} = \begin{bmatrix} \alpha + \beta & -\beta \\ -\beta & \beta \end{bmatrix}$$
(3.9)

Equation (3.8) is similar to Equation (3.2), and it transforms displacements at the coordinates to forces through the *stiffness matrix.*

Reciprocal Relation between the Stiffness and Flexibility Matrix

The application of Equation (3.3) to the present example is not apparent, because, for example, in Equation (3.6) $a_{11} = 1/\alpha$ and in Equation (3.9) $k_{11} = \alpha + \beta$ and these quantities are certainly not related by Equation (3.3). It turns out that when more than a single coordinate is considered the stiffness and flexibility matrices are the reciprocal of each other in a matrix sense. This is exemplified by the operations in Equation (3.10), in which the flexibility and stiffness matrix of Equations (3.6) and (3.9) are multiplied and yield the *unit matrix*†

$$\begin{bmatrix} 1 & 0 \\ 0 & 1 \end{bmatrix}$$

Any element of the unit matrix is obtained by the inner product of the row in $[a]$ and the column in $[k]$ that intersect at that element.

Col. 1   Col. 2

$$[k] \rightarrow \begin{bmatrix} \alpha + \beta & -\beta \\ -\beta & \beta \end{bmatrix}$$

$$[a] \rightarrow \begin{array}{c} \text{row 1} \\ \text{row 2} \end{array} \begin{bmatrix} \dfrac{1}{\alpha} & \dfrac{1}{\alpha} \\ \dfrac{1}{\alpha} & \dfrac{1}{\alpha} + \dfrac{1}{\beta} \end{bmatrix} \quad \begin{bmatrix} 1 & 0 \\ 0 & 1 \end{bmatrix} \leftarrow [a][k] \qquad (3.10)$$

([a] and [k] designate respectively the flexibility and stiffness matrices). For example, the value of 1 at the intersection of the first row of [a] and the first column of [k] is obtained by, see Equation (3.10)

$$\frac{1}{\alpha}(\alpha + \beta) + \frac{1}{\alpha}(-\beta) = 1$$

Similarly the zero at the intersection of the first row of [a] and second column of [k] is obtained from

$$\frac{1}{\alpha}(-\beta) + \frac{1}{\alpha}\beta = 0$$

---

† Matrix multiplication and the unit matrix are discussed in Chapter 4. The discussion here is a first exposure to this subject.

etc. The product in Equation (3.10) is written in compact notation as

$$[a][k] = [I] \qquad (3.11)$$

in which $[I]$ is the matrix with ones on the main diagonal and zeros elsewhere and is known as the *unit matrix*. Equation (3.11) is analogous to Equation (3.3) which applies to a single coordinate.

We shall now generalize the concepts of stiffness and flexibility matrices to structures with n coordinates.

3.4. FLEXIBILITY AND STIFFNESS MATRICES IN n COORDINATES

The procedures of the last section apply to structures with more than two coordinates, and can be generalized as follows:

Flexibility Matrix in n Coordinates

To generate a flexibility matrix in n coordinates proceed this way. Apply a unit force at coordinate 1 only and compute (or measure) the displacements $a_{i1}(i = 1, 2, \ldots, n)$ at all the coordinates; this yields the first column of the flexibility matrix. To generate the second column apply a unit force at coordinate 2 only and compute the displacements $a_{i2}(i = 1, 2, \ldots, n)$. Finally, to generate the nth column apply the unit force at coordinate n only and compute $a_{in}(i = 1, 2, \ldots, n)$. In general then, to generate the jth column of the flexibility matrix apply a unit force at coordinate j only and compute $a_{ij}(i = 1, 2, \ldots, n)$. This procedure indicates that the flexibility matrix is a *square matrix*; that is, it has the same number of rows and columns because n columns are generated and in each case n rows are recorded.

The flexibility matrix will be designated by $[a]$ with any of its elements a_{ij}, situated in row i and column j, defined as *the displacement at coordinate i due to a unit force at coordinate j only* (*zero forces at all the other coordinates*).

Stiffness Matrix in n Coordinates

To generate a stiffness matrix in n coordinates proceed as follows: Apply a unit displacement at coordinate 1 only and compute (or measure) the forces $k_{i1}(i = 1, 2, \ldots, n)$ required at all the coordinates; this yields the first column of the stiffness matrix. To generate the second column apply a unit displacement at coordinate 2 only and compute all k_{i2} $(i = 1, 2, \ldots, n)$. Finally, to generate the nth column apply a unit displacement at coordinate n only and compute k_{in} $(i = 1, 2, \ldots, n)$. In general, to generate the jth column of the stiffness matrix, apply a unit displacement at coordinate j only and compute the required forces k_{ij} $(i = 1, 2, \ldots, n)$. This procedure serves to indicate that the stiffness matrix is also a square matrix.

The stiffness matrix will be designated as $[k]$ with any of its elements, k_{ij}, situated in row i and column j, defined as *the force required at coordinate i to produce a unit displacement at coordinate j only* (*zero displacements at all other coordinates*).

Force Displacement Relations

Using the matrices $[a]$ and $[k]$, the force and displacement vectors at the coordinates are related by

$$\{u\} = [a]\{F\} \tag{3.12}$$

which in expanded form is

$$u_1 = \sum_{j=1}^{n} a_{1j}F_j = a_{11}F_1 + a_{12}F_2 + \cdots + a_{1n}F_n$$

$$u_2 = \sum_{j=1}^{n} a_{2j}F_j$$

$$\vdots$$

$$u_n = \sum_{j=1}^{n} a_{nj}F_j$$

That is, the ith element of $\{u\}$ in Equation (3.12) is equal to the sum of the products of the elements a_{ij} $(j = 1, 2, \ldots, n)$ in row i of $[a]$ and the corresponding elements, F_j, of $\{F\}$. Similarly,

$$\{F\} = [k]\{u\} \tag{3.13}$$

which is expanded as

$$F_1 = \sum_{j=1}^{n} k_{1j}u_j = k_{11}u_1 + k_{12}u_2 + \cdots + k_{1n}u_n$$

$$F_2 = \sum_{j=1}^{n} k_{2j}u_j$$

$$\vdots$$

$$F_n = \sum_{j=1}^{n} k_{nj}u_j$$

Reciprocal Relation between [a] and [k] in n Coordinates

As we shall prove in Chapter 4, Equation (3.11) will hold for any number of coordinates n, provided that $[a]$ and $[k]$ exist. The conditions under which $[a]$ or $[k]$ may not exist will be discussed in Section 3.6.

3.5. EXAMPLES

A number of examples will help to reinforce the concepts of the stiffness and flexibility matrix.

Example 1 (Figure 3.4)

To generate the first column of [a] for the three coordinates in Figure 3.4 we apply a unit force at coordinate 1 only which causes springs α and β to elongate an amount equal to a_{11}. From equilibrium the sum of the forces in springs α and β must be 1, or

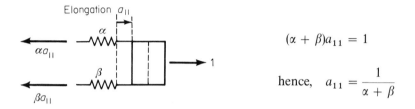

$$(\alpha + \beta)a_{11} = 1$$

$$\text{hence,} \quad a_{11} = \frac{1}{\alpha + \beta}$$

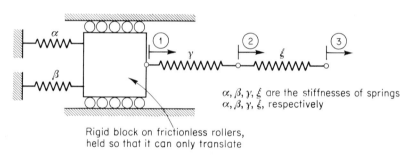

$\alpha, \beta, \gamma, \xi$ are the stiffnesses of springs $\alpha, \beta, \gamma, \xi$, respectively

Rigid block on frictionless rollers, held so that it can only translate

Figure 3.4.

The displacements a_{21} and a_{31} at coordinates 2 and 3, respectively, are the same as a_{11} because the unit force at 1 does not propagate to the right and therefore springs γ and ξ do not change in length.

We leave it as an exercise to the reader to generate the second and third columns of [a]. The complete matrix is

$$\begin{bmatrix} \dfrac{1}{\alpha + \beta} & \dfrac{1}{\alpha + \beta} & \dfrac{1}{\alpha + \beta} \\[3mm] \dfrac{1}{\alpha + \beta} & \dfrac{1}{\alpha + \beta} + \dfrac{1}{\gamma} & \dfrac{1}{\alpha + \beta} + \dfrac{1}{\gamma} \\[3mm] \dfrac{1}{\alpha + \beta} & \dfrac{1}{\alpha + \beta} + \dfrac{1}{\gamma} & \dfrac{1}{\alpha + \beta} + \dfrac{1}{\gamma} + \dfrac{1}{\xi} \end{bmatrix}$$

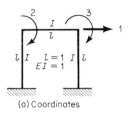

(a) Coordinates

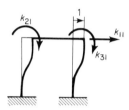

(b) Configuration for first
column of $[k]$

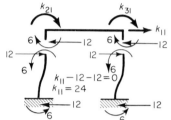

Free body to compute k_{11}
from equilibrium

$k_{11} - 12 - 12 = 0$
$k_{11} = 24$

Free bodies to compute
k_{21} and k_{31} from
equilibrium

$k_{21} + 6 = 0 \quad k_{31} + 6 = 0$
$k_{21} = -6 \quad k_{31} = -6$

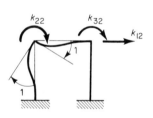

(c) Configuration for second
column of $[k]$

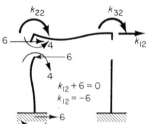

Free body to compute k_{12}

$k_{12} + 6 = 0$
$k_{12} = -6$

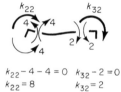

$k_{22} - 4 - 4 = 0 \quad k_{32} - 2 = 0$
$k_{22} = 8 \quad k_{32} = 2$

Free bodies to compute
k_{22} and k_{32}

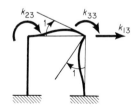

(d) Configuration for third
column of $[k]$

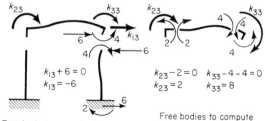

$k_{13} + 6 = 0$
$k_{13} = -6$

Free body to compute k_{13}

$k_{23} - 2 = 0 \quad k_{33} - 4 - 4 = 0$
$k_{23} = 2 \quad k_{33} = 8$

Free bodies to compute
k_{23} and k_{33}

Figure 3.5.

To generate the first column of $[k]$ in Figure 3.4 we apply a unit displacement at 1 only. This will cause springs α and β to elongate one unit and spring γ to shorten one unit, and will require a force $k_{11} = \alpha + \beta + \gamma$ at 1, $k_{21} = -\gamma$ at 2, and $k_{31} = 0$ at 3. The entire stiffness matrix is

$$\begin{bmatrix} \alpha + \beta + \gamma & -\gamma & 0 \\ -\gamma & \gamma + \xi & -\xi \\ 0 & -\xi & \xi \end{bmatrix}$$

(Verify columns 2 and 3.)

Suggested Exercise: Do problem 1.

Example 2 (Figure 3.5)

The computations leading to the stiffness matrix

$$\begin{bmatrix} 24 & -6 & -6 \\ -6 & 8 & 2 \\ -6 & 2 & 8 \end{bmatrix}$$

for the structure in Figure 3.5 are shown in the figure. In the computation we make use of the results obtained in Sections 2.8 and 2.9. The members of the frame are considered infinitely stiff axially and only displacements due to bending are accounted for. The moments and shears given in numbers are shown in the actual direction of their action, whereas the stiffness elements k_{ij} are shown in the positive direction of the coordinates.

To generate the flexibility matrix, $[a]$, for the frame of Figure 3.5 is much more complicated than to generate the stiffness matrix, $[k]$, and involves the solution of a three-times redundant structure when the elements of any column of $[a]$ are computed. We shall show later that $[a]$ can be obtained from $[k]$, and vice versa, so that in the present problem we can use $[k]$ to find $[a]$.

Example 3 (Figures 3.6 and 3.7)

Let us now show an example where $[a]$ can be generated more easily than $[k]$. In Figure 3.6(a) three coordinates are defined and the computations (by moment area) for the first column of $[a]$ are shown in Figure 3.6(b). The complete flexibility matrix $[a]$ is

$$\frac{l^3}{6EI} \begin{bmatrix} 2 & 5 & 8 \\ 5 & 16 & 28 \\ 8 & 28 & 54 \end{bmatrix}$$

in which the factor $l^3/6EI$ multiplies each element of the matrix.

To generate the stiffness matrix for the beam of Figure 3.6 is more involved and requires the solution of an indeterminate structure for each column of $[k]$. For instance, to generate the first column of $[k]$ we must compute the forces k_{i1} ($i = 1, 2, 3$) required to maintain the configuration shown in Figure 3.7, and this will lead to the solution of a three-times redundant structure.

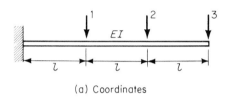

(a) Coordinates

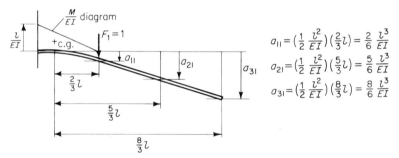

$$a_{11} = \left(\tfrac{1}{2}\tfrac{l^2}{EI}\right)\left(\tfrac{2}{3}l\right) = \tfrac{2}{6}\tfrac{l^3}{EI}$$

$$a_{21} = \left(\tfrac{1}{2}\tfrac{l^2}{EI}\right)\left(\tfrac{5}{3}l\right) = \tfrac{5}{6}\tfrac{l^3}{EI}$$

$$a_{31} = \left(\tfrac{1}{2}\tfrac{l^2}{EI}\right)\left(\tfrac{8}{3}l\right) = \tfrac{8}{6}\tfrac{l^3}{EI}$$

(b) Deflected configuration and $\frac{M}{EI}$ diagram
to generate the first column of $[a]$

Figure 3.6.

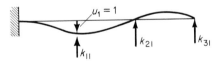

Figure 3.7. Deflected configuration to generate the first column of $[k]$.

Example 4 (Figures 3.8, 3.9, and 3.10)

The computations for the first column of $[a]$ for the fixed-free frame of Figure 3.8(a) are shown in Figure 3.8(b). Again only bending displacements

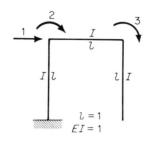

(a) Coordinates

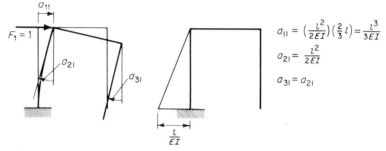

$$a_{11} = \left(\frac{l^2}{2EI}\right)\left(\frac{2}{3}l\right) = \frac{l^3}{3EI}$$

$$a_{21} = \frac{l^2}{2EI}$$

$$a_{31} = a_{21}$$

(b) Deflected configuration and computations for the first column of [a]

Figure 3.8.

are considered and the moment area method is used in the computations. The complete matrix [a] is

$$\begin{bmatrix} \frac{1}{3} & \frac{1}{2} & \frac{1}{2} \\ \frac{1}{2} & 1 & 1 \\ \frac{1}{2} & 1 & 2 \end{bmatrix}$$

The deflected configurations to compute the columns of [k] are shown in Figure 3.9. The computations for the second column of [k] are instructive and are illustrated in Figure 3.10. In this figure superposition is used to yield the deflected configuration in which $u_2 = 1$ and $u_1 = u_3 = 0$. In Figure 3.10(b), forces are applied at coordinates 1 and 2 only to cause displacements $u_1 = 0$ and $u_2 = 1$. This, however, causes a displacement $u_3^{(b)}$ at coordinate 3. To reduce u_3 to zero, we add Figure 3.10(c) such that u_1 and u_2 in Figure (b) are unaltered and $u_3^{(b)} + u_3^{(c)} = 0$.

Using the results of Section 2.8, Equation (2.6), we have, for Figure 3.10(b),

$$F_1^{(b)} = -6, \qquad F_2^{(b)} = 4$$

Since $u_3^{(b)} = 1$ in Figure 3.10(b), $F_3^{(c)}$ in Figure 3.10(c) must produce $u_3^{(c)} = -1$.

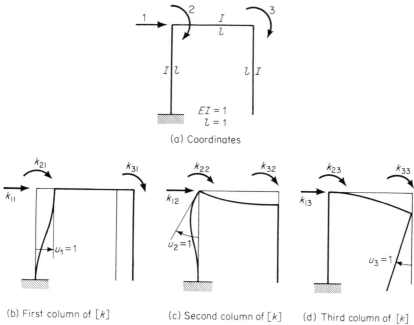

(a) Coordinates

(b) First column of $[k]$ (c) Second column of $[k]$ (d) Third column of $[k]$

Figure 3.9.

From moment area

$$F_3^{(c)} = -1$$

and from equilibrium

$$F_1^{(c)} = 0 \qquad \text{and} \qquad F_2^{(c)} = 1$$

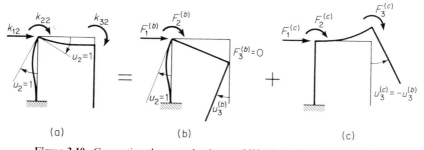

(a)   (b)   (c)

Figure 3.10. Computing the second column of $[k]$ (Fig. 3.9c) by superposition.

The forces at the coordinates in Figure 3.10(a) are computed by adding the corresponding forces in (b) and (c),

$$k_{12} = F_1^{(b)} + F_1^{(c)} = -6$$

$$k_{22} = F_2^{(b)} + F_2^{(c)} = 5$$

$$k_{32} = F_3^{(b)} + F_3^{(c)} = -1$$

The complete matrix $[k]$ for the frame of Figure 3.8(a) is

$$\begin{bmatrix} 12 & -6 & 0 \\ -6 & 5 & -1 \\ 0 & -1 & 1 \end{bmatrix}$$

Note the property of symmetry $a_{ij} = a_{ji}$ and $k_{ij} = k_{ji}$ in all the $[a]$ and $[k]$ matrices which we have derived. We shall discuss this property in a later chapter.

Example 5

The results for $[k]$ and $[a]$ referred to the same structure with the identical coordinates can be checked by applying Equation (3.11). For two co-ordinates this was demonstrated in Equation (3.10). We shall now apply this check to the frame in Example 4 as shown below.

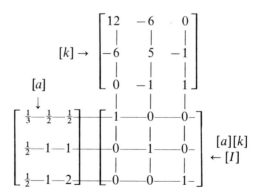

Any element, I_{ij}, in row i and column j of $[I]$ is obtained from the sum of the products of the elements in row i of $[a]$ and the corresponding elements in column j of $[k]$, or

$$I_{ij} = \sum_{l=1}^{n} a_{il}k_{lj} = a_{i1}k_{1j} + a_{i2}k_{2j} + a_{i3}k_{3j} + \cdots + a_{in}k_{nj} \qquad (3.14)$$

For instance, in the present example

$$I_{2,2} = \tfrac{1}{2}(-6) + 1(5) + 1(-1) = 1$$

$$I_{2,3} = \tfrac{1}{2}(0) + 1(-1) + 1(1) = 0$$

$$I_{3,2} = \tfrac{1}{2}(-6) + 1(5) + 2(-1) = 0$$

Suggested Exercises: Do problems 2, 3, 4, 5, 6, 7, and 8.

3.6. [a] AND [k] IN COORDINATES WITH CONSTRAINED MEASUREMENTS

In the last section we generated stiffness and flexibility matrices for structures with a set of coordinates in which the measurements of force and displacement were independent. In this section, we consider coordinates in which measurements of force or displacement are constrained (dependent) and see how this affects the matrices [a] and [k].

Constrained Displacement Measurements

Let the members of the frame in Figure 3.11 be infinitely stiff in their axial direction, then the following equation of constraint exists among the displacements:

$$u_1 = u_2$$

and the displacement measurements are, therefore, constrained. We now find it impossible to generate the stiffness matrix [k] for the four coordinates shown in Figure 3.11, because, according to the procedures of Section 3.4, each column of [k] is generated by applying a unit displacement at *only one coordinate, with no displacements at all other coordinates,* and this cannot be done in Figure 3.11.

The flexibility matrix [a] can still be generated because the forces at the four coordinates are independent and can be applied one at a time. The constraint on the displacements, however, will cause the first and second columns of [a] to be identical because the same displacements a_{i1} $(i = 1, 2, 3, 4)$ and a_{i2} $(i = 1, 2, 3, 4)$ will re-sult, respectively, from a unit

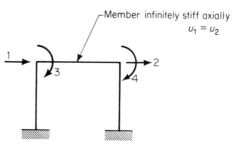

Figure 3.11. Frame with constrained displacements.

force at coordinate 1 only, and a unit force at coordinate 2 only. We say in this case that columns 1 and 2 are *linearly dependent* because one can be generated from the other.

Constrained Force Measurements

When a structure is in static equilibrium, the forces acting on it satisfy the equations of static equilibrium. In Chapter 2 we considered these equations as equations of constraint on the force measurements. Let us now see what happens when we try to generate the matrices $[a]$ and $[k]$ in a set of coordinates in which the force measurements are constrained.

In Figure 2.3(a) of Chapter 2 we show four coordinates for the beam. We now find it impossible to generate the flexibility matrix $[a]$ for this beam, because, according to the procedures of Section 3.4, each column of $[a]$ is generated by applying a unit force at *only one coordinate with no forces at all other coordinates*, and when we do so the beam will accelerate according to Newton's second law.

The stiffness matrix $[k]$ can still be generated and appears as follows (verify):

$$\frac{EI}{l} \begin{bmatrix} 4 & 2 & -6/l & 6/l \\ 2 & 4 & -6/l & 6/l \\ -6/l & -6/l & 12/l^2 & -12/l^2 \\ 6/l & 6/l & -12/l^2 & 12/l^2 \end{bmatrix}$$

An examination of this stiffness matrix shows that the elements of the fourth column can be obtained by adding the elements of the first and second columns and dividing by l. We say that the fourth column is *linearly dependent* on columns 1 and 2 because it can be obtained as a linear combination of them. Similarly, column 3 is linearly dependent on columns 1 and 2, and columns 3 and 4 are dependent. These dependencies are a direct result of the dependence among the force measurements at the coordinates in Figure 2.3. For instance, the force at coordinate 4 is the sum of the forces at coordinates 1 and 2 divided by l, that is,

$$F_4 = \frac{1}{l}(F_1 + F_2)$$

Similarly,

$$F_3 = -\frac{1}{l}(F_1 + F_2)$$

and

$$F_4 = -F_3$$

Note also that the same dependencies exist among the rows of the matrix because of symmetry (that is, any row i is identical to column i in matrix $[k]$ or $[a]$).

We summarize our findings as follows:

1. When the displacement measurements are constrained the stiffness matrix does not exist, and the flexibility matrix has linearly dependent columns and rows.

2. When the force measurements are constrained the flexibility matrix does not exist, and the stiffness matrix has linearly dependent columns and rows.

The flexibility matrix of a structure will exist when we provide supports to make the structure at least statically determinate so that it will be in equilibrium and will not accelerate when we try to generate $[a]$, and in addition we define a set of coordinates in which the force measurements are independent. For instance, for the beam of Figure 2.3, we can provide supports and define coordinates as shown in Figure 3.12 so that corresponding flexibility matrices will exist. (These are shown below each figure.)

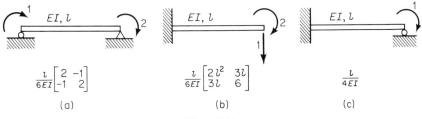

$$\frac{\imath}{6EI}\begin{bmatrix} 2 & -1 \\ -1 & 2 \end{bmatrix}$$

$$\frac{\imath}{6EI}\begin{bmatrix} 2\imath^2 & 3\imath \\ 3\imath & 6 \end{bmatrix}$$

$$\frac{\imath}{4EI}$$

(a)   (b)   (c)

Figure 3.12.

3.7. STIFFNESS AND FLEXIBILITY OF SYSTEMS AND ELEMENTS

As we have indicated earlier, one of our prime objectives will be to synthesize the stiffness and flexibility matrices of a structure from those of its elements. We have done this already in the examples of this chapter; for example, in Figure 3.5, the stiffness of the frame was obtained by compounding the stiffnesses of the elements; in Figure 3.8, the flexibility matrix was obtained by compounding the flexibilities of the elements. To formalize the synthesis process, it is convenient to distinguish between the stiffness and flexibility matrices of a system (the entire structure) and those of its elements, and also between the vectors of force and displacement at the coordinates of the system and those at the coordinates of the elements. To do so we shall adopt the following notation:

	System	Element
Flexibility matrix	$[a]$	$[\alpha]$
ijth element	a_{ij}	α_{ij}
Stiffness matrix	$[k]$	$[\kappa]$
ijth element	k_{ij}	κ_{ij}
Force vector	$\{F\}$	$\{P\}$
Displacement vector	$\{u\}$	$\{\delta\}$

Let us illustrate this notation by examples and show how the stiffness matrix of an element was used in Figure 3.5 to synthesize the stiffness matrix of the system.

The force and displacement vectors for the system of Figure 3.5 are related by [see Equation (3.12)],

$$\{u\} = [a]\{F\}$$

in which

$$u_i = \sum_{j=1}^{3} a_{ij}F_j$$

and, [see Equation (3.13)]

$$\{F\} = [k]\{u\}$$

in which

$$F_i = \sum_{j=1}^{3} k_{ij}u_j$$

The beam in Figures 2.3 and 3.12 can be considered as an element in the system of Figure 3.5. Taking Figure 3.12(a), for instance, we write

$$\{\delta\} = [\alpha]\{P\} \tag{3.15}$$

in which

$$\delta_i = \sum_{j=1}^{2} \alpha_{ij}P_j = \alpha_{i1}P_1 + \alpha_{i2}P_2$$

and

$$\{P\} = [\kappa]\{\delta\} \tag{3.16}$$

in which

$$P_i = \sum_{j=1}^{2} \kappa_{ij}\delta_j = \kappa_{i1}\delta_1 + \kappa_{i2}\delta_2$$

$\{\delta\} = \begin{Bmatrix} \delta_1 \\ \delta_2 \end{Bmatrix}$ is the vector of element displacements

$\{P\} = \begin{Bmatrix} P_1 \\ P_2 \end{Bmatrix}$ is the vector of element forces

$$[\alpha] = \frac{l}{6EI}\begin{bmatrix} 2 & -1 \\ -1 & 2 \end{bmatrix}, \qquad [\kappa] = \frac{EI}{l}\begin{bmatrix} 4 & 2 \\ 2 & 4 \end{bmatrix}$$

For the beam of Figure 2.3 we can write

$$\{P\} = [\kappa]\{\delta\}$$

in which

$$P_i = \sum_{j=1}^{4} \kappa_{ij}\delta_j = \kappa_{i1}\delta_1 + \kappa_{i2}\delta_2 + \kappa_{i3}\delta_3 + \kappa_{i4}\delta_4$$

$[\kappa]$ is given in Section 3.6. We cannot write, however, the displacements in terms of the forces, because $[\alpha]$ does not exist for the coordinates in Figure 2.3.

Let us see how this last matrix equation can be used to construct the matrix $[k]$ for Figure 3.5. The expanded form of the last matrix equation is

$$\begin{Bmatrix} P_1 \\ P_2 \\ P_3 \\ P_4 \end{Bmatrix} = \frac{EI}{l} \begin{bmatrix} 4 & 2 & -6/l & 6/l \\ 2 & 4 & -6/l & 6/l \\ -6/l & -6/l & 12/l^2 & -12/l^2 \\ 6/l & 6/l & -12/l^2 & 12/l^2 \end{bmatrix} \begin{Bmatrix} \delta_1 \\ \delta_2 \\ \delta_3 \\ \delta_4 \end{Bmatrix} \tag{3.17}$$

To generate, for example, the second column of $[k]$ in Figure 3.5, we transport the beam of Figure 2.3 (with its coordinates) as a rigid body and superimpose it on the left-hand column of the deflected configuration in Figure 3.5(c). Suppose that in doing so we match coordinates 1 and 3 of the element with coordinates 2 and 1 of the system respectively. To make our element match the deflected configuration of the column we apply $\delta_1 = 1$ and $\delta_2 = \delta_3 = \delta_4 = 0$. Substituting these values in Equation (3.17) and recalling that $EI = l = 1$ in Figure 3.5, we obtain

$$\begin{Bmatrix} P_1 \\ P_2 \\ P_3 \\ P_4 \end{Bmatrix} = \begin{Bmatrix} 4 \\ 2 \\ -6 \\ 6 \end{Bmatrix}$$

These are the values recorded in the free body diagram of the column in Figure 3.5(c).

The same procedure is followed for the beam in Figure 3.5(c). Figure 2.3 is transported and placed on the beam with its coordinates 1 and 2 matching, respectively, coordinates 2 and 3 of the system. To produce the deflected configuration of the beam in Figure 3.5(c), again we set $\delta_1 = 1$, and $\delta_2 = \delta_3 = \delta_4 = 0$, and from Equation (3.17)

$$\begin{Bmatrix} P_1 \\ P_2 \\ P_3 \\ P_4 \end{Bmatrix} = \begin{Bmatrix} 4 \\ 2 \\ -6 \\ 6 \end{Bmatrix}$$

Only $P_1 = 4$ and $P_2 = 2$ are recorded in Figure 3.5(c) for clarity.

The approach illustrated here will be developed as a systematic procedure in Chapters 7, 8, and 9 through the use of the tools of matrix algebra.

3.8. COMPUTING DISPLACEMENTS AND FORCES AT COORDINATES FROM VIRTUAL WORK

There are a number of methods to compute displacement at any coordinate of a structure. These methods are treated in detail in the literature[11–13, 15–19]. In this section we shall review the method of virtual work, which is the most versatile, and show how it is used to compute displacements and forces at the coordinates of a structure. The fundamental relation in this method is

$$\text{external virtual work} = \text{internal virtual work} \qquad (3.18)$$

The virtual work on each side of the equation is computed by applying to the structure virtual forces, or virtual displacements as follows:

Computing Displacements

Virtual forces. When a structure is undergoing displacements,† we can compute the displacement at any desired coordinate by applying there a virtual (fictitious) force. We require that this virtual force be in equilibrium with its corresponding internal virtual forces in the structure. The virtual force at the coordinate is considered to "ride," at its full value, along the real displacement at that coordinate, and at the same time the internal virtual forces are "riding," at their full values, along the corresponding real internal displacements (which are compatible with the real external displacements). The product

$$\text{(virtual force)(real displacement)}$$

at the coordinate of interest is called the *external virtual work*; the product

$$\text{(internal virtual forces)(internal real displacements)}$$

is called the *internal virtual work*. From Equation (3.18) these two products are equal, or

$$
\overbrace{
\begin{pmatrix} \text{virtual} \\ \text{force} \end{pmatrix}
\begin{pmatrix} \text{real} \\ \text{displacement} \end{pmatrix}
}^{\text{virtual forces in equilibrium}}
=
\begin{pmatrix} \text{internal} \\ \text{virtual} \\ \text{forces} \end{pmatrix}
\underbrace{
\begin{pmatrix} \text{internal} \\ \text{real} \\ \text{displacements} \end{pmatrix}
}_{\text{Real displacements compatible}}
\qquad (3.19)
$$

---

† The cause of the displacements may be due to applied forces, temperature changes, lack of fit, settlement of supports, or a combination of these causes.

If we apply a virtual force of unity, then Equation (3.19) yields the desired real displacement on the left-hand side

$$
\overset{\text{in equilibrium}}{(1)\begin{pmatrix}\text{real}\\\text{displacement}\\\text{desired}\end{pmatrix} = \begin{pmatrix}\text{internal}\\\text{virtual}\\\text{forces}\end{pmatrix}\begin{pmatrix}\text{internal}\\\text{real}\\\text{displacements}\end{pmatrix}}_{\text{compatible}}
\qquad (3.20)
$$

The method of virtual forces is also known as the method of *complementary virtual work* and is attributed to Engesser[11,16]. It has the further advantage of being applicable to computing displacements of structures whose materials have a nonlinear stress-strain relation.

Computing Forces

Virtual Displacements. When a force acting at a coordinate is not known, it can be computed from the internal forces in the structure (which are in equilibrium with the external forces) by applying a virtual displacement at that coordinate. Here we require that this virtual displacement be compatible with its corresponding internal virtual displacements. Now we consider the real force to "ride," at its full value, along the virtual displacement at the coordinate, and the real internal forces to "ride," at their full values, along the internal virtual displacements. Applying Equation (3.18), we have

$$
\begin{pmatrix}\text{virtual}\\\text{displacement}\end{pmatrix}\begin{pmatrix}\text{real}\\\text{force}\end{pmatrix} = \overset{\text{in equilibrium}}{\begin{pmatrix}\text{internal}\\\text{virtual}\\\text{displacements}\end{pmatrix}\begin{pmatrix}\text{internal}\\\text{real}\\\text{forces}\end{pmatrix}}_{\text{compatible}}
\qquad (3.21)
$$

When the virtual displacement is set equal to unity, Equation (3.21) yields the desired force

$$
(1)\begin{pmatrix}\text{real}\\\text{force}\\\text{desired}\end{pmatrix} = \overset{\text{in equilibrium}}{\begin{pmatrix}\text{internal}\\\text{virtual}\\\text{displacements}\end{pmatrix}\begin{pmatrix}\text{internal}\\\text{real}\\\text{forces}\end{pmatrix}}_{\text{compatible}}
\qquad (3.22)
$$

The virtual displacement approach is also used to compute displacements. The procedure is to consider the virtual external force real, and the real displacements virtual, in which case in Equation (3.21) the real force is set equal to unity and the virtual displacement on the left-hand side is actually the desired real displacement.[15,pp.96–97]. (For further discussion of Equation (3.22) and its applications see References[20,21].)

Before we can apply Equation (3.20) or (3.22) we must derive expressions for the internal displacements which may be a combination of any of the following forms: (1) axial, (2) bending, (3) shear, (4) torsional.

Expressions for Internal Displacements

1. *Axial displacements:* Consider a segment dx at section x of a bar (Figure 3.13). The force at section x is $P(x)$ and the cross-sectional area is $A(x)$. The incremental change in length $\Delta(dx)$ of the segment is

$$\Delta(dx) = \varepsilon \, dx$$

where ε designates strain. Substituting Hooke's law,

$$\varepsilon = \frac{\sigma}{E}$$

where σ designates stress and E is the modulus of elasticity, we have

$$\Delta (dx) = \frac{\sigma}{E} dx$$

Assuming the stress σ to be uniformly distributed over the area, then $\sigma = P(x)/A(x)$, and

$$\Delta(dx) = \frac{P(x)}{EA(x)} dx \tag{3.23}$$

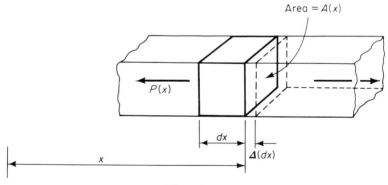

Figure 3.13.

2. *Bending displacement:* The beam in Figure 3.14 is subjected to a bending moment $M(x)$ at section x. For a segment of length dx at section x the change in length of the extreme fiber, which is a distance c from the

neutral axis, is $\varepsilon\,dx$, and for small deflections the rotation $d\theta$ of section x is

$$d\theta = \frac{\varepsilon\,dx}{c}$$

Substituting σ/E for ε and recalling that σ is the stress at the extreme fiber, then from elementary beam theory[22]

$$\sigma = \frac{M(x)c}{I(x)}$$

where $I(x)$ is the moment of inertia of the cross section at x about the neutral axis. Then $d\theta$ becomes

$$d\theta = \frac{M(x)}{EI(x)}\,dx \qquad\qquad (3.24)$$

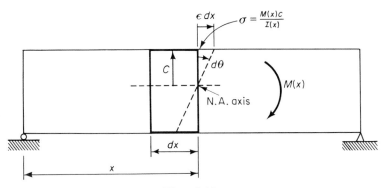

Figure 3.14.

3. *Shear displacement:* The segment dx of Figure 3.15 is subjected to shear $V(x)$ at section x. The shear strain, γ, is given by $\gamma = \tau/G$ where G is the modulus of elasticity in shear, and τ is the shear stress. Assuming the shear stress to be uniform over the area $A(x)$, then $\gamma = V(x)/GA(x)$ and the shear displacement of segment dx becomes

$$\gamma\,dx = \frac{V(x)}{GA(x)}\,dx$$

In more general form this expression is

$$\gamma\,dx = K\frac{V(x)}{GA(x)}\,dx \qquad\qquad (3.25)$$

where K is a factor which depends on the shape of the cross section, and accounts for the fact that the stress τ is not uniform over the cross section. For rectangular cross sections $K = 1.2$, and for wide flange sections (WF) $K \approx 1$.

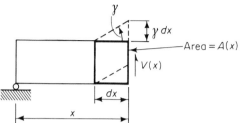

Figure 3.15.

4. *Torsion displacement:* The segment dx of the circular shaft in Figure 3.16 is acted upon by a torque $T(x)$ at section x. The increment in torsional displacement (rotation), $d\phi$, is given by $d\phi = \gamma \, dx/r$. But[11] $\gamma = T(x)r/GJ(x)$ [in which $J(x)$ is the polar moment of inertia at x for a circular cross section and r is its radius], therefore $d\phi$ becomes

$$d\phi = \frac{T(x)}{GJ(x)} dx \tag{3.26}$$

For cross sections other than circular, $J(x)$ must be replaced by a torsion constant which depends on the shape of the cross section [11, 16, 23].

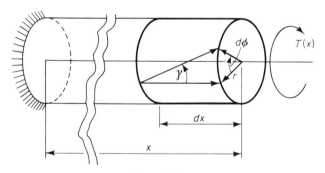

Figure 3.16.

3.9. COMPUTING COEFFICIENTS a_{ij} AND k_{ij} FROM VIRTUAL WORK

Now that we have the four possible forms of incremental displacements we can apply Equations (3.20) and (3.22) to compute coefficients a_{ij} and k_{ij} respectively. The example that follows illustrates the application of

Equation (3.20) to computing flexibility coefficients a_{ij}. The application of Equation (3.22) to computing stiffness coefficients k_{ij} is left as an exercise to the reader. See Problem 13.

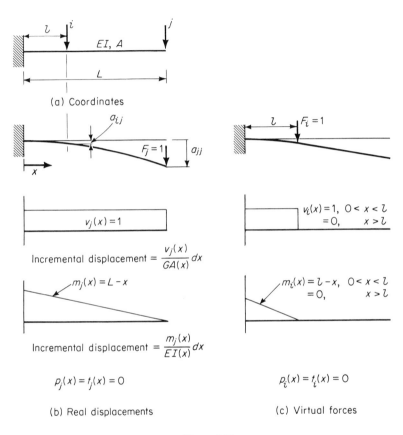

Figure 3.17.

In Figure 3.17 it is desired to compute the flexibility coefficient a_{ij}. First we apply a unit force (real) at j and compute the internal (real) forces $p_j(x)$, $m_j(x)$, $v_j(x)$, and $t_j(x)$, from which we obtain the real internal incremental displacements by substituting in Equations (3.23)–(3.26) inclusive. [See Figure 3.17(b).] Then we apply a unit virtual force at coordinate i and compute the internal virtual forces $p_i(x)$, $m_i(x)$, $v_i(x)$, $t_i(x)$. To obtain the total internal virtual work, we integrate, over the length of the structure, the product of the incremental real internal displacements and the corresponding internal virtual forces which makes Equation (3.20) appear as follows:

$$(1)a_{ij} = \int_0^L p_i(x)\frac{p_j(x)}{EA(x)}\,dx + \int_0^L m_i(x)\frac{m_j(x)}{EI(x)}\,dx + \int_0^L v_i(x)\frac{v_j(x)}{GA(x)}\,dx$$

$$+ \int_0^L t_i(x)\frac{t_j(x)}{GJ(x)}\,dx \qquad (3.27)$$

[The right-hand side of Equation (3.27) can also be used to compute k_{ij}, provided the internal forces with subscripts i and j are associated with unit displacements at coordinates i and j respectively. See Problem 13.]

The evaluation of the integrals in Equation (3.27) can be performed by the conventional procedures[24], or can be aided by special techniques to simplify the amount of labor. For instance, when only moment terms are involved (second integral in Equation 3.27) then the methods of moment area, conjugate beam, or visual integration can be used†[16, pp.47-48]. Also, when the cross-sectional properties $A(x)$, $I(x)$, and $J(x)$ vary with x, so that integration becomes difficult or impossible, then a numerical procedure is usually used to evaluate the integrals in Equation (3.27)[15].

In the example of Figure 3.17 only two virtual work terms on the right-hand side of Equation (3.27) are nonzero, these are the moment and shear terms. Also, because A and I are constant, and because the range of $v_i(x)$ and $m_i(x)$ makes it possible to change the upper limit of integration in Equation (3.27) to l, Equation (3.27) becomes

$$a_{ij} = \int_0^l v_i(x)\frac{v_j(x)}{GA}\,dx + \int_0^l m_i(x)\frac{m_j(x)}{EI}\,dx$$

$$= \frac{1}{GA}\int_0^l dx + \frac{1}{EI}\int_0^l (l-x)(L-x)\,dx$$

$$= \frac{l}{GA} + \frac{1}{EI}\left(l^2\frac{L-l}{2} + \frac{l^3}{3}\right)$$

In many applications some of the terms in Equation (3.27) contribute very little compared to others and are neglected in the computations. For instance, in plane frame problems both the axial and shear terms are small compared to the moment term and are disregarded[17].

We note here that the concepts of stiffness and flexibility developed in this chapter are valid no matter how many of the terms on the right of Equation (3.27) are considered. For clarity and simplicity, we often concern

---

† A table for integrals involving common shapes of moment diagrams appears in [25, 26].

ourselves in this book with the bending term only, when frames are considered.

Suggested Exercises: Do problems 9, 10, 11, 12, and 13.

PROBLEMS

Problem 1: Set $\alpha = \beta = \gamma = \xi = 1$ kip/inch in Figure 3.4.
   a. Determine the force vector required to cause a displacement

$$\left\{ \begin{array}{c} u_1 \\ u_2 \\ u_3 \end{array} \right\} = \left\{ \begin{array}{c} 1 \text{ in.} \\ -2 \text{ in.} \\ -0.5 \text{ in.} \end{array} \right\}$$

   b. Compute the displacement vector caused by force vector

$$\left\{ \begin{array}{c} F_1 \\ F_2 \\ F_3 \end{array} \right\} = \left\{ \begin{array}{c} 20 \text{ kip} \\ -15 \text{ kip} \\ 10 \text{ kip} \end{array} \right\}$$

Problem 2: Check $[a]$ and $[k]$ of Example 1 by applying Equation (3.11) as was done in Example 5.

Problems 3, 4, 5: Generate the stiffness matrix for each of the following structures with coordinates as shown.

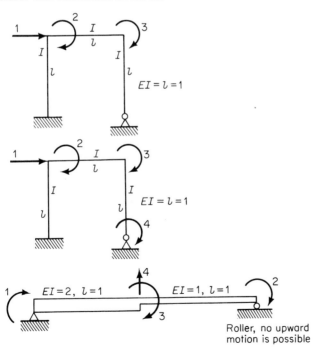

Problem 6: Generate the stiffness matrix for the structure of Figure 2.16, Chapter 2.

Problem 7: Generate the stiffness matrix for the structure of Problem 6, Chapter 2.

Problem 8: Generate the stiffness matrix for the structure of Problem 5, Chapter 2.

Problem 9: Set up the integrals to compute a_{ij} in the figure shown. Consider all virtual work terms in Equation (3.27) significant. Member 1 is perpendicular to the plane of the paper, and has length L_1 and uniform sectional properties A_1, I_1, J_1. Members 2 and 3 are in the plane of the paper with lengths and uniform sectional properties as shown in the figure. The coordinates i and j are also in the plane of the paper.

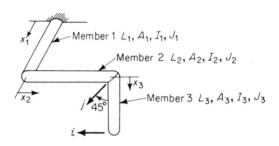

Problem 10: Generate the flexibility matrix of the beam in Figure 3.6(a) using Equation (3.27).

Problem 11: Generate the flexibility matrix of Figure 3.8 using Equation (3.27).

Problem 12: Generate the flexibility matrix for the structure of Problem 5, Chapter 3 using Equation (3.27). Check your answer by applying Equation 3.11. The stiffness matrix for the structure is given in the answer to Problem 5.

Problem 13: Show that the right-hand side of Equation (3.27) can be used to compute stiffness coefficients k_{ij} at the coordinates of a structure if the internal forces in this equation are interpreted as follows: $p_i(x)$, $m_i(x)$, $v_i(x)$, $t_i(x)$ are the internal forces associated with a unit displacement at coordinate i only, and $p_j(x)$, $m_j(x)$, $v_j(x)$, $t_j(x)$ are the internal forces associated with a unit displacement at coordinate j only.

CHAPTER 4

DETERMINANTS
AND MATRICES

4.1. GENERAL INTRODUCTION

In Chapter 3 we motivated the need for matrix notation and matrix algebra when the concepts of stiffness and flexibility coefficients were introduced. We found matrices useful in organizing information such as the coefficients a_{ij}, k_{ij} and—matrix equations useful in transforming information in a compact manner (Equations 3.12 and 3.13). These characteristics of organization and compactness, made matrices and matrix algebra useful in many fields, particularly since the advent of digital computers because the availability of the computer shifted the emphasis from problem solution to efficient problem formulation. Since formulation of complex problems often involves handling large quantities of information, these are best organized and manipulated by matrix methods.

In this chapter we shall introduce the fundamental tools of matrix algebra which will enable us to develop, in subsequent chapters, matrix methods for formulating problems in structures.†

4.2. INTRODUCTION TO DETERMINANTS AND MATRICES

Before proceeding with a general treatment of determinants and matrices we consider a case in which they are both involved.

---

† For an expanded treatment of matrices consult References [27–30].

Let us rewrite, for convenience, Equation (3.8) in the following form:

$$\begin{bmatrix} k_{11} & k_{12} \\ k_{21} & k_{22} \end{bmatrix} \begin{Bmatrix} u_1 \\ u_2 \end{Bmatrix} = \begin{Bmatrix} F_1 \\ F_2 \end{Bmatrix} \tag{4.1}$$

Using this equation, we can compute the forces F_1 and F_2 required to cause any desired displacements u_1, u_2 if the matrix of coefficients $[k]$ is available. Suppose that $[k]$ has been generated (Equation 3.9 for Figure 3.3) but we are asked to compute the displacements u_1 and u_2 caused by given forces F_1 and F_2. In this case, we can write Equation (4.1) in expanded form

$$k_{11}u_1 + k_{12}u_2 = F_1$$

$$k_{21}u_1 + k_{22}u_2 = F_2$$

and solve for u_1 and u_2. For instance, multiplying the first equation by k_{22} and the second by k_{12} and subtracting, we eliminate u_2 and have

$$(k_{11}k_{22} - k_{12}k_{21})u_1 = F_1k_{22} - F_2k_{12}$$

Similarly eliminating u_1 we have

$$(k_{11}k_{22} - k_{12}k_{21})u_2 = F_2k_{11} - F_1k_{21}$$

or

$$u_1 = \frac{F_1k_{22} - F_2k_{12}}{k_{11}k_{22} - k_{12}k_{21}}$$

$$u_2 = \frac{F_2k_{11} - F_1k_{21}}{k_{11}k_{22} - k_{12}k_{21}} \tag{4.2}$$

The denominator, in each of Equations (4.2), is the same, and is obtained by a manipulation of the elements of $[k]$. This manipulation is written symbolically as follows:

$$\begin{vmatrix} k_{11} & k_{12} \\ k_{21} & k_{22} \end{vmatrix} = k_{11}k_{22} - k_{12}k_{21} \tag{4.3}$$

Namely, the two lines that bound the four coefficients constitute an operator in the same sense that the symbols $+$, $-$, Σ, d/dt, $\int$ do. They indicate that element $(1, 1)$ multiplies element $(2, 2)$, element $(1, 2)$ multiplies element $(2, 1)$, and the products are subtracted as shown in Equation (4.3). The left side of Equation (4.3) is called a *second-order determinant*. A first-order determinant has a single element, and an *n*th-order determinant has *n* rows and *n* columns of elements between the vertical lines; however, a determinant of any order represents a single number.

Using Equation (4.3) which defines a second-order determinant, Equations (4.2) become

$$u_1 = \frac{\begin{vmatrix} F_1 & k_{12} \\ F_2 & k_{22} \end{vmatrix}}{\begin{vmatrix} k_{11} & k_{12} \\ k_{21} & k_{22} \end{vmatrix}} \qquad u_2 = \frac{\begin{vmatrix} k_{11} & F_1 \\ k_{21} & F_2 \end{vmatrix}}{\begin{vmatrix} k_{11} & k_{12} \\ k_{21} & k_{22} \end{vmatrix}} \qquad (4.4)$$

In these equations the denominator is the determinant of matrix $[k]$. The numerator is a determinant formed from the elements of $[k]$ in which the column on the right of Equation (4.1) replaces the first column of $[k]$ when the first unknown, u_1, is computed, and it replaces the second column of $[k]$ when u_2 is computed. In compact notation Equations (4.4) can be written as

$$u_1 = \frac{|k|_1}{|k|}, \qquad u_2 = \frac{|k|_2}{|k|} \qquad (4.5)$$

in which $|k|$ is the determinant of $[k]$ and the subscripts in $|k|_1$ and $|k|_2$ indicate which column of $|k|$ has been replaced by $\{F\}$ in the numerator.

Equations (4.5) can be extended to n linear equations with n unknowns, in which case the unknowns u_i are computed from determinants of order n

$$u_i = \frac{|k|_i}{|k|} \qquad i = 1, 2, \ldots, n \qquad (4.6)$$

We shall consider the evaluation of nth-order determinants in the next section. Equation (4.6) is known as *Cramer's rule* for solving linear equations.

In matrix form Equations (4.2) can be written as

$$\begin{Bmatrix} u_1 \\ u_2 \end{Bmatrix} = \begin{bmatrix} \dfrac{k_{22}}{|k|} & -\dfrac{k_{12}}{|k|} \\ -\dfrac{k_{21}}{|k|} & \dfrac{k_{11}}{|k|} \end{bmatrix} \begin{Bmatrix} F_1 \\ F_2 \end{Bmatrix} \qquad (4.7)$$

The square matrix in this equation is the *inverse* of matrix $[k]$; it is designated compactly as $[k]^{-1}$ and is formed from $[k]$ using determinants. $[k]$ and $[k]^{-1}$ are the inverse or the reciprocal of each other in the sense discussed in Section 3.3.

In summary let us emphasize the distinction between a matrix and a determinant. A matrix of order $m \times n$ is merely an arrangement of numbers in m rows and n columns in which the position is of significance. A determinant of order n, when evaluated, is a single number obtained by manipulating n rows and n columns of numbers. In our computer model of Chapter

1, a matrix of m rows and n columns requires $m \times n$ compartments for storage, whereas a determinant of any order, once evaluated, will require a single compartment.

4.3. THEORY OF DETERMINANTS

nth-order Determinant: The symbol

$$|a| = \begin{vmatrix} a_{11} & a_{12} & \cdots & a_{1n} \\ a_{21} & a_{22} & \cdots & a_{2n} \\ \cdot & \cdot & \cdots & \cdot \\ a_{n1} & a_{n2} & \cdots & a_{nn} \end{vmatrix}$$

represents a determinant of a square matrix of order $n \times n$, and is called a *determinant of order n*. The symbol has no meaning unless an equal number of rows and columns is enclosed between the vertical lines. The element in row i and column j of determinant $|a|$ is designated as a_{ij}.

Minor: The *minor*, M_{ij}, of element a_{ij} in determinant $|a|$ is defined as the subdeterminant obtained after row i and column j are deleted from $|a|$. For instance, the minors M_{11}, M_{12}, and M_{23} of elements a_{11}, a_{12}, and a_{23} in the determinant

$$|a| = \begin{vmatrix} a_{11} & a_{12} & a_{13} \\ a_{21} & a_{22} & a_{23} \\ a_{31} & a_{32} & a_{33} \end{vmatrix}$$

are, respectively, given by

$$M_{11} = \begin{vmatrix} a_{22} & a_{23} \\ a_{32} & a_{33} \end{vmatrix}, \qquad M_{12} = \begin{vmatrix} a_{21} & a_{23} \\ a_{31} & a_{33} \end{vmatrix}, \qquad M_{23} = \begin{vmatrix} a_{11} & a_{12} \\ a_{31} & a_{32} \end{vmatrix}$$

Cofactor: The *cofactor* A_{ij} of element a_{ij} in determinant $|a|$ is defined as a signed minor of a_{ij} in which the sign is given by $(-1)^{i+j}$,

$$\text{cofactor of element } a_{ij} = A_{ij} = (-1)^{i+j}M_{ij}$$

For instance, cofactors A_{11}, A_{12}, and A_{23} of elements a_{11}, a_{12}, and a_{23} in determinant $|a|$ are, respectively, given by

$$A_{11} = (-1)^{1+1}M_{11}, \qquad A_{12} = (-1)^{1+2}M_{12}, \qquad A_{23} = (-1)^{2+3}M_{23}$$

Evaluation of Determinants by Cofactors (Laplace Expansion)

We can expand the second-order determinant in Equation (4.3) by using any row or any column in the following way:

1. Multiply the elements of row 1 by their corresponding cofactors and add

$$k_{11}(-1)^{1+1}k_{22} + k_{12}(-1)^{1+2}k_{21} = k_{11}k_{22} - k_{12}k_{21}$$

2. Multiply the elements of row 2 by their cofactors and add

$$k_{21}(-1)^{2+1}k_{12} + k_{22}(-1)^{2+2}k_{11} = k_{11}k_{22} - k_{12}k_{21}$$

3. Multiply the elements of column 1 by their cofactors and add

$$k_{11}(-1)^{1+1}k_{22} + k_{21}(-1)^{2+1}k_{12} = k_{11}k_{22} - k_{12}k_{21}$$

4. Multiply the elements of column 2 by their cofactors and add

$$k_{12}(-1)^{1+2}k_{21} + k_{22}(-1)^{2+2}k_{11} = k_{11}k_{22} - k_{12}k_{21}$$

In each case we obtained the value of the determinant. This procedure can be extended to expand a determinant of order n by using any single row or column as follows:

1. Select any row i ($i = 1, 2, \ldots, n$) of $|a|$ and write

$$|a| = \sum_{j=1}^{n} a_{ij}A_{ij} \tag{4.8}$$

   in which the a_{ij} ($j = 1, 2, \ldots, n$) are the elements of row i and the $A_{ij}(j = 1, 2, \ldots, n)$ are the corresponding cofactors.
2. Select any column j ($j = 1, 2, \ldots, n$) of $|a|$ and write

$$|a| = \sum_{i=1}^{n} a_{ij}A_{ij} \tag{4.9}$$

   in which the a_{ij} and A_{ij} are the elements and cofactors of column j.

The expanded form of Equations (4.8) or (4.9) is the value of the denominator used in Equation (4.6) when n unknowns are computed from a set of n linear equations with a matrix of coefficients $[a]$. Equations (4.8) and (4.9) also define the general meaning of the operator represented by the two vertical bars used to denote determinants.

As an example we use Equation (4.9) to evaluate the following determinant (the first column is used):

$$
\begin{array}{c}
a_{11} \\
a_{21} \\
a_{31}
\end{array}
\begin{vmatrix}
7 & 1 & -2 \\
1 & 4 & 1 \\
-2 & 1 & 7
\end{vmatrix}
=
\overset{a_{11}A_{11}}{7\begin{vmatrix} 4 & 1 \\ 1 & 7 \end{vmatrix}}
+
\overset{a_{21}A_{21}}{1(-1)\begin{vmatrix} 1 & -2 \\ 1 & 7 \end{vmatrix}}
+
\overset{a_{31}A_{31}}{(-2)\begin{vmatrix} 1 & -2 \\ 4 & 1 \end{vmatrix}}
$$

$$= 7(28 - 1) - 1(7 + 2) - 2(1 + 8) = 162$$

When a determinant of order 4 is evaluated it is first expanded as a sum of determinants of order 3, then each of these is expanded in terms of determinants of order 2. The same procedure is followed for determinants of order n. First the expansion contains determinants of order $(n - 1)$, these are expanded in terms of determinants of order $(n - 2)$, etc., until we end with determinants of order 2.

Suggested Exercise: Do problem 1.

4.4. USEFUL PROPERTIES OF DETERMINANTS

From Equations (4.8) and (4.9) we deduce the following:

1. If all elements a_{ij} in a row or a column of $|a|$ are zero, then $|a| = 0$.
2. If only one element a_{kl} in a row k or a column l of $|a|$ is not zero, then $|a| = a_{kl}A_{kl}$.
3. Multiplying $|a|$ by any factor is equivalent to multiplying all the elements of any one row or column of $|a|$ by the same factor. For instance,

$$5 \begin{vmatrix} 1 & 3 \\ 2 & 4 \end{vmatrix} = \begin{vmatrix} 5 & 3 \\ 10 & 4 \end{vmatrix} = \begin{vmatrix} 5 & 15 \\ 2 & 4 \end{vmatrix}$$

4. The value of $|a|$ is not altered when its rows and columns are interchanged, for example,

$$\begin{vmatrix} 1 & 2 \\ 3 & 4 \end{vmatrix} = \begin{vmatrix} 1 & 3 \\ 2 & 4 \end{vmatrix}$$

5. When two rows or two columns of $|a|$ are interchanged, the sign of $|a|$ is changed, for instance,

$$\begin{vmatrix} 1 & 2 \\ 3 & 4 \end{vmatrix} = - \begin{vmatrix} 2 & 1 \\ 4 & 3 \end{vmatrix}$$

6. If two rows or columns of $|a|$ are identical, $|a| = 0$. This follows from 5. Why?
7. The value of $|a|$ is not altered when the elements of any row (or column) are multiplied by a factor, and the results are added to corresponding elements of any other row (or column). This follows from Property 6.

For example, let us multiply column 1 of $|a|$ by a factor α and add it to column 3. If $|a|$ is of order 3, then according to Property 7,

$$
\begin{vmatrix} a_{11} & a_{12} & a_{13} \\ a_{21} & a_{22} & a_{23} \\ a_{31} & a_{32} & a_{33} \end{vmatrix} = \begin{vmatrix} a_{11} & a_{12} & (a_{13} + \alpha a_{11}) \\ a_{21} & a_{22} & (a_{23} + \alpha a_{21}) \\ a_{31} & a_{32} & (a_{33} + \alpha a_{31}) \end{vmatrix}
$$

To prove this equality, expand the right-hand side using column 3 and its cofactors. The cofactors for column 3 are the same for the determinant on either side of the equation.

$$
(a_{13} + \alpha a_{11})A_{13} + (a_{23} + \alpha a_{21})A_{23} + (a_{33} + \alpha a_{31})A_{33}
$$
$$
= (a_{13}A_{13} + a_{23}A_{23} + a_{33}A_{33}) + \alpha(a_{11}A_{13} + a_{21}A_{23} + a_{31}A_{33})
$$

The quantity in the first parentheses on the right of the equal sign is the value of $|a|$. The quantity in the second parentheses is equivalent to the expansion of the following determinant with two identical columns

$$
\begin{vmatrix} a_{11} & a_{12} & a_{11} \\ a_{21} & a_{22} & a_{21} \\ a_{31} & a_{32} & a_{31} \end{vmatrix}
$$

From Property 6 this determinant is zero; hence, the two foregoing determinants are equal.

8. From Properties 7 and 1 we deduce that a determinant with dependent rows† or columns is zero. This is so because we can use Property 7 to reduce to zeros all the elements of a dependent row or column, without altering the value of the determinant, hence it must equal zero because of Property 1. For instance, in the determinant

$$
\begin{vmatrix} 1 & 1.5 & 2.5 \\ 2 & 2 & 3 \\ 3 & 1 & 0.5 \end{vmatrix}
$$

column 1 is a linear combination of 2 and 3; that is, column 1 = 4(column 2) − 2(column 3). Invoking rule 7 we can first subtract 4(column 2) from column 1, and then add 2(column 3), which will reduce column 1 to zeros.

9. Property 6 can also be used to deduce the following: When the elements a_{ij} of any row i of $|a|$ are multiplied by corresponding

---

† Rows are dependent when at least one of them can be generated by a linear combination of other rows. Similarly for columns.

cofactors A_{kj} of any other row $k \neq i$, then the sum of the products is zero

$$\sum_{j=1}^{n} a_{ij}A_{kj} = 0, \qquad i \neq k \tag{4.10}$$

Similarly, when the elements a_{ij} of any column j of $|a|$ are multiplied by corresponding cofactors A_{il} of any other column $l \neq j$, then the sum of the products is zero

$$\sum_{i=1}^{n} a_{ij}A_{il} = 0, \qquad j \neq l \tag{4.11}$$

These results occur because expression (4.10) is equivalent to the expansion of a determinant with identical rows i and k, and Equation (4.11) is equivalent to the expansion of a determinant with identical columns j and l (see proof of Property 7).

Property 9 will be used to develop the inverse of a matrix, we therefore suggest that the reader master it.

4.5. EVALUATING DETERMINANTS BY WORKING FOR ZEROS (PIVOTAL CONDENSATION METHOD)

The properties of the last section can be used to simplify the evaluation of a determinant. We demonstrate this for a determinant of order 3, but the application of the technique to an nth-order determinant will be apparent.

Consider the determinant

$$|a| = \begin{vmatrix} a_{11} & a_{12} & a_{13} \\ a_{21} & a_{22} & a_{23} \\ a_{31} & a_{32} & a_{33} \end{vmatrix}$$

in which all the elements are different from zero. Let us factor out a_{11} from the first row, then using Property 3, we have

$$|a| = a_{11} \begin{vmatrix} 1 & \dfrac{a_{12}}{a_{11}} & \dfrac{a_{13}}{a_{11}} \\ a_{21} & a_{22} & a_{23} \\ a_{31} & a_{32} & a_{33} \end{vmatrix}$$

We now apply Property 7 to reduce to zero all the elements of the first column except the first one. To generate a zero in position (2, 1) we multiply row 1 by a_{21} and subtract the result from the second row. Similarly for a zero in position $(3, 1)$ we multiply row 1 by a_{31} and subtract the result from row 3. $|a|$ will then have the form

$$|a| = a_{11} \begin{vmatrix} 1 & \dfrac{a_{12}}{a_{11}} & \dfrac{a_{13}}{a_{11}} \\ 0 & a_{22} - \dfrac{a_{12}}{a_{11}}a_{21} & a_{23} - \dfrac{a_{13}}{a_{11}}a_{21} \\ 0 & a_{32} - \dfrac{a_{12}}{a_{11}}a_{31} & a_{33} - \dfrac{a_{13}}{a_{11}}a_{31} \end{vmatrix}$$

Applying Property 2 we have

$$|a| = a_{11} \begin{vmatrix} a_{22} - \dfrac{a_{12}}{a_{11}}a_{21} & a_{23} - \dfrac{a_{13}}{a_{11}}a_{21} \\ a_{32} - \dfrac{a_{12}}{a_{11}}a_{31} & a_{33} - \dfrac{a_{13}}{a_{11}}a_{31} \end{vmatrix}$$

When $|a|$ is of order n we work for zeros in the first column to reduce it to a product of $a_{11}|b|$ where $|b|$ is a determinant of order $(n - 1)$. The same procedure is applied to $|b|$ so that $|a| = a_{11}b_{11}|c|$ where $|c|$ is of order $(n - 2)$. This process is continued until $|a|$ is reduced to a product of $(n - 2)$ numbers and a determinant of order 2.

The method described here is known as the *method of pivotal condensation*[28] where the pivot is the element which is reduced to unity.

Example

The following determinant is evaluated by the method of working for zeros.

$$\begin{vmatrix} -2 & 1 & 7 \\ 1 & 4 & 1 \\ 7 & 1 & -2 \end{vmatrix} = -2 \begin{vmatrix} 1 & -0.5 & -3.5 \\ 0 & 4.5 & 4.5 \\ 0 & 4.5 & 22.5 \end{vmatrix} = -2 \begin{vmatrix} 4.5 & 4.5 \\ 4.5 & 22.5 \end{vmatrix} = -162$$

Suggested Exercise: Do problem 2.

4.6. MATRICES: DEFINITIONS AND NOTATION

A matrix of order $m \times n$ is an arrangement of elements in m rows and n columns designated as follows:

$$[a] = \begin{bmatrix} a_{11} & a_{12} & \cdots & a_{1n} \\ a_{21} & a_{22} & \cdots & a_{2n} \\ \cdot & \cdot & \cdots & \cdot \\ a_{m1} & a_{m2} & \cdots & a_{mn} \end{bmatrix}$$

The elements a_{ij} of the matrix can be real numbers, complex numbers, or functions of variables. The first subscript i designates the row position of an element, and the second subscript j designates the column position. Rows are counted from the top down and columns from left to right.

An $(m \times n)$ matrix in which all elements $a_{ij} = 0$ is called a *null matrix* or a *zero matrix*.

Square Matrix

When a matrix has an equal number of rows and columns $(m = n)$ it is called a *square matrix*. The diagonal of a square matrix which extends from the upper left to the lower right and contains the element a_{ii} $(i = 1, 2, \ldots, n)$ is known as its *principal diagonal*.

A *symmetric matrix* is a square matrix in which $a_{ij} = a_{ji}$ for all i and j; that is, the matrix is symmetric about the principal diagonal.

A *diagonal matrix* is a square matrix with nonzero elements only on the principal diagonal; that is, $a_{ij} = 0$ for $i \neq j$, $a_{ij} \neq 0$ for $i = j$.

An *identity matrix*, or a *unit matrix*, is a diagonal matrix with all the elements of the principal diagonal equal to unity, $a_{ii} = 1$, $(i = 1, 2, \ldots, n)$.

The determinant $|a|$ formed from all the elements of a square matrix is known as the determinant of $[a]$.

A single number is a square matrix of order 1×1 known as *a scalar*.

Column Matrix: A matrix of order $m \times 1$ with m rows and a single column is known as a *column matrix* or *column vector*, and is designated by brackets as we did for the force and displacement vectors $\{F\}$ and $\{u\}$ in Chapter 2.

Transpose of a Matrix. When corresponding rows and columns of a matrix $[a]$ are interchanged the resulting matrix is called the *transposed matrix of* $[a]$ and is designated as $[a]^T$ (some books use a prime, $[a]'$). For instance, the transposed matrix $[a]^T$ of the 2×3 matrix

$$[a] = \begin{bmatrix} a_{11} & a_{12} & a_{13} \\ a_{21} & a_{22} & a_{23} \end{bmatrix} = \begin{bmatrix} 1 & 3 & 2 \\ -4 & 0 & 5 \end{bmatrix}$$

is the 3×2 matrix

$$[a]^T = \begin{bmatrix} a_{11}^T & a_{12}^T \\ a_{21}^T & a_{22}^T \\ a_{31}^T & a_{32}^T \end{bmatrix} = \begin{bmatrix} 1 & -4 \\ 3 & 0 \\ 2 & 5 \end{bmatrix}$$

in which any element, a_{ij}^T, of the transposed matrix is obtained from element

a_{ji} of the original matrix, or

$$a_{ij}^T = a_{ji}$$

Row Matrix. A matrix of order $1 \times n$ with one row and n columns is known as a *row matrix* or *row vector*. We shall designate a row matrix as the transpose of a column matrix. Hence $\{F\}^T$ and $\{u\}^T$ are respectively row matrices of force and displacement

$$\{u\}^T = [u_1, u_2, \ldots, u_n]$$
$$\{F\}^T = [F_1, F_2, \ldots, F_n]$$

4.7. MATRIX ALGEBRA: EQUALITY, ADDITION, SUBTRACTION, SCALAR MULTIPLICATION

We now define the rules that permit the manipulation of matrices and form the foundation of matrix algebra.

Equality of Matrices

Two matrices $[a]$ and $[b]$ are said to be equal if

1. They are of the same order, and
2. All elements a_{ij} of $[a]$ are equal to the corresponding elements b_{ij} of $[b]$. That is,

$$[a] = [b]$$

when

$$\text{order of } [a] = \text{order of } [b]$$

and

$$a_{ij} = b_{ij} \qquad \text{for all } i \text{ and } j$$

Addition of Matrices

Matrices of the same order can be added. Any element ij in the resulting matrix is the sum of the elements ij in the added matrices. That is,

$$[d] = [a] + [b] + [c]$$

when

$$d_{ij} = a_{ij} + b_{ij} + c_{ij}, \qquad \text{for all } i \text{ and } j$$

Subtraction of Matrices

Subtraction of matrices is similar to addition except that corresponding elements are subtracted. That is,

$$[d] = [a] - [b] - [c]$$

when

$$d_{ij} = a_{ij} - b_{ij} - c_{ij} \qquad \text{for all } i \text{ and } j$$

Or

$$[d] = [a] - [b] + [c]$$

when

$$d_{ij} = a_{ij} - b_{ij} + c_{ij} \qquad \text{for all } i \text{ and } j$$

Scalar Multiplication of a Matrix

When a scalar α multiplies a matrix $[a]$, then each element a_{ij} is multiplied by α. Namely,

$$[c] = \alpha[a]$$

implies

$$c_{ij} = \alpha a_{ij} \qquad \text{for all } i \text{ and } j$$

4.8. MATRIX MULTIPLICATION

We used matrix multiplication in Chapter 3. For instance in Equation (3.10) two square matrices were multiplied and on the right-hand side of Equation (3.12) a square matrix multiplied a column matrix. In general, when a matrix $[a]$ of order $m \times r$ is multiplied by a matrix $[b]$ of order $r \times n$, the resulting matrix $[c]$ has as many rows as $[a]$ and as many columns as $[b]$, and any element c_{ij} of $[c]$ is the *inner product*† of row i in $[a]$ and column j in $[b]$. That is, in the matrix product $[a][b]$

$$[c] \quad = \quad [a] \qquad [b]$$
$$\text{order} \to m \times n \quad m \times r \quad r \times n$$

$$c_{ij} = \sum_{k=1}^{r} a_{ik}b_{kj} \tag{4.12}$$

$$i = 1, 2, \ldots, m \qquad j = 1, 2, \ldots, n$$

---

† An inner product of row i and column j is the sum of the products of their corresponding elements.

The matrix multiplication of Equation (4.12) is defined only when the number of columns in $[a]$ is equal to the number of rows in $[b]$, in which case $[a]$ and $[b]$ are said to be *conformable matrices* for multiplication.

It is helpful to use the following geometric scheme in multiplying matrix $[a]$ by matrix $[b]$ to generate matrix $[c]$.

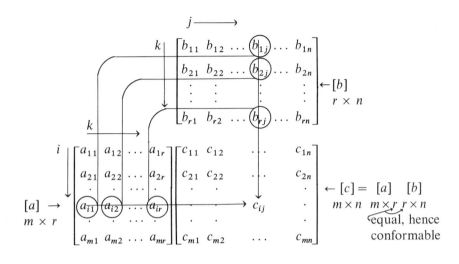

In this scheme any element c_{ij} of $[c]$ is at the intersection of row i in $[a]$ and column j in $[b]$. This helps to visualize why $[a]$ determines the number of rows in $[c]$, and $[b]$ determines the number of columns in $[c]$, and why the number of columns in $[a]$ must equal the number of rows in $[b]$, but has no effect on the order of matrix $[c]$.

Example

The multiplication $[a][b] = [c]$

$$\begin{array}{ccc} [a] & [b] & [c] \end{array}$$

$$\begin{bmatrix} 2 & 3 & 6 \\ 4 & 1 & 0 \end{bmatrix} \begin{bmatrix} 1 & 1 & 3 \\ 2 & 5 & 9 \\ 0 & 1 & 0 \end{bmatrix} = \begin{bmatrix} c_{11} & c_{12} & c_{13} \\ c_{21} & c_{22} & c_{23} \end{bmatrix}$$

$$\begin{array}{cccc} \text{order} & 2 \times 3 & 3 \times 3 & 2 \times 3 \end{array}$$

equal o.k.

can be performed by the geometric scheme as follows:

$$
\begin{array}{c}
[b]\begin{bmatrix} 1 & 1 & 3 \\ 2 & 5 & 9 \\ 0 & 1 & 0 \end{bmatrix} \\
[a]\begin{bmatrix} 2 & 3 & 6 \\ 4 & 1 & 0 \end{bmatrix} \begin{bmatrix} 8 & 23 & 33 \\ 6 & 9 & 21 \end{bmatrix}[c]
\end{array}
$$

For instance, c_{23} is obtained from row 2 of $[a]$ and column 3 of $[b]$

$$c_{23} = 4 \times 3 + 1 \times 9 + 0 \times 0 = 21$$

and

$$c_{22} = 4 \times 1 + 1 \times 5 + 0 \times 1 = 9$$

(Verify the other results.)

Suggested Exercises: Do problems 3 and 4.

Properties Connected With Matrix Multiplication

1. *In general, matrix multiplication is not commutative;* that is,

$$[a][b] \neq [b][a]$$

This is so because the product $[a]\ [b]$ may be conformable, whereas the
$\underset{m \times r\ r \times n}{}$
product $[b][a]$ is not $(m \neq n)$, and the products may be unequal although
conformable, as for instance,

$$
\begin{bmatrix} 1 & 1 \\ 0 & 1 \end{bmatrix}\begin{bmatrix} 1 & 2 \\ 3 & 4 \end{bmatrix} \neq \begin{bmatrix} 1 & 2 \\ 3 & 4 \end{bmatrix}\begin{bmatrix} 1 & 1 \\ 0 & 1 \end{bmatrix}
$$

Because of this property, we distinguish between *premultiplication* and
postmultiplication of matrices. In the product $[a][b]$, $[b]$ is premultiplied
by $[a]$, and in $[b][a]$, $[b]$ is postmultiplied by $[a]$.

Suggested Exercises: Do problems 5 and 6.

2. *Zero Product.* The product of two nonzero matrices can yield a null
matrix. For instance,

$$
\begin{bmatrix} 0 & 3 \\ 0 & 8 \end{bmatrix}\begin{bmatrix} 5 & 9 \\ 0 & 0 \end{bmatrix} = \begin{bmatrix} 0 & 0 \\ 0 & 0 \end{bmatrix}
$$

3. *Continued Products, Associative, and Distributive Laws.* The associative law of ordinary algebra applies to matrix algebra. That is,

$$[d] = ([a][b])[c] = [a]([b][c]) \quad \text{(associative law)}$$

and the parentheses can be eliminated because the result is not altered by the sequence of multiplication; that is, we can first do $[a][b]$ and then post-multiply by $[c]$, or first do $[b][c]$ and then premultiply by $[a]$. Any element ij of $[d]$ in the preceding multiplication is given by

$$d_{ij} = \sum_k \sum_l a_{ik} b_{kl} c_{lj}$$

(Verify.)

It is important to check conformability before proceeding to carry out a continuous multiplication. This is conveniently done by writing under each matrix its order (rows × columns) as shown

$$\underset{m \times r}{[a]} \quad \underset{r \times s}{[b]} \quad \underset{s \times t}{[c]} \quad \underset{t \times v}{[d]} \quad \underset{v \times n}{[e]} = \underset{m \times n}{[\text{result}]}$$

equal equal equal equal

The matrix that results from a continuous product has as many rows, m, as the first matrix in the product and as many columns, n, as the last.

The distributive law of ordinary algebra also applies to matrix algebra, that is,

$$[a]([b] + [c]) = [a][b] + [a][c]$$

or $\qquad\qquad\qquad\qquad\qquad\qquad\qquad$ distributive law

$$([b] + [c])[a] = [b][a] + [c][a]$$

4.9. THE INVERSE MATRIX

In Chapter 3 we showed that, for a linear structure with a single coordinate,

$$ak = 1 \quad \text{(see Equation 3.3)}$$

That is, a and k are the inverse of each other. For a linear structure with two coordinates or more, we wrote a similar relation using matrices $[a]$ and $[k]$,

$$[a][k] = [I] \quad \text{(see Equation 3.11)}$$

and stated that $[a]$ and $[k]$ are the inverse of each other in a matrix sense.

We see that the identity matrix $[I]$ in matrix algebra is analogous to 1 in ordinary algebra. In fact in ordinary algebra a number b is not altered when multiplied by 1

$$b \cdot 1 = 1 \cdot b = b$$

and in matrix algebra a matrix $[b]$ is not altered when premultiplied or post-multiplied by $[I]$ (verify, see Problem 6)

$$[b][I] = [I][b] = [b] \qquad (4.13)$$

Inverse of a Matrix

An inverse of a square matrix $[a]$ is a square matrix of the same order which will yield the identity matrix when it premultiplies or postmultiplies $[a]$. The inverse of $[a]$ is designated as $[a]^{-1}$, hence, from this definition,

$$[a]^{-1}[a] = [I]$$
$$[a][a]^{-1} = [I] \qquad (4.14)$$

The inverse of a matrix $[a]$ is defined only when $[a]$ is a square matrix, and it exists only when the rows and columns of $[a]$ are independent, or when $|a| \neq 0$ (see Property 8, Section 4.4).

The maximum number of linearly independent rows or columns of $[a]$ is called the *rank* of $[a]$. Hence, when the rank of a square matrix $[a]$ is equal to its order (that is, $|a| \neq 0$), it has an inverse.

A square matrix $[a]$ is said to be *singular* when $|a| = 0$, and *nonsingular* when $|a| \neq 0$.

Computing the Inverse of $[a]$ *from its Cofactors.* Given a nonsingular matrix $[a]$ of order n we can find its inverse by using Equations (4.8) and (4.10), which are repeated here, for convenience, in the following form:

$$\sum_{j=1}^{n} a_{ij}A_{kj} = |a|, \qquad \text{for } i = k$$
$$= 0, \qquad \text{for } i \neq k \qquad (4.15)$$

As a first step we construct a new matrix of the cofactors A_{ij} of the elements a_{ij} of $[a]$.

$$[A] = \begin{bmatrix} A_{11} & A_{12} & \dots & A_{1n} \\ A_{21} & A_{22} & \dots & A_{2n} \\ \vdots & \vdots & & \vdots \\ A_{n1} & A_{n2} & \dots & A_{nn} \end{bmatrix}$$

The transpose of this matrix is called the *adjoint of* $[a]$ and is designated compactly as adj [a].†

$$\text{adj} [a] = [A]^T = \begin{bmatrix} A_{11} & A_{21} & \cdots & A_{n1} \\ A_{12} & A_{22} & \cdots & A_{n2} \\ \vdots & \vdots & & \vdots \\ A_{1n} & A_{2n} & \cdots & A_{nn} \end{bmatrix}$$

Any column i of adj [a] consists of the cofactors of row i of [a],

$$\text{element } ji \text{ of adj } [a] = A_{ji}^T = A_{ij}$$

Next we premultiply $[A]^T$ by [a] and use, for convenience, the geometric scheme of matrix multiplication (Section 4.8), then from Equation (4.15)

We can therefore write

$$[a] \text{ adj } [a] = |a|[I]$$

or

$$[a]\left(\frac{1}{|a|} \text{ adj } [a]\right) = [I]$$

From the definition of the inverse matrix, it follows that

$$[a]^{-1} = \frac{1}{|a|} \text{ adj } [a] \qquad (4.16)$$

From Equation (4.16) we understand why $[a]^{-1}$ does not exist when $|a| = 0$, that is, when [a] is singular.

---

† It is also possible to generate adj [a] by writing the matrix of cofactors for $[a]^T$.

Example

To generate the inverse of

$$[a] = \begin{bmatrix} 1 & -2 & 3 \\ 2 & 0 & -3 \\ 1 & 1 & 1 \end{bmatrix}$$

we first compute $|a|$ from Equation (4.8) or (4.9). Using the first column of $[a]$ in Equation (4.9) we have

$$|a| = 1 \times 3 + 2 \times 5 + 1 \times 6 = 19$$

Since $|a| \neq 0$ we know that $[a]^{-1}$ exists so we proceed to generate adj $[a]$ by finding the matrix of cofactors $[A]$ and transposing it. (We have the first column of $[A]$ from the computations for $|a|$.)

$$[A] = \begin{bmatrix} 3 & -5 & 2 \\ 5 & -2 & -3 \\ 6 & 9 & 4 \end{bmatrix}, \quad \text{adj}\,[a] = [A]^T = \begin{bmatrix} 3 & 5 & 6 \\ -5 & -2 & 9 \\ 2 & -3 & 4 \end{bmatrix}$$

The inverse is computed from Equation (4.16)

$$[a]^{-1} = \tfrac{1}{19} \begin{bmatrix} 3 & 5 & 6 \\ -5 & -2 & 9 \\ 2 & -3 & 4 \end{bmatrix}$$

To check the result we perform the multiplication $[a][a]^{-1}$ which must yield the identity matrix

$$\tfrac{1}{19} \begin{bmatrix} 3 & 5 & 6 \\ -5 & -2 & 9 \\ 2 & -3 & 4 \end{bmatrix} \leftarrow [a]^{-1}$$

$$[a] \rightarrow \begin{bmatrix} 1 & -2 & 3 \\ 2 & 0 & -3 \\ 1 & 1 & 1 \end{bmatrix} \tfrac{1}{19} \begin{bmatrix} 19 & 0 & 0 \\ 0 & 19 & 0 \\ 0 & 0 & 19 \end{bmatrix} \leftarrow [a][a]^{-1} = [I]$$

Suggested Exercises: Do problems 7 and 8.

4.10. MATRIX EQUATIONS

A *matrix equation* is an equation in terms of matrices. For instance, Equations (3.12) and (3.13) are matrix equations. We can perform the following operations on each side of a matrix equation: add and subtract matrices, premultiply and postmultiply by a matrix, provided that these operations are consistent with the rules of addition and multiplication. We can also transpose or invert each side of a matrix equation when the inverse is defined and exists.

Let us repeat Equations (3.12) and (3.13) and assume that they represent the force displacement relations at n coordinates of a structure.

$$\{u\} = [a]\{F\} \tag{4.17}$$

$$\{F\} = [k]\{u\} \tag{4.18}$$

If we premultiply each side of Equation (4.17) by $[a]^{-1}$ (assuming it exists), then from Equations (4.14) and (4.13), we have

$$[a]^{-1}\{u\} = \{F\}$$

Comparing this equation with Equation (4.18), we conclude that

$$[k] = [a]^{-1}$$

Or alternatively we can substitute for $\{F\}$, from Equation (4.18) in Equation (4.17),

$$\{u\} = [a][k]\{u\}$$

from which we conclude that

$$[a][k] = [I] \tag{4.19}$$

and from Equation (4.14)

$$[a] = [k]^{-1}$$

$$[k] = [a]^{-1}$$

Equation (4.19) is a generalization of Equation (3.11) which was shown to be true for a specific example. Stated in words Equation (4.19) reads: The stiffness and flexibility matrix corresponding to a structure with a prescribed set of coordinates are the inverse of each other.

4.11. STIFFNESS MATRIX [k], AND FLEXIBILITY MATRIX [a] IN CO-ORDINATES WITH CONSTRAINED MEASUREMENTS

We now use Equation (4.19) to summarize our findings in Section 3.6 in the light of the tools of matrix algebra.

When the displacement measurements are constrained (dependent), [a] exists (can be constructed), but it has linearly dependent rows and columns; consequently, it is singular and its inverse [k] does not exist (cannot be constructed).

When the force measurements are constrained $[k]$ exists (can be constructed), but it has linearly dependent rows and columns; consequently, it is singular and its inverse, $[a]$, does not exist (cannot be constructed).

4.12. THE REVERSAL LAW

The inverse of a product of nonsingular square matrices is equal to the product of their individual inverses taken in reverse order, or

$$([a][b][c][d])^{-1} = [d]^{-1}[c]^{-1}[b]^{-1}[a]^{-1} \qquad (4.20)$$

This can be verified by premultiplying each side of Equation (4.20) first by $[d]$ then by $[c]$, $[b]$, and $[a]$.

A reversal law similar to Equation (4.20) holds for the transpose of a product of matrices (here the matrices must only be conformable).

$$([a][b][c][d])^{T} = [d]^{T}[c]^{T}[b]^{T}[a]^{T} \qquad (4.21)$$

4.13. PARTITIONED MATRICES

It is often convenient to partition a matrix by introducing vertical and horizontal lines as follows:

$$[K] = \left[\begin{array}{cc|cc} 4 & 2 & -6 & 6 \\ 2 & 4 & -6 & 6 \\ \hline -6 & -6 & 12 & -12 \\ 6 & 6 & -12 & 12 \end{array}\right] = \left[\begin{array}{c|c} [K]_{11} & [K]_{12} \\ \hline [K]_{21} & [K]_{22} \end{array}\right] \qquad (4.22)$$

Each array of numbers bounded by the original brackets and the newly introduced lines is called a *submatrix*, and the original matrix in partitioned form is referred to as a *partitioned matrix*. The submatrices are conveniently identified by subscripts as if they were elements; that is, first and second subscript designate row and column position respectively. In the foregoing example

$$[K]_{11} = \begin{bmatrix} 4 & 2 \\ 2 & 4 \end{bmatrix}, \qquad [K]_{12} = \begin{bmatrix} -6 & 6 \\ -6 & 6 \end{bmatrix}$$

$$[K]_{21} = \begin{bmatrix} -6 & -6 \\ 6 & 6 \end{bmatrix}, \qquad [K]_{22} = \begin{bmatrix} 12 & -12 \\ -12 & 12 \end{bmatrix}$$

and each submatrix is of order 2×2, but any other partitioning of matrices is possible, such as, for instance,

$$\begin{bmatrix} 1 & 2 & 3 \\ \hline 3 & 0 & 8 \\ 6 & 5 & 4 \end{bmatrix} \qquad \begin{bmatrix} 4 & 2 & 3 & 1 & 0 & 1 \\ \hline 7 & 9 & 0 & 3 & 4 & 6 \\ 5 & 7 & 1 & 0 & 8 & 2 \end{bmatrix}$$

Addition and Subtraction of Partitioned Matrices

Partitioned matrices can be added or subtracted in terms of the sub-matrices treated as elements provided that they are partitioned the same way so that corresponding submatrices are of the same order. For example, in the following equation all submatrices with the same subscripts are of the same order.

$$\begin{bmatrix} [a]_{11} & [a]_{12} \\ [a]_{21} & [a]_{22} \end{bmatrix} + \begin{bmatrix} [b]_{11} & [b]_{12} \\ [b]_{21} & [b]_{22} \end{bmatrix} = \begin{bmatrix} [a]_{11} + [b]_{11} & [a]_{12} + [b]_{12} \\ [a]_{21} + [b]_{21} & [a]_{22} + [b]_{22} \end{bmatrix} \quad (4.23)$$

Multiplication of Partitioned Matrices

Two partitioned matrices can be multiplied in terms of the submatrices treated as elements, provided that all resulting matrix products are conformable. For example, let us consider the product $[a][b] = [c]$ with the matrices partitioned as shown.

$$\overset{[a]}{\begin{bmatrix} A_{11} & A_{12} \\ \hline A_{21} & A_{22} \end{bmatrix}} \overset{[b]}{\begin{bmatrix} B_{11} & B_{12} \\ \hline B_{21} & B_{22} \end{bmatrix}} = \overset{[c]}{\begin{bmatrix} C_{11} & C_{12} \\ \hline C_{21} & C_{22} \end{bmatrix}} \quad (4.24)$$

The height and width are respectively representative of the number of rows and columns in a matrix or submatrix, and each capital letter represents a submatrix. Now when we carry out the multiplication, treating submatrices A_{ij} and B_{ij} as elements, we have

$$C_{11} = A_{11}B_{11} + A_{12}B_{21} \qquad C_{12} = A_{11}B_{12} + A_{12}B_{22}$$

$$C_{21} = A_{21}B_{11} + A_{22}B_{21} \qquad C_{22} = A_{21}B_{12} + A_{22}B_{22}$$

This indicates that for conformability the column partitioning in matrix $[a]$ must be the same as the row partitioning in matrix $[b]$. This partitioning is shown by the heavy dashed line in Equation (4.24). The row partitioning in $[a]$ is arbitrary but determines the corresponding row partitioning in the resulting product $[c]$. This is indicated by the horizontal dashed line in $[a]$ and $[c]$. Similarly the column partitioning in $[b]$ is arbitrary but determines the corresponding column partitioning in [c]. This is shown by the vertical dashed line in [b] and [c].

Suggested Exercise: Do problem 9.

4.14. AN EXAMPLE OF PARTITIONED MATRICES IN STRUCTURES

We wish to generate the 2 × 2 stiffness matrix for the stepped beam of Figure 4.1. Since we derived, in Section 3.6, the stiffness matrix for the prismatic beam of Figure 2.3 in Chapter 2, we find it easier to define two more coordinates at the step in Figure 4.1 and generate a 4 × 4 stiffness matrix for the four coordinates shown in Figure 4.2. Proceeding by the method of Chapter 3 we obtain

$$[k] = \begin{bmatrix} 8 & 0 & 4 & 12 \\ 0 & 4 & 2 & -6 \\ 4 & 2 & 12 & 6 \\ 12 & -6 & 6 & 36 \end{bmatrix}$$

which can be used in the following matrix equation for the four coordinates of Figure 4.2

$$\{F\} = [k]\{u\}$$

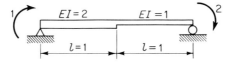

Figure 4.1.

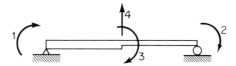

Figure 4.2.

But we wish to compute the 2 × 2 stiffness matrix for Figure 4.1. This is equivalent to saying that we wish to establish in Figure 4.2 the relation

$$\begin{Bmatrix} F_1 \\ F_2 \end{Bmatrix} = [k]^* \begin{Bmatrix} u_1 \\ u_2 \end{Bmatrix}$$

between the forces and displacement at coordinates 1 and 2 only, with the forces at 3 and 4 zero, by finding a corresponding 2×2 stiffness matrix $[k]^*$. We therefore partition $\{F\}$ and $\{u\}$ to separate the coordinates of interest 1 and 2 from the others. This causes the matrix equation written for the 4 coordinates in Figure 4.2 to appear as follows:

$$\left\{\begin{matrix} \{F\}^* \\ \hline \{0\} \end{matrix}\right\} = \left[\begin{matrix} [k]_{11} & | & [k]_{12} \\ \hline [k]_{21} & | & [k]_{22} \end{matrix}\right] \left\{\begin{matrix} \{u\}^* \\ \hline \{u\}^0 \end{matrix}\right\} \tag{4.25}$$

in which

$$\{F\}^* = \left\{\begin{matrix} F_1 \\ F_2 \end{matrix}\right\}, \qquad \{0\} = \left\{\begin{matrix} 0 \\ 0 \end{matrix}\right\}$$

$$\{u\}^* = \left\{\begin{matrix} u_1 \\ u_2 \end{matrix}\right\}, \qquad \{u\}^0 = \left\{\begin{matrix} u_3 \\ u_4 \end{matrix}\right\}$$

The 4×4 stiffness matrix $[k]$ must be partitioned in a way which is consistent with the partitioning of $\{F\}$ and $\{u\}$, therefore submatrices $[k]_{ij}$ are each of order 2×2.

Treating submatrices as elements we can write Equation (4.25) as the following two matrix equations:

$$\{F\}^* = [k]_{11}\{u\}^* + [k]_{12}\{u\}^0 \tag{4.26}$$

$$\{0\} = [k]_{21}\{u\}^* + [k]_{22}\{u\}^0 \tag{4.27}$$

Since we wish to obtain an equation in terms of vectors $\{F\}^*$ and $\{u\}^*$ only, we eliminate $\{u\}^0$ from Equation (4.26) as follows: Premultiply Equation (4.27) by $[k]_{22}^{-1}$, then

$$\{u\}^0 = -[k]_{22}^{-1}[k]_{21}\{u\}^*$$

Substitute this result in Equation (4.26) to obtain

$$\{F\}^* = [k]^*\{u\}^*$$

in which

$$[k]^* = [k]_{11} - [k]_{12}[k]_{22}^{-1}[k]_{21} \tag{4.28}$$

is the desired stiffness matrix. $[k]^*$ is referred to as the *reduced stiffness matrix.*

For the present example,

$$[k]^* = \begin{bmatrix} 8 & 0 \\ 0 & 4 \end{bmatrix} - \begin{bmatrix} 4 & 12 \\ 2 & -6 \end{bmatrix} \begin{bmatrix} 12 & 6 \\ 6 & 36 \end{bmatrix}^{-1} \begin{bmatrix} 4 & 2 \\ 12 & -6 \end{bmatrix}$$

$$= \begin{bmatrix} 8 & 0 \\ 0 & 4 \end{bmatrix} - \frac{1}{11}\begin{bmatrix} 48 & -16 \\ -16 & 20 \end{bmatrix} = \frac{1}{11}\begin{bmatrix} 40 & 16 \\ 16 & 24 \end{bmatrix}$$

Suggested Exercises: Do problems 10 and 11.

4.15. INVERSION BY PARTITIONED MATRICES

Suppose that we have a computer and a program for matrix inversion which can handle matrices of order $\leqslant n$. To invert a matrix of order $m > n$ we can partition it and generate its inverse in a way that will involve the inversion of submatrices of order $\leqslant n$. Here is how this is accomplished:

Let the inverse of matrix $[a]$ of order $m > n$ be designated as $[b]$. We partition these matrices the same way in rows and columns and write

$$
\begin{array}{c}
\text{columns} \\
\begin{array}{cc} r & s \end{array}
\end{array}
$$

$$
\text{rows} \quad
\begin{array}{c} r \\ s \end{array}
\left[\begin{array}{c|c} A_{11} & A_{12} \\ \hline A_{21} & A_{22} \end{array}\right]
\left[\begin{array}{c|c} B_{11} & B_{12} \\ \hline B_{21} & B_{22} \end{array}\right]
=
\left[\begin{array}{c|c} I & 0 \\ \hline 0 & I \end{array}\right]
\qquad (4.29)
$$

$$
[a] \qquad\qquad [b]
$$

All capital letters in Equation (4.29) are submatrices with I and 0 designating respectively the identity matrix and the null matrix. A_{11} and A_{22} are square matrices of order r and s, respectively, each smaller than $n (r < n,$ $s < n)$. The objective is to find the submatrices B_{ij} of the inverse matrix in terms of the submatrices A_{ij} of $[a]$. To do this we write Equation (4.29) as the following four matrix equations:

$$
\begin{aligned}
A_{11}B_{11} + A_{12}B_{21} &= I \\
A_{11}B_{12} + A_{12}B_{22} &= 0 \\
A_{21}B_{11} + A_{22}B_{21} &= 0 \\
A_{21}B_{12} + A_{22}B_{22} &= I
\end{aligned}
\qquad (4.30)
$$

Using these four equations and remembering that the inverse is defined only for a square matrix we can solve for the four submatrices B_{ij}. For instance, B_{22} can be computed as follows. Premultiply each term in the second of Equations (4.30) by A_{11}^{-1} and write

$$
B_{12} = -A_{11}^{-1}A_{12}B_{22}
$$

Substitute this in the fourth of Equations (4.30) to obtain

$$
(A_{22} - A_{21}A_{11}^{-1}A_{12})B_{22} = I
$$

The matrix in the parentheses is square and of order s, the same order as B_{22} and I in the fourth of Equations (4.30), therefore we can premultiply by its inverse and write

$$
B_{22} = (A_{22} - A_{21}A_{11}^{-1}A_{12})^{-1}
$$

Operating similarly on the first and third of Equations (4.30) we obtain B_{11} and B_{21}. The complete inverse is given by

$$[a]^{-1} = [b] = \begin{bmatrix} (A_{11} - A_{12}A_{22}^{-1}A_{21})^{-1} & | & -A_{11}^{-1}A_{12}B_{22} \\ \hline -A_{22}^{-1}A_{21}B_{11} & | & B_{22} \end{bmatrix}_{\substack{r \\ }}^{\substack{r \\ }} \quad (4.31)$$

(Verify.) In Equation (4.31) all submatrices which are inverted are of order r or s, each smaller than n.

4.16. INVERSION BY WORKING FOR ZEROS: THE GAUSS–JORDAN METHOD

The inverse of a matrix can also be obtained by a method similar to the one used in Section (4.5) to evaluate determinants by "working for zeros." In this method, the matrix $[a]$ of order n which is to be inverted is first premultiplied by a square matrix $[t_1]$ which causes the product $[t_1][a] = [b]$ to have the first column of the identity matrix of order n. Next, matrix $[b]$ is premultiplied by $[t_2]$ which causes the resulting matrix $[c] = [t_2][t_1][a]$ to have the first two columns of the identity matrix. This is repeated n times until the final product yields the identity matrix of order n; that is,

$$[t_n][t_{n-1}] \cdots [t_3][t_2][t_1][a] = [I] \quad (4.32)$$

By definition then,

$$[a]^{-1} = [t_n][t_{n-1}] \cdots [t_3][t_2][t_1] \quad (4.33)$$

Let us illustrate the method by finding the inverse of a matrix $[a]$ of order 3. The application to matrices of higher order will be apparent. We use, for convenience, the geometric scheme for multiplication as follows:

$$\begin{bmatrix} a_{11} & a_{12} & a_{13} \\ a_{21} & a_{22} & a_{23} \\ a_{31} & a_{32} & a_{33} \end{bmatrix} \leftarrow [a]$$

$$[t_1] \rightarrow \begin{bmatrix} \dfrac{1}{a_{11}} & 0 & 0 \\ -\dfrac{a_{21}}{a_{11}} & 1 & 0 \\ -\dfrac{a_{31}}{a_{11}} & 0 & 1 \end{bmatrix} \begin{bmatrix} 1 & b_{12} & b_{13} \\ 0 & b_{22} & b_{23} \\ 0 & b_{32} & b_{33} \end{bmatrix} \leftarrow [t_1][a] = [b]$$

$$[t_2] \rightarrow \begin{bmatrix} 1 & -\dfrac{b_{12}}{b_{22}} & 0 \\ 0 & \dfrac{1}{b_{22}} & 0 \\ 0 & -\dfrac{b_{32}}{b_{22}} & 1 \end{bmatrix} \begin{bmatrix} 1 & 0 & c_{13} \\ 0 & 1 & c_{23} \\ 0 & 0 & c_{33} \end{bmatrix} \leftarrow [t_2][t_1][a] = [c]$$

$$[t_3] \rightarrow \begin{bmatrix} 1 & 0 & -\dfrac{c_{13}}{c_{33}} \\ 0 & 1 & -\dfrac{c_{23}}{c_{33}} \\ 0 & 0 & \dfrac{1}{c_{33}} \end{bmatrix} \begin{bmatrix} 1 & 0 & 0 \\ 0 & 1 & 0 \\ 0 & 0 & 1 \end{bmatrix} \leftarrow [t_3][t_2][t_1][a] = [I]$$

Notice that matrix $[b]$ has a form which is similar to the determinant in Section 4.5 after the first operation on it. This is so because the function of matrix $[t_1]$ is similar to this first operation. Row 2 of $[t_1]$ reduces element $(2, 1)$ to zero by adding row 2 and $-a_{21}/a_{11}$ times row 1, and row 3 of $[t_1]$ reduces element $(3, 1)$ to zero by adding row 3 and $-a_{31}/a_{11}$ times row 1. Element a_{11} is used as a *pivot* in this operation.

As an example we compute the inverse of the matrix $[a]$ on facing page. To avoid rewriting matrices $[t_i]$ in longhand computations, the following geometric scheme can be used (each letter represents its corresponding matrix)

$$[a]$$
$$[t_1] \quad [t_1 a]$$
$$[t_2][t_2 t_1] \quad [t_2 t_1 a] \quad [t_3 t_2 t_1] = [a]^{-1}$$
$$[t_3][t_3 t_2 t_1][t_3 t_2 t_1 a] \leftarrow [I]$$

Suggested Exercise: Do problem 12.

$$[t_1]\to \begin{bmatrix} 1 & 0 & 0 \\ -2 & 1 & 0 \\ -3 & 0 & 1 \end{bmatrix}$$

$$\begin{bmatrix} -1 & 1 & 0 \\ 2 & -1 & 0 \\ 1 & -2 & 1 \end{bmatrix} \to [t_2][t_1]$$

$$\begin{bmatrix} 1 & -3 & 2 \\ 1 & 1 & -1 \\ -1 & 2 & -1 \end{bmatrix} \to [t_3][t_2][t_1]=[a]^{-1}$$

$$\begin{bmatrix} 1 & 0 & 0 \\ 0 & 1 & 0 \\ 0 & 0 & 1 \end{bmatrix} \to [I]$$

$$[a]\to \begin{bmatrix} 1 & 1 & 1 \\ 2 & 1 & 3 \\ 3 & 1 & 4 \end{bmatrix}$$

$$[t_1]\to \begin{bmatrix} 1 & 1 & 1 \\ 0 & -1 & 1 \\ 0 & -2 & 1 \end{bmatrix}$$

$$[t_2]\to \begin{bmatrix} 1 & 0 & 2 \\ 0 & 1 & -1 \\ 0 & 0 & -1 \end{bmatrix}$$

$$[t_3]\to \begin{bmatrix} 1 & 0 & 0 \\ 0 & 1 & 0 \\ 0 & 0 & 1 \end{bmatrix}$$

$$[t_1]\to \begin{bmatrix} 1 & 0 & 0 \\ -2 & 1 & 0 \\ -3 & 0 & 1 \end{bmatrix}$$

$$[t_2]\to \begin{bmatrix} 1 & 1 & 0 \\ 0 & -1 & 0 \\ 0 & -2 & 1 \end{bmatrix}$$

$$[t_3]\to \begin{bmatrix} 1 & 0 & 2 \\ 0 & 1 & -1 \\ 0 & 0 & -1 \end{bmatrix}$$

4.17. MATRIX OPERATIONS ON THE COMPUTER

The manipulation of matrices is greatly facilitated by using a computer. Let us see now how we can use the automatic programming language of Fortran (introduced in Chapter 1) to write programs for manipulating matrices. For simplicity, we assume that all data are in the computer and concern ourselves only with the instructions involving the manipulation of matrices.

Program to Add Two Matrices

Table 4.1 represents a program designed to add two matrices of order $M \times N$ and store the result in Matrix $[C]$.

TABLE 4.1

PROGRAM TO ADD TWO MATRICES

Statement Number	Fortran Statement
1	DO 3 $I = 1, M$
2	DO 3 $J = 1, N$
3	$C(I, J) = A(I, J) + B(I, J)$

In this program we have two do loops, one nested within the other. The operations called for by the do loops are performed as follows: First the computer sets $I = 1$, then goes to statement 2 and satisfies the inner do loop of statements 2 and 3 for all J from 1 to N; that is, the first rows of $[A]$ and $[B]$ are added. Next I is set equal to 2 and the inner do loop is again satisfied for $J = 1, 2, \ldots N$; that is, the second rows are added. This is continued until all M rows are added. As a rule in Fortran, an inner do loop (nested within an outer do loop) is always satisfied completely for each cycle of the outer loop (in our program satements 1 to 3 inclusive constitute the outer loop).

Programs for Subtraction, Transposition, and Multiplication

Tables 4.2, 4.3, and 4.4 show, respectively, programs for subtracting two matrices, transposing matrix $[A]$ and storing the result in $[B]$, and performing the multiplication $[A][B]$ ($[A]$ is of order $M \times L$ and $[B]$ of order $L \times N$) and storing the result in $[C]$.

Table 4.4 has three do loops. Here again an inner do loop is completely satisfied for each cycle of an outer loop. Namely, first $I = 1$, $J = 1$, and

$K = 1, 2, \ldots, L$; then $I = 1$, $J = 2$, and $K = 1, 2, \ldots, L$; next $I = 1$, $J = 3$, and $K = 1, 2, \ldots, L$; and so on, until finally $I = 1$, $J = N$, and $K = 1$, $2, \ldots, L$. This generates the first row of $[C]$. Next the same cycles are repeated for $I = 2$ to generate the second row of $[C]$, and so on, until finally, row M of $[C]$ is generated.

TABLE 4.2

PROGRAM TO SUBTRACT TWO MATRICES

Statement Number	Fortran Statement

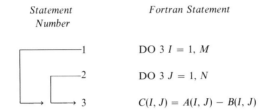

1	DO 3 $I = 1$, M
2	DO 3 $J = 1$, N
3	$C(I, J) = A(I, J) - B(I, J)$

TABLE 4.3

PROGRAM TO TRANSPOSE A MATRIX

Statement Number	Fortran Statement

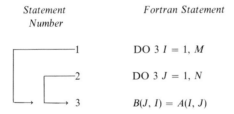

1	DO 3 $I = 1$, M
2	DO 3 $J = 1$, N
3	$B(J, I) = A(I, J)$

TABLE 4.4

PROGRAM TO MULTIPLY TWO MATRICES

Statement Number	Fortran Statement

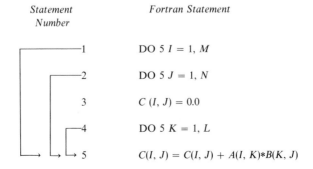

1	DO 5 $I = 1$, M
2	DO 5 $J = 1$, N
3	$C (I, J) = 0.0$
4	DO 5 $K = 1$, L
5	$C(I, J) = C(I, J) + A(I, K)*B(K, J)$

Suggested Exercise: It will be instructive for the reader to follow the operations of the computer in Table 4.4 as it executes the multiplication $[A][B]$ with

$$[A] = \begin{bmatrix} 1 & 0 & 4 & 9 \\ 2 & 1 & 0 & 3 \\ 3 & 2 & 5 & 2 \end{bmatrix} \qquad [B] = \begin{bmatrix} -1 & 7 \\ 2 & 5 \\ 0 & 2 \\ -3 & 1 \end{bmatrix}$$

Here $M = 3$, $L = 4$, and $N = 2$. Consider the elements A_{ik} and B_{kj} of $[A]$ and $[B]$ to be stored in the computer in compartments with corresponding addresses $A(I, K)$ and $B(K, J)$. For instance, in Figure 4.3 we have compartment $A(2, 4)$ which stores $A_{2,4} = 3$.

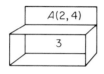

Figure 4.3. Compartment A (2, 4) with element $A_{2,4}$.

The compartments with addresses $C(I, J)$ contain arbitrary numbers when the execution of the program begins. Also, note that the inner loop of statements 4 and 5 is equivalent to Equation (4.12); that is,

$$C_{ij} = \sum_{k=1}^{l} A_{ik}B_{kj}$$

But the equal sign in statement 5 does not have the conventional meaning. (See Section 1.14).

Suggested Exercise: Do problem 13.

4.18. MATRIX PROGRAMMING LANGUAGE–MATRIX INTERPRETIVE ROUTINES

When the operations of Tables 4.1, 4.2, 4.3, or 4.4 are part of a larger program, they are referred to as *subroutines* (subprograms); the complete program is known as the *main program.* Very often the main program will be required to execute a subroutine several times, each time for different matrices. In such cases, one can avoid repeating the subroutine each time it must be executed, by using a symbolic statement which refers to it and is interpreted by the program. For instance, the statement MULT (A, B, C) is enough to instruct the computer to refer to the subroutine of *matrix MULTiplication*, multiply $[A]$ by $[B]$, and store the result in $[C]$. Similarly, other matrices can be manipulated by the same subroutine. For example, the statement MULT (STF, DISPL, FORCE) will cause the first matrix in the parentheses to be multiplied by the second and the result to be stored in the third, that is,

$$[FORCE] = [STF][DISPL]$$

Note that this is equivalent to the matrix equation

$$\{F\} = [k]\{u\}$$

or to the equation

$$[F] = [k][u]$$

when the structure is analyzed for a number of loading conditions.

A matrix programming scheme which uses and interprets such symbolic language, and manipulates matrices by referring to subroutines, is called a *matrix interpretive routine* or a *matrix interpretive scheme*. Several types of such routines are available. The example at the end of this section shows how such a routine works.

Table 4.5 shows some examples of the "vocabulary" in a matrix interpretive routine language. Note that the letters A, B, C are dummy parameters and can be replaced by other matrix names such as STF, FORCE, etc.

TABLE 4.5

EXAMPLES OF STATEMENTS IN A MATRIX INTERPRETIVE ROUTINE

READ	A
ADD	(A, B, C)
SUB	(A, B, C)
MULT	(A, B, C)
TRANS	(A, B)
COPY	(A, B)
INVERT	A
PRINT	A

Here is what takes place when the computer encounters the statements of Table 4.5:

READ A: the computer reads a matrix from a specified input media and stores it in A (the order of the matrix should be specified but we omit this for clarity).

ADD (A, B, C): the operation $[A] + [B]$ is performed and the result stored in $[C]$.

SUB (A, B, C): the operation $[A] - [B]$ is performed and the result stored in $[C]$.

MULT (A, B, C): the operation $[A][B]$ is performed and the result stored in $[C]$.

TRANS (A, B): matrix $[A]$ is transposed and the result stored in $[B]$.

COPY (A, B): matrix $[A]$ is stored in $[B]$.

INVERT A: matrix $[A]$ is inverted and the result is stored in $[A]$, replacing the original matrix. This is the first statement in which the matrix that the computer operates on is destroyed in the course of the operations. If $[A]$ is required in subsequent computations it can first be copied into $[B]$ by the instruction COPY (A, B), and then inverted.

PRINT A: matrix A is printed through a specified output media.

As an example of the application of a matrix programming language let us compute the reduced stiffness matrix $[k]^*$ of Equation (4.28). The program is shown in Table 4.6 with STF11, STF12, STF21, and STF22 designating the four submatrices $[k]_{ij}$ in Equation (4.28).

TABLE 4.6

PROGRAM TO COMPUTE A REDUCED STIFFNESS MATRIX (EQUATION 4.28)

Statement Number	Statement
1	READ STF11, STF12, STF22
2	TRANS (STF12, STF21)
3	INVERT STF22
4	MULT (STF12, STF22, A)
5	MULT (A, STF21, B)
6	SUB (STF11, B, RSTF)
7	PRINT RSTF

The following operations are performed as the program of Table 4.6 is executed:

Statement 1: STF11, STF12, and STF22 are stored in the computer.
Statement 2: STF12 is transposed and the result stored in STF21. This was possible because $[k]_{21} = [k]_{12}^T$ on account of the symmetry of $[k]$.
Statement 3: STF22 is inverted and the inverse replaces STF22 so that from here on when we refer to STF22 we actually get its inverse.
Statement 4: $[A] = [k]_{12}[k]_{22}^{-1}$
Statement 5: $[B] = [k]_{12}[k]_{22}^{-1}[k]_{21}$
Statement 6: $[k]^* = [k]_{11} - [k]_{12}[k]_{22}^{-1}[k]_{21}$. In the program $[k]^*$ is designated by RSTF (reduced stiffness).
Statement 7: RSTF is printed.

Suggested Exercises: Do problems 14 and 15.

PROBLEMS

Problem 1: Use Equation (4.8) or (4.9) to evaluate the following determinants

$$
\begin{vmatrix} 2 & -1 & 5 & 1 \\ 1 & 4 & 6 & 3 \\ 4 & 2 & 7 & 4 \\ 3 & 1 & 2 & 5 \end{vmatrix}
\qquad
\begin{vmatrix} 1 & 0 & 0 & 0 \\ 7.5 & 7 & 0 & 0 \\ 9.31 & 0.75 & 1 & 0 \\ 11 & 3 & -1.9 & 2 \end{vmatrix}
$$

Problem 2: Evaluate the following determinants:

$$
\begin{vmatrix} 1 & -2 & 1 \\ -2 & 2 & 3 \\ 1 & 3 & 3 \end{vmatrix}
\qquad
\begin{vmatrix} 2 & -1 & 6 \\ 4 & 1 & 2 \\ 3 & 5 & 7 \end{vmatrix}
\qquad
\begin{vmatrix} 2 & 7 & 5 & 8 \\ 7 & -1 & 2 & 5 \\ 1 & 0 & 4 & 2 \\ -3 & 6 & -1 & 2 \end{vmatrix}
$$

Problem 3: In Section 3.5 Example 1, Figure 3.4 set $\alpha = \beta = \gamma = \xi = 1$, so that the stiffness matrix becomes

$$
[k] = \begin{bmatrix} 3 & -1 & 0 \\ -1 & 2 & -1 \\ 0 & -1 & 1 \end{bmatrix}
$$

Suppose that the structure in Figure 3.4 is to be subjected to four different force vectors (one at a time) at the coordinates so that each will yield a specified displacement vector. The four displacement vectors are given by

$$
[u] = \begin{bmatrix} u_{11} & u_{12} & u_{13} & u_{14} \\ u_{21} & u_{22} & u_{23} & u_{24} \\ u_{31} & u_{32} & u_{33} & u_{34} \end{bmatrix}
$$

where the first subscript designates the coordinate and the second subscript identifies the force vector causing the displacement. Using Equation (3.13), compute the force vectors required to produce displacements $[u]$.

Problem 4: Given the matrices

$$
\{a\} = \begin{Bmatrix} 4 \\ 4 \\ 1 \\ 0 \end{Bmatrix}, \quad \{b\} = \begin{Bmatrix} 2 \\ 1 \\ 0 \\ 1 \end{Bmatrix}, \quad [c] = \begin{bmatrix} 1 & 0 & 2 & 4 \\ 2 & 1 & 1 & 3 \end{bmatrix}
$$

$$[d] = \begin{bmatrix} 1 & 2 & 1 & 0 \\ 2 & 1 & 1 & 0 \\ 3 & 0 & 0 & 2 \end{bmatrix}, \quad [e] = \begin{bmatrix} 1 & 1 & 9 & 3 & 1 \\ 2 & 0 & 6 & 2 & 1 \\ 3 & 2 & 7 & 3 & 0 \\ 0 & 5 & 8 & 1 & 1 \end{bmatrix}$$

execute the following operations (if possible) according to the rules of matrix algebra.

1. $\{a\}^T\{b\}$

2. $\{b\}\{a\}^T$

3. $[c]\{b\}$

4. $\{b\}[c]$

5. $\{b\}^T[e]$

6. $\{a\}^T[e]^T$

7. $\{a\}^T[d]^T$

8. $[d][e]$

9. $[e][d]$

10. $[e]^T[d]^T$

Problem 5: Show that when $[a]$ and $[b]$ are diagonal matrices

$$[a][b] = [b][a]$$

Problem 6: Show that

$$[I][a] = [a][I]$$

where $[I]$ is the unit matrix.

Problem 7: Find the inverse of each of the following matrices:

(1) $\begin{bmatrix} 1 & 2 \\ 3 & 4 \end{bmatrix}$ (2) $\begin{bmatrix} a_{11} & a_{12} \\ a_{21} & a_{22} \end{bmatrix}$ (3) $\begin{bmatrix} k_{11} & k_{12} \\ k_{21} & k_{22} \end{bmatrix}$

(4) $\begin{bmatrix} 6 & 1 & -5 \\ -2 & -5 & 4 \\ -3 & 3 & -1 \end{bmatrix}$ (5) $\begin{bmatrix} -7 & 6 & -1 \\ 1 & 0 & -1 \\ 1 & -2 & 1 \end{bmatrix}$ (6) $\begin{bmatrix} 1.5 & -1 & 1 \\ 0.5 & 1 & -1 \\ -1.5 & 1 & 3 \end{bmatrix}$

Problem 8: Find the inverse of the stiffness matrix $[k]$ for the structures of Figures 3.4 and 3.5. What do the resulting matrices signify? (Set $\alpha = \beta = \gamma = \xi = 1$ in Figure 3.4.)

Problem 9: Given the following matrix multiplication, $[a][b] = [c]$, establish the row partitioning in $[a]$ and $[b]$, and the column partitioning in $[c]$, then verify the result of the multiplication by operating on the submatrices.

$$\begin{bmatrix} 1 & 2 & 1 \\ 1.5 & 0 & 0.5 \\ 1 & 5 & 0 \end{bmatrix} \begin{bmatrix} 4 & 2 & 3 & 1 & 0 & 1 \\ 2 & 1 & 0 & 3 & 1 & 6 \\ 5 & 2 & 1 & 0 & 0 & 2 \end{bmatrix} = \begin{bmatrix} 13 & 6 & 4 & 7 & 2 & 15 \\ 8.5 & 4 & 5 & 1.5 & 0 & 2.5 \\ 14 & 7 & 3 & 16 & 5 & 31 \end{bmatrix}$$

Problem 10: Consider only coordinate 1 defined for the structure of Figure 3.5 (Example 2, Section 3.5). Derive the reduced stiffness coefficient k^* using the 3×3 stiffness matrix of the same structure given in Section 3.5, Example 2.

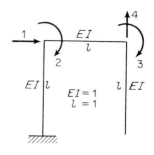

Problem 11: Derive the 4×4 stiffness matrix for the structure shown. Use this matrix to compute the reduced 3×3 stiffness matrix for the structure in Figure 3.9, Section 3.5.

Figure for problem 11.

Problem 12: Use the Gauss-Jordan method to invert the following matrices:

$$\begin{bmatrix} 12 & -6 & 0 \\ -6 & 5 & -1 \\ 0 & -1 & 1 \end{bmatrix} \qquad \begin{bmatrix} 1 & -2 & 3 \\ 2 & 0 & -3 \\ 1 & 1 & 1 \end{bmatrix} \qquad \begin{bmatrix} 2 & 4 & 3 & 2 \\ 3 & 6 & 5 & 2 \\ 2 & 5 & 2 & -3 \\ 4 & 5 & 14 & 14 \end{bmatrix}$$

Problem 13: Explain the meaning of statement 5, Table 4.4, Section 4.17. Give an example.

Problem 14: Given the matrices

$$\{u\} = \begin{Bmatrix} 2 \\ 4.5 \\ 8.5 \end{Bmatrix} \qquad \{F\} = \begin{Bmatrix} -3 \\ 2 \\ 4 \end{Bmatrix} \qquad [F] = \begin{bmatrix} 2 & -3 & 3 & 2 \\ 1 & 4 & -4 & 0 \\ 0 & -5 & 0 & 0 \end{bmatrix}$$

$$[a] = \tfrac{1}{6}\begin{bmatrix} 2 & 3 & 3 \\ 3 & 6 & 6 \\ 3 & 6 & 12 \end{bmatrix} \qquad [k] = \begin{bmatrix} 12 & -6 & 0 \\ -6 & 5 & -1 \\ 0 & -1 & 1 \end{bmatrix}$$

which are related to a set of 3 coordinates of a structure, execute the following operations:

1. $\{F\}^T\{u\}$
2. $\{F\}\{u\}^T$
3. $[a]\{F\}$
4. $[a][F]$
5. $\{F\}^T[a]$

6. $\tfrac{1}{2}\{F\}^T[a]\{F\}$
7. $\{u\}^T[k]$
8. $\tfrac{1}{2}\{u\}^T[k]\{u\}$
9. $(\{u\}^T[k]\{u\})^T$
10. $(\{F\}^T[a]\{F\})^T$

Problem 15: Use the procedures and results of Section 4.14 to solve problems 6, 7 and 8 of Chapter 2.

5

SOLUTION OF LINEAR EQUATIONS

5.1. INTRODUCTION

Solving simultaneous linear equations is one of the most important parts of the field of numerical analysis. Simultaneous linear equations occur very frequently in structural analysis, in network analysis, in dynamics, as well as in many other branches of engineering and physics. Even the solution of differential equations involves simultaneous equations when the boundary conditions are satisfied, and often the complete solution of ordinary and partial differential equations by numerical methods is reduced to the solution of linear equations[33].

In the analysis of linear structures considered in this book we shall also require the solution of linear equations. When the forces at the coordinates are given, we shall solve for the corresponding displacements, and when the displacements are given we shall solve for the corresponding forces.

In this chapter we consider some useful concepts and methods connected with the solution of linear equations.†

5.2. SOLUTION BY MATRIX INVERSION: CRAMER'S RULE

A set of n linear equations in n unknowns u_i $(i = 1, 2, \ldots, n)$ with coefficients k_{ij}, and free constants (not multiplying the unknowns) F_i appears as follows:

$$
\begin{aligned}
k_{11}u_1 + k_{12}u_2 + \cdots + k_{1n}u_n &= F_1 \\
k_{21}u_1 + k_{22}u_2 + \cdots + k_{2n}u_n &= F_2 \\
\phantom{k_{21}u_1} \cdot \phantom{k_{22}u_2} \cdot \cdot \phantom{k_{2n}u_n} \cdot \\
k_{n1}u_1 + k_{n2}u_2 + \cdots + k_{nn}u_n &= F_n
\end{aligned}
\tag{5.1}
$$

† For an expanded treatment of the subject consult References [31–37].

In matrix form these equations become

$$[k]\{u\} = \{F\} \tag{5.2}$$

We recognize this matrix equation as the one representing the force displacement relation of a structure through the stiffness matrix (see Equations 3.13 and 4.18), but for our purposes, let it represent a set of linear equations in general in which the u_i ($i = 1, 2, \ldots, n$) are the unknowns, and k_{ij}, F_i are known constants.†

If the matrix of coefficients $[k]$ is nonsingular ($|k| \neq 0$), then each side of Equation (5.2) can be premultiplied by $[k]^{-1}$ to solve for $\{u\}$

$$\{u\} = [k]^{-1}\{F\} \tag{5.3}$$

In view of the definition of an inverse as given by Equation (4.16) we can also write Equation (5.3) in the form

$$\{u\} = \frac{1}{|k|} \text{adj}\,[k]\{F\} \tag{5.4}$$

Now any unknown u_i in Equation (5.4) is obtained as $1/|k|$ times the matrix product of row i of adj $[k]$ and $\{F\}$

$$u_i = \frac{1}{|k|}(\text{row } i \text{ of adj }[k])\{F\} \tag{5.5}$$

But the elements of row i of adj $[k]$ are the cofactors of column i of $[k]$, (see Section 4.9), hence the product

$$(\text{row } i \text{ of adj }[k])\{F\}$$

is equivalent to the value of the determinant of matrix $[k]$ in which column i has been replaced by $\{F\}$. We denote this determinant by $|k|_i$ so that Equation (5.5) becomes

$$u_i = \frac{|k|_i}{|k|} \qquad i = 1, 2, \ldots, n \tag{5.6}$$

This is the expression of *Cramer's rule* which was first stated in Equation (4.6).

5.3. HOMOGENEOUS EQUATIONS

When $\{F\} = \{0\}$ in Equation (5.2), the resulting set of equations in unknowns u_i

$$[k]\{u\} = \{0\} \tag{5.7}$$

---

† In structures $[k]$ is always symmetric, but relative to the discussions in this chapter it need not be symmetric.

is called a system of *homogeneous equations*. If $[k]$ is nonsingular in Equation (5.7), then using Equation (5.3) or (5.6), we have the unique solution

$$\{u\} = \{0\}$$

which is referred to as the *trivial solution*. However if $[k]$ is singular, then in addition to the trivial solution, which always satisfies the equations, we also have other solutions which are obtained as follows:

Consider the following homogeneous equations

$$\begin{bmatrix} 0 & -1 & 1 \\ 4 & -1 & -1 \\ 4 & -2 & 0 \end{bmatrix} \begin{Bmatrix} u_1 \\ u_2 \\ u_3 \end{Bmatrix} = \begin{Bmatrix} 0 \\ 0 \\ 0 \end{Bmatrix} \tag{5.8}$$

The matrix of coefficients is singular because row 3 is a linear combination of rows 1 and 2. This is equivalent to saying that the third equation adds no new information to that given by the first and second equations. In fact many more equations, such as the third equation, can be written by other linear combinations of the first two equations. The first two equations are independent and from them we can solve for two unknowns in terms of a third one. For example,

$$\begin{bmatrix} 0 & -1 \\ 4 & -1 \end{bmatrix} \begin{Bmatrix} u_1 \\ u_2 \end{Bmatrix} = \begin{Bmatrix} -u_3 \\ u_3 \end{Bmatrix}$$

or

$$\begin{Bmatrix} u_1 \\ u_2 \end{Bmatrix} = \begin{bmatrix} 0 & -1 \\ 4 & -1 \end{bmatrix}^{-1} \begin{Bmatrix} -u_3 \\ u_3 \end{Bmatrix}$$

Therefore, the solution to Equation (5.8), when the matrix of coefficients is singular, is not unique because u_3 can have any arbitrary value, but once u_3 is assigned a value, u_1 and u_2 are uniquely established.

In general when Equation (5.7) (or Equation 5.2 with $\{F\} \neq \{0\}$) involves n equations in n unknowns, and r of these equations (with both sides of the equal sign included) can be expressed as a linear combination of the remaining $(n - r)$, then we can use these $(n - r)$ independent equations to solve for $(n - r)$ of the unknowns in terms of the remaining r unknowns.

5.4. CONSISTENT AND INCONSISTENT EQUATIONS

In summary we state the following: A system of n homogeneous equations in n unknowns will have nontrivial solutions when the matrix of coefficients is singular.

A system of n nonhomogeneous equations ($\{F\} \neq \{0\}$ in Equation 5.2) in n unknowns will have a unique solution when the matrix of coefficients $[k]$ is nonsingular, and an infinite number of solutions when $[k]$ is singular.

In either case, homogeneous or nonhomogeneous, the systems of equations is said to be *consistent* as long as a solution, whether unique or not, exists. A system of equations is *inconsistent* when there exists no solution that will satisfy them.

5.5. SOLUTION BY ELIMINATION

The most common method for solving linear equations taught in elementary algebra, is the method of elimination of unknowns. In this method we take one of the n equations in which the first unknown is present and use it to eliminate the first unknown from the remaining $(n-1)$ equations. Next we select an equation, from these $(n-1)$, in which the second unknown is present and use it to eliminate the second unknown from the remaining $(n-2)$ equations. This procedure is continued until the following set of equations is obtained for the unknowns u_i

$$a_{11}u_1 + a_{12}u_2 + a_{13}u_3 + \cdots + a_{1n}u_n = c_1$$
$$b_{22}u_2 + b_{23}u_3 + \cdots + b_{2n}u_n = c_2$$
$$c_{33}u_3 + \cdots + c_{3n}u_n = c_3 \qquad (5.9)$$
$$\vdots \qquad \vdots$$
$$\alpha_{nn}u_n = c_n$$

Starting with the nth of Equations (5.9) we solve for u_n, and then, by substituting its value in the equation above it, we solve for u_{n-1}, and so on. The matrix of coefficients in Equation (5.9) is called a *triangular matrix*, and the process of elimination described here reduces the original matrix of coefficients to the triangular form. This method is favored, in many cases, to solve large systems of equations (n large)[75].

The Gauss–Jordan method of Section 4.16 is a form of an elimination method which reduces a matrix of coefficients to the identity matrix. If we apply the chain of products, $[t_n] \ldots [t_1]$, in Equation (4.32), to each side of the equation

$$[k]\{u\} = \{F\}$$

we obtain the same result as in Equation (5.3)

$$\{u\} = [k]^{-1}\{F\}$$

which is the desired solution.

The solution in the form of Equation (5.3) represents a very desirable way of retaining the information derived from the solution in case it is necessary to solve the equations for several sets of constants $\{F\}$ while $[k]$, (and therefore $[k]^{-1}$), remains unaltered.

5.6. SOLUTION BY ITERATION

Linear equations can be solved by iteration methods which involve successive approximations. A common iteration method is the *Gauss–Seidel* method.

A system of equations most suitable for solution by iteration is a *diagonally dominant* system which has the following property: In each equation the absolute value of a coefficient of a different unknown is larger than, or equal to, the sum of the absolute values of the other coefficients. Usually the largest coefficients are the elements k_{ii} of the principal diagonal in the matrix of coefficients $[k]$. Many systems of linear equations in engineering are of the diagonal type. For instance, the stiffness matrices for the structures in Section 3.5, Examples 1, 2, and 4 will lead to diagonally dominant systems of equations.

Using the Gauss–Seidel method we proceed as follows: Referring to Equations (5.1) we start the first cycle of the iteration by setting all $u_i = 0$ for $i = 2, 3, \ldots, n$ in the first equation, and solving for $u_1^{(1)}$ (the superscript indicates the cycle number in the iteration). Substituting this value of $u_1^{(1)}$ in the second equation with $u_i = 0$ for $i = 3, 4, \ldots, n$, we solve for $u_2^{(1)}$. Next we substitute $u_1^{(1)}$, $u_2^{(1)}$, and $u_i = 0$ for $i = 4, 5, \ldots, n$, in the third equation and solve for $u_3^{(1)}$. This is continued until all $u_i^{(1)}$ ($i = 1, 2, \ldots, n$) have been evaluated. Now we return to the first equation to start a second cycle of the iteration. First $u_1^{(2)}$ is computed by substituting $u_i^{(1)}$ ($i = 2, 3, \ldots, n$) in the first equation. $u_1^{(2)}$ replaces $u_1^{(1)}$. Next $u_1^{(2)}$ and $u_i^{(1)}$ ($i = 3, 4, \ldots, n$) are substituted in the second equation and $u_2^{(2)}$ is computed and replaces $u_2^{(1)}$. This is continued until all $u_i^{(2)}$ ($i = 1, 2, \ldots, n$) have been computed, and then a third cycle is started to generate $u_i^{(3)}$ ($i = 1, 2, \ldots, n$) which replace $u_i^{(2)}$ ($i = 1, 2, \ldots, n$). This process is continued until results obtained in successive cycles are the same, or the difference between them is within acceptable bounds.

The first cycle of the iteration must not necessarily begin with $u_i = 0$ ($i = 2, 3, \ldots, n$); any guessed values for these u_i will do. The same holds true for any intermediate cycle; we can substitute any guessed values for the unknowns instead of their values from the preceding cycle. If the guesses are good, convergence may be accelerated; if they are poor, it may be prolonged. The process is also self-correcting, because wrong values of u_i can be considered as another guess in the iteration.

Let us illustrate the method by solving for the displacements of the structure in Section 3.5, Example 2, caused by forces $F_1 = 18$, $F_2 = 8$,

$F_3 = -10$ (the stiffness matrix is given in Section 3.5). From Equation (3.13)

$$\begin{bmatrix} 24 & -6 & -6 \\ -6 & 8 & 2 \\ -6 & 2 & 8 \end{bmatrix} \begin{Bmatrix} u_1 \\ u_2 \\ u_3 \end{Bmatrix} = \begin{Bmatrix} 18 \\ 8 \\ -10 \end{Bmatrix}$$

These equations are rewritten in a more convenient form for the iteration as

$$u_1 = \tfrac{3}{4} + \tfrac{1}{4}u_2 + \tfrac{1}{4}u_3 \qquad \text{(a)}$$
$$u_2 = 1 + \tfrac{3}{4}u_1 - \tfrac{1}{4}u_3 \qquad \text{(b)} \qquad\qquad (5.10)$$
$$u_3 = -\tfrac{5}{4} + \tfrac{3}{4}u_1 - \tfrac{1}{4}u_2 \qquad \text{(c)}$$

On the right-hand side of these equations we always substitute the last available approximations for the unknowns u_i from the preceding steps in the iteration cycles. Let us start the first cycle of iteration by setting $u_2 = u_3 = 0$

Cycle 1

From Equation (5.10a) $u_1^{(1)} = \dfrac{3}{4}$

From Equation (5.10b) $u_2^{(1)} = 1 + \dfrac{3}{4}\cdot\dfrac{3}{4} = \dfrac{25}{16}$

From Equation (5.10c) $u_3^{(1)} = -\dfrac{5}{4} + \dfrac{3}{4}\cdot\dfrac{3}{4} - \dfrac{1}{4}\cdot\dfrac{25}{16} = -\dfrac{69}{64}$

Cycle 2

From Equation (5.10a) $u_1^{(2)} = \dfrac{3}{4} + \dfrac{1}{4}\cdot\dfrac{25}{16} - \dfrac{1}{4}\cdot\dfrac{69}{64} = \dfrac{223}{256}$

From Equation (5.10b) $u_2^{(2)} = 1 + \dfrac{3}{4}\cdot\dfrac{223}{256} + \dfrac{1}{4}\cdot\dfrac{69}{64} = \dfrac{1969}{1024}$

From Equation (5.10c) $u_3^{(2)} = -\dfrac{5}{4} + \dfrac{3}{4}\cdot\dfrac{223}{256} - \dfrac{1}{4}\cdot\dfrac{1969}{1024} = -\dfrac{4413}{4096}$

The computations can be continued to any desired accuracy. The answers in the present problem are

$$u_1 = 1, \qquad u_2 = 2, \qquad u_3 = -1.$$

The answers after the second cycle are not far off.

The Gauss–Seidel iteration is very useful in structural analysis and is discussed in detail as applied to frames in Chapter 11.

5.7. SOLUTION BY RELAXATION

The reader who is familiar with the method of moment distribution[12,14,47] will recall that it is a relaxation method. In this method joints of the structure are locked and relaxed in successive steps, and moments, which are a function of the unknown rotations, are distributed. The solution to the desired moments is obtained by adding the increments distributed in the relaxation process.

The basic principle of the relaxation method as applied to linear equations, in general, is as follows: Let us rewrite Equation (5.1) in the following form,

$$\sum_j k_{ij}u_j - F_i = 0, \qquad i = 1, 2, \ldots, n$$

or

$$[k]\{u\} - \{F\} = \{0\} \tag{5.11}$$

Equation (5.11) will be satisfied when we substitute the correct values of all u_i. In the relaxation method, we begin with an approximate solution to the u_i which may not satisfy Equation (5.11), that is, the right-hand side may not be zero and there is a residual, denoted by R_i, in each equation

$$R_i = \sum_j k_{ij}u_j - F_i, \qquad i = 1, 2, \ldots, n$$

or

$$\{R\} = [k]\{u\} - \{F\} \tag{5.12}$$

The relaxation procedure continues by adding increments (positive or negative) to the initial approximations to the unknowns u_i until the R_i $(i = 1, 2, \ldots, n)$ become negligible.

We illustrate the method by solving the equations

$$\begin{bmatrix} 3 & 1 & 2 \\ 2 & -3 & -1 \\ 1 & 2 & 1 \end{bmatrix} \begin{Bmatrix} u_1 \\ u_2 \\ u_3 \end{Bmatrix} - \begin{Bmatrix} 3 \\ -3 \\ 4 \end{Bmatrix} = \begin{Bmatrix} 0 \\ 0 \\ 0 \end{Bmatrix} \tag{5.13}$$

The solution is aided by Table 5.1 which shows the incremental changes δR_i in the residuals corresponding to incremental changes, δu_i, in the unknowns. For instance, when $\delta u_1 = 1$, $\delta u_2 = \delta u_3 = 0$ (first row of Table 5.1), then the changes δR_1, δR_2, δR_3, correspond, respectively, to the elements of the first column in the matrix of coefficients in Equation (5.13), and these are recorded in the first row of Table 5.1 under δR_1, δR_2, δR_3. In general the right-hand side of Table 5.1, (under the δR_i), is the transpose of the matrix of coefficients in the linear equations.

TABLE 5.1

INCREMENTS IN RESIDUALS CORRESPONDING
TO INCREMENTS IN THE UNKNOWNS

δu_1	δu_2	δu_3	δR_1	δR_2	δR_3
1	0	0	3	2	1
0	1	0	1	−3	2
0	0	1	2	−1	1

We begin the relaxation by setting $u_i = 0$ for all i and recording the corresponding residuals (these correspond to the fixed end moments at the joints in moment distribution when all the unknown joint rotations are set equal to zero). Next we add increments to the unknowns and adjust the corresponding residuals by using Table 5.1, until the residuals $R_i = 0$, or are very close to zero. This procedure as applied to Equations (5.13) is illustrated in Table 5.2. Under the R_i in Table 5.2, we record the total current value of the residual so that we will know to stop when $R_i = 0$. On the left of the table we record only the increments in δu_i. The final solution for the unknowns u_i is the sum of the increments $\delta u_i^{(j)}$, which lead to $R_i = 0$.

TABLE 5.2

RELAXATION COMPUTATIONS

Cycle Number p	δu_1	δu_2	δu_3	R_1	R_2	R_3
1	0	0	0	−3	3	−4
2	1	0	0	0	5	−3
3	0	2	0	2	−1	1
4	0	0	−1	0	0	0

$$u_i = \sum_j^p \delta u_i^{(j)} = \qquad 1 \qquad 2 \qquad -1$$

In the present example we begin with $u_i = 0$ ($i = 1, 2, 3$) in the first row of Table 5.2 and record the corresponding residuals −3, 3, and −4. Next we observe that, using the results in the first row of Table 5.1, we can reduce R_1 to zero. We therefore add the increment $\delta u_1 = 1$ in the second row of Table 5.2 and adjust the residuals R_i as shown. Next we use row 2 of Table 5.1

(multiplied by two) to bring R_2 closer to zero. The third row in Table 5.1 can now be used to reduce to zero all the R_i in row 3 of Table 5.2. The relaxation is now complete and the final solution is obtained by adding the $\delta u_i^{(j)}$ increments as follows:

$$u_i = \sum_{j=1}^{p} \delta u_i^{(j)} \qquad i = 1, 2, \ldots, n$$

in which p designates the number of relaxation cycles.

5.8. ILL-CONDITIONED EQUATIONS

In Section 5.2 we demonstrated that the determinant of the coefficients plays an important role in the solution of linear equations. In Equation (5.6) this determinant appears in the denominator. Therefore, when the determinant is nearly zero, we may run into computational difficulties by dealing with small differences in large numbers in which a slight change in accuracy may result in completely different solutions. Systems of equations with such difficulties are said to be *ill conditioned* and usually involve equations which are nearly linearly dependent.

For example, the equations

$$2u_1 - 5u_2 = 80$$

$$2.001u_1 - 5.003u_2 = 80.038$$

are almost identical (that is, "almost" dependent). Their solution is $u_1 = 50$, $u_2 = 4$. Now, just a slight change in the free constant of the second equation from 80.038 to 80.040 changes the solution to

$$u_1 = 40 \quad \text{and} \quad u_2 = 0$$

When equations are ill conditioned they can be solved best by elimination. Matrix inversion will be very difficult or impossible, and relaxation may fail because small residuals can be obtained although we are still far from the solution. We observed this in the preceding example in which the difference $80.040 - 80.038 = 0.002$ may be regarded as a residual.

It is best to avoid ill-conditioned equations whenever possible. We shall do so in structural analysis by defining coordinates which will lead to linear equations that are not ill conditioned. This will be accomplished by choosing coordinates in which the stiffness and flexibility matrices are not likely to have nearly dependent rows and columns. In selecting such coordinates,† we shall be assisted by the physical considerations relating to the behavior of the structure and the discussion in this section.

Suggested Exercises: Do problems 1, 2, 3, 4, 5, 6, 7 and 8.

---

† See Section 8.3 on choice of redundants.

5.9. EIGENVALUE PROBLEMS[†]

At this point we have developed sufficient background to introduce the concepts associated with eigenvalue problems which are of great importance in dynamics of structures and in stability studies as well as in other fields of engineering. Let us begin with an example of a problem in structures and use it as a springboard to generalize the concepts.

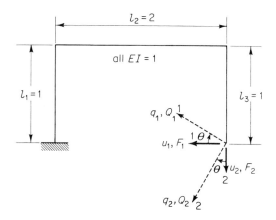

Figure 5.1. Structure with two coordinate systems, u (solid line arrows) and q (dashed line arrows).

Example

The structure of Figure 5.1 has members of uniform rigidity $EI = 1$ and lengths as shown. The flexibility matrix for the coordinates shown by the arrows with the solid lines in Figure 5.1 is designated with subscript u as $[a]_u$ and has the following elements in the present problem.

$$\begin{bmatrix} a_{11} & a_{12} \\ a_{21} & a_{22} \end{bmatrix}_u = \begin{bmatrix} \frac{8}{3} & 3 \\ 3 & \frac{20}{3} \end{bmatrix}$$

The force-displacement relationship (Equation 3.12) for the same coordinates is as follows

$$\begin{Bmatrix} u_1 \\ u_2 \end{Bmatrix} = \begin{bmatrix} a_{11} & a_{12} \\ a_{21} & a_{22} \end{bmatrix}_u \begin{Bmatrix} F_1 \\ F_2 \end{Bmatrix} \tag{5.14}$$

[†] Sections 5.9 and 5.10 are intended to introduce the reader to eigenvalue problems which are treated in Dynamics of Structures, Reference 39.

Since in the present example each element in $[a]_u$ is different from zero, it is apparent that a force at any one coordinate causes displacements u_i at both coordinates.

Our objective is to use $[a]_u$ to find a new set of two coordinates at the free tip of the structure (arrows with dashed lines in Figure 5.1) and a corresponding flexibility matrix, such that a force applied at one of these coordinates will produce a displacement at only that coordinate. This is the essence of the elastic center method in structural analysis[13, 15, 22].

Let us designate the force and displacement measurements in the new coordinates by Q_i and q_i, respectively, and the corresponding flexibility matrix by $[a]_q$. Our objective, then, is to find new coordinates and a corresponding flexibility matrix $[a]_q$, which is diagonal, so that

$$\begin{Bmatrix} q_1 \\ q_2 \end{Bmatrix} = \begin{bmatrix} a_{11} & 0 \\ 0 & a_{22} \end{bmatrix}_q \begin{Bmatrix} Q_1 \\ Q_2 \end{Bmatrix} \tag{5.15}$$

or

$$q_1 = a_{11}^{(q)} Q_1$$

$$q_2 = a_{22}^{(q)} Q_2$$

in which the superscript (q) identifies the q coordinate system.

It turns out that all the desired information can be obtained from matrix $[a]_u$ in the coordinates which identify the u measurements. The desired values $a_{11}^{(q)}$ and $a_{22}^{(q)}$ are the *eigenvalues* of matrix $[a]_u$, and the orientation of the new coordinates in which measurements q are identified are the *eigenvectors* of matrix $[a]_u$. Eigenvalues and eigenvectors are defined only for a square matrix, and the problem which is formulated to solve for the eigenvalues and eigenvectors is called an *eigenvalue problem*.

Formulation of the Eigenvalue Problem

To formulate the eigenvalue problem for the present example, we proceed as follows:

Apply a unit force $Q_1 = 1$ in Figure 5.1. By definition, this will cause displacements $q_1 = a_{11}^{(q)}$ and $q_2 = 0$. The force $Q_1 = 1$ and the corresponding displacement $q_1 = a_{11}^{(q)}$ can be expressed in terms of measurements F_i and u_i, respectively (see Figure 5.1).

$$F_1 = 1 \cdot \cos \theta \qquad u_1 = a_{11}^{(q)} \cos \theta$$

$$F_2 = -1 \cdot \sin \theta \qquad u_2 = -a_{11}^{(q)} \sin \theta$$

Substituting these values in Equation (5.14), we have

$$\begin{bmatrix} a_{11} & a_{12} \\ a_{21} & a_{22} \end{bmatrix}_u \begin{Bmatrix} \cos \theta \\ -\sin \theta \end{Bmatrix} = a_{11}^{(q)} \begin{Bmatrix} \cos \theta \\ -\sin \theta \end{Bmatrix} \tag{5.16}$$

Similarly, setting $Q_2 = 1$ yields $q_2 = a_{22}^{(q)}$, $q_1 = 0$, and

$$F_1 = \sin \theta \qquad u_1 = a_{22}^{(q)} \sin \theta$$

$$F_2 = \cos \theta \qquad u_2 = a_{22}^{(q)} \cos \theta$$

Again using these values in Equation (5.14),

$$\begin{bmatrix} a_{11} & a_{12} \\ a_{21} & a_{22} \end{bmatrix}_u \left\{ \begin{matrix} \sin \theta \\ \cos \theta \end{matrix} \right\} = a_{22}^{(q)} \left\{ \begin{matrix} \sin \theta \\ \cos \theta \end{matrix} \right\} \tag{5.17}$$

Equations (5.16) and (5.17) are similar in that in each equation the same column vector appears on each side of the equation. This column is the *eigenvector* which corresponds to the *eigenvalue* $a_{ii}^{(q)}$ on the right-hand side of the equation. Let us designate the eigenvalue by λ and the eigenvector by $\{\gamma\}$, then Equations (5.16) and (5.17) take the general form

$$[a]_u \{\gamma\} = \lambda \{\gamma\} \tag{5.18}$$

This equation represents the general formulation of an eigenvalue problem.

Computing the Eigenvalues and Eigenvectors

To compute λ and $\{\gamma\}$, we write Equation (5.18) as

$$[a]_u \{\gamma\} - \lambda \{\gamma\} = \{0\}$$

or, introducing the identity matrix $[I]$,

$$[a]_u \{\gamma\} - \lambda [I] \{\gamma\} = \{0\} \tag{5.19}$$

because

$$\lambda [I] \{\gamma\} = \lambda \{\gamma\}$$

From Equation (5.19), we have

$$([a]_u - \lambda [I]) \{\gamma\} = \{0\} \tag{5.20}$$

This is a set of homogeneous linear equations in the unknowns γ_i. From Section 5.3, we recall that Equation (5.20) will have a nontrivial solution only when the determinant of $([a]_u - \lambda [I])$ is zero, or

$$\begin{vmatrix} a_{11}^{(u)} - \lambda & a_{12}^{(u)} \\ a_{21}^{(u)} & a_{22}^{(u)} - \lambda \end{vmatrix} = 0 \tag{5.21}$$

This condition will enable us to solve for the eigenvalues λ_i. Expanding the determinant of Equation (5.21), we have

$$(a_{11}^{(u)} - \lambda)(a_{22}^{(u)} - \lambda) - a_{21}^{(u)} a_{12}^{(u)} = 0$$

or

$$\lambda^2 - (a_{11}^{(u)} + a_{22}^{(u)})\lambda + a_{11}^{(u)} a_{22}^{(u)} - a_{21}^{(u)} a_{12}^{(u)} = 0$$

Substituting the known values of $a_{ij}^{(u)}$, the last equation becomes

$$\lambda^2 - \tfrac{28}{3}\lambda + \tfrac{79}{9} = 0$$

and solving for the roots λ (slide rule accuracy is used),

$$\lambda = \frac{14}{3} \pm \sqrt{\frac{117}{9}}$$

$$\lambda_1 = 1.06 \qquad \lambda_2 = 8.28 \tag{5.22}$$

Hence the solution of Equation (5.21) led to the eigenvalues λ_1 and λ_2 of $[a]_u$.

Now we use λ_1 and λ_2 to solve for their corresponding eigenvectors. Substituting $\lambda_1 = 1.06$ in Equation (5.20) we can solve for $\{\gamma\}^{(1)}$ corresponding to λ_1 but not uniquely as discussed in Section 5.3. It can also be seen by comparing Equation (5.18) and Equation (5.16) that we are concerned only with the value of θ, and therefore the ratio $\gamma_2^{(1)}/\gamma_1^{(1)} = -\tan\theta$ is all we must evaluate, in which $\gamma_1^{(1)}$ and $\gamma_2^{(1)}$ are the elements of $\{\gamma\}^{(1)}$. From the first of Equations (5.20) we have (the second equation may also be used),

$$(a_{11}^{(u)} - \lambda_1)\gamma_1^{(1)} + a_{12}^{(u)}\gamma_2^{(1)} = 0$$

Dividing through by $\gamma_1^{(1)}$ and substituting the values of $a_{ij}^{(u)}$ and λ_1, we can solve for $\gamma_2^{(1)}/\gamma_1^{(1)} = -\tan\theta$

$$(\tfrac{8}{3} - 1.06) + 3(-\tan\theta) = 0$$

or

$$\tan\theta = 0.5355$$

$$\gamma_1^{(1)} = \cos\theta = 0.882$$

and

$$\gamma_2^{(1)} = -\sin\theta = -0.472$$

Hence the first eigenvalue and corresponding eigenvector are

$$\lambda_1 = a_{11}^{(q)} = 1.06$$

and

$$\{\gamma\}^{(1)} = \left\{ \begin{array}{c} 0.882 \\ -0.472 \end{array} \right\}$$

Similarly substituting $\lambda_2 = 8.28$ in one of Equations (5.20) (say the first) we solve for $\gamma_1^{(2)}$ and $\gamma_2^{(2)}$ by finding $\tan\theta = \gamma_1^{(2)}/\gamma_2^{(2)}$ (compare Equations

5.18 and 5.17). The second eigenvalue and corresponding eigenvector are

$$\lambda_2 = a_{22}^{(q)} = 8.28$$

and

$$\{\gamma\}^{(2)} = \begin{Bmatrix} 0.472 \\ 0.882 \end{Bmatrix}$$

The two eigenvectors $\{\gamma\}^{(1)}$ and $\{\gamma\}^{(2)}$ identify the new coordinate system by describing how measurements q_i in the new coordinates are transformed to measurements u_i in the original coordinates

$$\begin{Bmatrix} u_1 \\ u_2 \end{Bmatrix} = \begin{bmatrix} \{\gamma\}^{(1)} & \vdots & \{\gamma\}^{(2)} \end{bmatrix} \begin{Bmatrix} q_1 \\ q_2 \end{Bmatrix}$$

or

$$\begin{Bmatrix} u_1 \\ u_2 \end{Bmatrix} = \begin{bmatrix} \gamma_{11} & \gamma_{12} \\ \gamma_{21} & \gamma_{22} \end{bmatrix} \begin{Bmatrix} q_1 \\ q_2 \end{Bmatrix} \tag{5.23}$$

and in general

$$\{u\} = [\gamma]\{q\}$$

The matrix $[\gamma]$ is a transformation matrix which is constructed from the eigenvectors with the jth eigenvector occupying the jth column, and gives the directions of the new coordinates. In our example

$$[\gamma] = \begin{bmatrix} 0.882 & 0.472 \\ -0.472 & 0.882 \end{bmatrix}$$

Other Familiar Eigenvalue Problems

The reader may recognize that the example considered here is similar to the problem of finding principal moments of inertia of an area and the corresponding coordinates [38] (axes), or finding principal stresses acting on an element and the corresponding coordinates[11]. Each of these problems is an eigenvalue problem in which the principal moments of inertia and the principal stresses are the eigenvalues, and the orientation of the corresponding axes is determined from the eigenvectors.

In structures, eigenvalue problems are encountered very often in structural dynamics[21, 28, 39] and in studies of stability of structures[40]. In dynamics the natural frequencies are related to the eigenvalues and the mode shapes are represented by the eigenvectors. In stability problems the buckling loads are related to the eigenvalues and the buckled configurations are represented by the eigenvectors.

5.10. GENERALIZATION OF CONCEPTS IN AN EIGENVALUE PROBLEM

We now summarize and generalize the basic concepts associated with an eigenvalue problem.

Eigenvalue Problem and Eigenvalues

The equation [see Equations (5.18) and (5.20)]

$$[a]\{\gamma\} = \lambda\{\gamma\} \tag{5.24}$$

or

$$([a] - \lambda[I])\{\gamma\} = \{0\} \tag{5.25}$$

is the general formulation of an eigenvalue problem.† When $[a]$ is of order n it has n eigenvalues $\lambda_i (i = 1, 2, \ldots, n)$ which are computed from the expansion of the determinant

$$|B| = 0 \tag{5.26}$$

in which

$$[B] = [a] - \lambda[I] \tag{5.27}$$

$[B]$ is called the *characteristic matrix* of $[a]$, and $|B|$ is the *characteristic function* of $[a]$. $|B|$ is an nth-order polynomial in λ and can be expanded in the form

$$|B| = \lambda^n + C_1\lambda^{n-1} + \cdots + C_{n-1}\lambda + C_n = 0 \tag{5.28}$$

in which the C_i are constants which are derived from the elements of $[a]$. Equation (5.26) or Equation (5.28) is called the *characteristic equation* of $[a]$.

Eigenvectors

The ith eigenvector $\{\gamma\}^{(i)}$ corresponding to the ith eigenvalue λ_i is determined as follows: Substitute λ_i in $[B]$ (Equation 5.27) and designate the resulting matrix by $[B_i]$. From the definition of an inverse, we can write

$$[B_i][B_i]^{-1} = [I]$$

or

$$[B_i] \text{ adj } [B_i] = |B_i|[I] \tag{5.29}$$

But from Equation (5.26) $|B_i| = 0$ if a nontrivial solution to Equation (5.25) exists. Hence Equation (5.29) becomes

$$[B_i] \text{ adj } [B_i] = [0]$$

---

† Matrix $[a]$ in Equation 5.25 is a square matrix in general, and is not necessarily symmetrical.

To generate any column of the null matrix on the right-hand side of the last equation we multiply $[B_i]$ by the corresponding column of adj $[B_i]$. Therefore

$$[B_i] \text{ (any column of adj } [B_i]) = \{0\} \tag{5.30}$$

Writing Equation (5.25) for λ_i and $\{\gamma\}^{(i)}$ we have

$$[B_i]\{\gamma\}^{(i)} = \{0\} \tag{5.31}$$

(Recall that $[B_i] = [a] - \lambda_i[I]$)

Comparing Equations (5.30) and (5.31), we conclude that the ith eigenvector, $\{\gamma\}^{(i)}$, is proportional to any column of the matrix adj $[B_i]$, that is,

$$\{\gamma\}^{(i)} = \alpha \text{ (any column of adj } [B_i]) \tag{5.32}$$

in which α is an arbitrary constant of proportionality. The columns in Equation (5.32) are proportional and not equal because, as pointed out in Section 5.3, $\{\gamma\}^{(i)}$ cannot be solved for uniquely from a set of homogeneous equations, such as Equation (5.25).

The Modal Matrix

The matrix $[\gamma]$ constructed from the eigenvectors is called the *modal matrix* of $[a]$ and it relates the measurements q in the new coordinates, in which the eigenvalues are defined, to the measurements u in the coordinates in which $[a]$ is defined

$$\{u\} = [\gamma]\{q\} \tag{5.33}$$

Iteration

The eigenvalues and eigenvectors of a matrix can also be obtained by an iterative technique in which approximations to the eigenvectors are selected and the process converges to the correct eigenvalues and corresponding eigenvectors[28, 34, 39].

Suggested Exercises: Do problems 9 and 10.

PROBLEMS

Problems 1, 2, 3, 4: Solve the following equations by matrix inversion, by iteration, and by relaxation:

1.
$$\begin{bmatrix} 4 & 2 & 0 \\ 2 & 8 & 2 \\ 0 & 2 & 4 \end{bmatrix} \begin{Bmatrix} x_1 \\ x_2 \\ x_3 \end{Bmatrix} = \begin{Bmatrix} 4 \\ 12 \\ 8 \end{Bmatrix}$$

2.
$$\begin{bmatrix} 1 & 2 & 0 \\ 2 & -1 & -2 \\ -1 & 1 & 3 \end{bmatrix} \begin{Bmatrix} x_1 \\ x_2 \\ x_3 \end{Bmatrix} = \begin{Bmatrix} 1 \\ 3 \\ 2 \end{Bmatrix}$$

3.
$$\begin{bmatrix} 1 & -1 & 1 \\ 3 & -2 & -2 \\ -2 & -1 & -3 \end{bmatrix} \begin{Bmatrix} x_1 \\ x_2 \\ x_3 \end{Bmatrix} = \begin{Bmatrix} -1 \\ 1 \\ -2 \end{Bmatrix}$$

4.
$$\begin{bmatrix} -2 & 1 & -4 \\ 4 & 1 & 2 \\ -3 & 2 & -5 \end{bmatrix} \begin{Bmatrix} x_1 \\ x_2 \\ x_3 \end{Bmatrix} = \begin{Bmatrix} -7 \\ 4 \\ -2 \end{Bmatrix}$$

Problems 5, 6, 7, 8: Find the nontrivial solutions to the following equations:

5.
$$\begin{bmatrix} -1 & 2 \\ 3 & 1 \end{bmatrix} \begin{Bmatrix} x_1 \\ x_2 \end{Bmatrix} = \begin{Bmatrix} 0 \\ 0 \end{Bmatrix}$$

6.
$$\begin{bmatrix} 4 & 2 & -6 \\ 2 & 4 & -6 \\ -6 & -6 & 12 \end{bmatrix} \begin{Bmatrix} u_1 \\ u_2 \\ u_3 \end{Bmatrix} = \begin{Bmatrix} 0 \\ 0 \\ 0 \end{Bmatrix}$$

7.
$$\begin{bmatrix} -1 & -2 & 2 \\ 3 & -2 & 1 \\ 2 & -1 & 2 \end{bmatrix} \begin{Bmatrix} x_1 \\ x_2 \\ x_3 \end{Bmatrix} = \begin{Bmatrix} 0 \\ 0 \\ 0 \end{Bmatrix}$$

8.
$$\begin{bmatrix} -2 & 1 & -3 \\ 2 & -1 & 0.5 \\ 1 & -0.5 & -1 \\ 3 & -1.5 & 2 \end{bmatrix} \begin{Bmatrix} x_1 \\ x_2 \\ x_3 \end{Bmatrix} = \begin{Bmatrix} 0 \\ 0 \\ 0 \\ 0 \end{Bmatrix}$$

Problem 9: Find the eigenvalues and eigenvectors of the following matrix:

$$\begin{bmatrix} 4.38 & 2.58 \\ 1.95 & 2.58 \end{bmatrix}$$

Problem 10: Find the eigenvalues and eigenvectors of the following matrix:

$$\begin{bmatrix} 10.5 & 3.89 \\ 10.5 & 11.67 \end{bmatrix}$$

CHAPTER 6

ENERGY CONCEPTS IN STRUCTURES

6.1. INTRODUCTION

In this chapter, we use the tools of matrix algebra to derive some important concepts relating to strain energy and to the properties of the stiffness and flexibility matrices of structures.

Our discussion deals with ideal elastic structures which are *conservative*. In such structures the work done by externally applied forces, F_i, acting through corresponding displacements, u_i, which they produce, is stored in the deflected structure in the form of kinetic and strain energy, and all damping forces or energy dissipative forces in the structure are zero.

6.2. STRAIN ENERGY

When a conservative structure is subjected to forces which are applied gradually so that at any stage in the loading history the structure is in static equilibrium (that is, no net resultant force acts on the structure at any time), then no velocities will develop and the kinetic energy associated with the mass of the structure will be zero. In this case all the work, W, done by the applied forces on their corresponding displacements is stored in the structure in the form of strain energy, U, or

$$W = U \qquad (6.1)$$

This strain energy depends only on the final configuration of the structure, and is independent of the loading path (history), or the manner in which this configuration was obtained. For example, when forces F_i $(i = 1, 2, \ldots, n)$

cause a certain deflected configuration of a structure, this same configuration and associated strain energy can be obtained by applying the forces F_i in any order or all at the same time, provided that the forces are applied gradually.

Strain energy can have the following four forms which correspond to the internal incremental displacements and associated internal forces discussed in Section 3.8:

1. Strain energy due to normal stresses (axial forces)
2. Strain energy due to bending stresses (bending moments)
3. Strain energy due to shear stresses (shear forces)
4. Strain energy due to torsion stresses (torques)

For example, in the structure of Figure 6.1 all four forms of strain energy are present when force F_i is applied as shown.

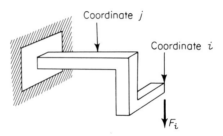

Figure 6.1.

Suppose that force F_i in Figure 6.1 is applied gradually and causes a final displacement u_i as shown in Figure 6.2(a). The force displacement relationship shown is not linear but is elastic (that is, same loading and

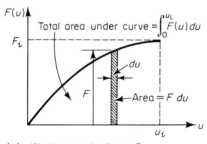

(a)   Work done by force F_i

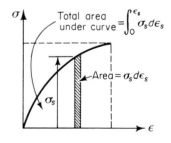

(b)   Strain energy of form s per unit volume, corresponding to work done by force F_i in Figure (a)

Figure 6.2.

unloading path). The work, W, done by force F_i when it caused a final displacement, u_i, is given by

$$W = \int_0^{u_i} F(u)\, du \tag{6.2}$$

The corresponding strain energy, U, stored in the structure is given by

$$U = \sum_{s=1}^{4} \int_V \left(\int_0^{\varepsilon_s} \sigma_s\, d\varepsilon_s \right) dV \tag{6.3}$$

in which σ_s and ε_s represent, respectively, stress and strain, and subscript s takes on the values 1, 2, 3, 4, corresponding, respectively, to axial, bending, shear, and torsion stress and associated strain. The inner integral $\int_0^{\varepsilon_s} \sigma_s\, d\varepsilon_s$ represents the energy per unit volume for energy form s, as shown in Figure 6.2(b). The outer integral is taken over the entire volume, V, of the structure for each energy form, and all four energy forms ($s = 1, 2, 3, 4$) are added to give the total energy in the system. Note that the product $\sigma_s\, d\varepsilon_s$ has, of course, the units of energy per unit of volume

$$\left(\frac{\text{lb}}{\text{in.}^2} \right) \left(\frac{\text{in.}}{\text{in.}} \right) = \left(\frac{\text{lb–in.}}{\text{in.}^3} \right)$$

When the structure of Figure 6.1 is linear, then the curve of Figure 6.2(a) is replaced by a straight line so that $F(u) = k_{ii}u$ (k_{ii} is the stiffness coefficient), and Equation (6.2) becomes

$$W = \int_0^{u_i} k_{ii}u\, du = \tfrac{1}{2} k_{ii}u_i^2 = \tfrac{1}{2} F_i u_i \tag{6.4}$$

Similarly, when the structure is linear, σ_s and ε_s are linearly related and the inner integral in Equation (6.3) takes the form

$$\int_0^{\varepsilon_s} \sigma_s\, d\varepsilon_s = \tfrac{1}{2} \sigma_s \varepsilon_s$$

so that Equation (6.3) becomes

$$U = \tfrac{1}{2} \sum_{s=1}^{4} \int_V \sigma_s \varepsilon_s\, dV \tag{6.5}$$

If the structure is linear and in addition the stresses, σ_s, are linearly distributed over the cross sections of the structure as considered in Section 3.8, then Equation (6.5) can be written

$$U = \frac{1}{2} \int_L \frac{P^2(x)}{EA(x)}\, dx + \frac{1}{2} \int_L \frac{M^2(x)}{EI(x)}\, dx + \frac{1}{2} \int_L \frac{V^2(x)}{GA(x)}\, dx + \frac{1}{2} \int_L \frac{T^2(x)}{GJ(x)}\, dx \tag{6.6}$$

in which $P(x)$, $M(x)$, $V(x)$, and $T(x)$ are, respectively, the internal axial force, bending moment, shear, and torque at x caused by force F_i. The integrals are taken over the entire length, L, of the structure.

6.3. SYMMETRY PROPERTY OF THE STIFFNESS AND FLEXIBILITY MATRICES

We can use the fact that the strain energy in a structure is independent of the loading history to prove that the stiffness and flexibility matrices are symmetrical. Let us do this by means of a simple example:

The beam in Figure 6.3 is acted upon by forces F_i and F_j causing displacements u_i and u_j. Since the loading sequence has no effect on the final value of the strain energy, U, this same energy will be obtained in the following two loading sequences in which all forces are applied gradually.

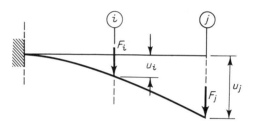

Figure 6.3.

Loading Sequence I (Figure 6.4)

First, place F_i which causes displacement $a_{ii}F_i$ at i. The work done by F_i on displacement $a_{ii}F_i$ is

$$\tfrac{1}{2}a_{ii}F_i^2$$

Next apply F_j which causes at coordinate i a displacement $a_{ij}F_j$ and at coordinate j a displacement $a_{jj}F_j$. The corresponding work done by forces F_i and F_j on these displacements is

$$a_{ij}F_iF_j + \tfrac{1}{2}a_{jj}F_j^2$$

(There is no $\tfrac{1}{2}$ in the first term because F_i is in its full value when displacement $a_{ij}F_j$ takes place at i.)

The total strain energy, U_I, in loading sequence I is

$$U_I = \tfrac{1}{2}a_{ii}F_i^2 + a_{ij}F_iF_j + \tfrac{1}{2}a_{jj}F_j^2 \tag{6.7a}$$

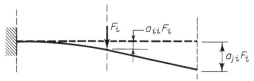

(a)   Place F_i first (gradually);   work $= \frac{1}{2}a_{ii}F_i^2$

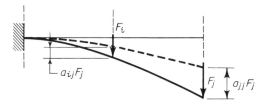

(b)   Leave F_i as in (a) and place
F_j gradually;   work $= a_{ij}F_iF_j + \frac{1}{2}a_{jj}F_j^2$

Total strain energy U_{I} stored
in loading sequence $\mathrm{I} = \frac{1}{2}a_{ii}F_i^2 + a_{ij}F_iF_j + \frac{1}{2}a_{jj}F_j^2$

Figure 6.4. Loading sequence I.

Loading Sequence II (Figure 6.5)

Place F_j first which does an amount of work

$$\tfrac{1}{2}a_{jj}F_j^2$$

Next place F_i which causes the following amount of work to be done by F_j and F_i

$$a_{ji}F_iF_j + \tfrac{1}{2}a_{ii}F_i^2$$

The total strain energy, U_{II}, in loading sequence II is

$$U_{\mathrm{II}} = \tfrac{1}{2}a_{ii}F_i^2 + a_{ji}F_iF_j + \tfrac{1}{2}a_{jj}F_j^2 \tag{6.7b}$$

Since

$$U_{\mathrm{I}} = U_{\mathrm{II}}$$

then comparing Equations (6.7a) and (6.7b), we conclude that

$$a_{ij} = a_{ji} \tag{6.8}$$

This is known as *Maxwell's reciprocity relationship* and it indicates that the flexibility matrix of a structure is symmetrical.

A procedure similar to that shown in Figures (6.3), (6.4), and (6.5) can be used to show that $k_{ij} = k_{ji}$. Use the following two loading sequences in which all forces are applied gradually to produce forces F_i, F_j, and displacements u_i and u_j in Figure 6.3.

Loading Sequence I : First produce u_i only with $u_j = 0$, then produce u_j, yielding

$$U_{\mathrm{I}} = \tfrac{1}{2}k_{ii}u_i^2 + k_{ji}u_iu_j + \tfrac{1}{2}k_{jj}u_j^2$$

Loading Sequence II : First produce u_j only with $u_i = 0$, then produce u_i, yielding

$$U_{\mathrm{II}} = \tfrac{1}{2}k_{ii}u_i^2 + k_{ij}u_iu_j + \tfrac{1}{2}k_{jj}u_j^2$$

Equating U_{I} and U_{II} leads to

$$k_{ij} = k_{ji} \tag{6.9}$$

which indicates that the stiffness matrix of a structure is symmetrical. We leave it as an exercise for the reader to verify the last result by generating the expressions for U_{I} and U_{II} from figures analogous to Figures 6.4 and 6.5 in which stiffness coefficients and displacements are involved instead of flexibility coefficients and forces.

Equations (6.8) and (6.9) can also be derived from virtual work by using Equations (3.20) and (3.22). For instance, using Equation (3.20) to compute the flexibility coefficient a_{ji} will lead to the same expression as that which

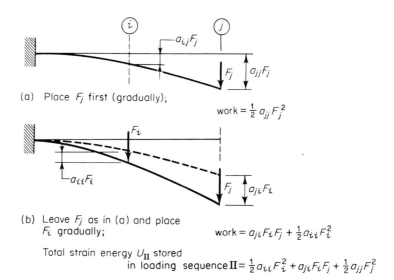

(a) Place F_j first (gradually);

work $= \tfrac{1}{2}a_{jj}F_j^2$

(b) Leave F_j as in (a) and place F_i gradually;

work $= a_{ji}F_iF_j + \tfrac{1}{2}a_{ii}F_i^2$

Total strain energy U_{II} stored
in loading sequence II $= \tfrac{1}{2}a_{ii}F_i^2 + a_{ji}F_iF_j + \tfrac{1}{2}a_{jj}F_j^2$

Figure 6.5. Loading sequence II.

appears on the right-hand side of Equation (3.27) and consequently $a_{ij} = a_{ji}$. A similar use of Equation (3.22) to compute k_{ij} and k_{ji} will lead to $k_{ij} = k_{ji}$.

6.4. STRAIN ENERGY IN TERMS OF STIFFNESS AND FLEXIBILITY MATRICES

When a linear structure is acted upon by a number of forces F_i ($i = 1, 2, \ldots, n$) which are applied gradually, the strain energy, U, in the structure is equal to the work done by these forces on the corresponding displacement u_i. Using the right-hand side of Equation (6.4) and summing on i, we have

$$U = \tfrac{1}{2} \sum_{i=1}^{n} F_i u_i \qquad (6.10)$$

In matrix form, this equation is

$$U = \tfrac{1}{2} \{u\}^T \{F\} \qquad (6.11)$$

or

$$U = \tfrac{1}{2} \{F\}^T \{u\} \qquad (6.12)$$

Substituting $[k]\{u\}$ for $\{F\}$ in Equation (6.11) gives

$$U = \tfrac{1}{2} \{u\}^T [k] \{u\} \qquad (6.13)$$

and substituting $[a]\{F\}$ for $\{u\}$ in Equation (6.12)

$$U = \tfrac{1}{2} \{F\}^T [a] \{F\} \qquad (6.14)$$

Equations (6.13) and (6.14) represent the strain energy in the structure in terms of the stiffness and flexibility matrix, respectively.

Let us transpose each side of Equation (6.13) using the reversal law of Section 4.12, and write

$$U = \tfrac{1}{2} \{u\}^T [k]^T \{u\} \qquad (6.15)$$

The left-hand side is unchanged because the transpose of a scalar is the same as the scalar. The right-hand sides of Equations (6.13) and (6.15) are also identical because, from Equation (6.9), we concluded that the stiffness matrix of a structure is symmetrical, or

$$[k]^T = [k] \qquad (6.16)$$

Similarly, transposing each side of Equation (6.14), we have

$$U = \tfrac{1}{2} \{F\}^T [a]^T \{F\} \qquad (6.17)$$

which is identical to Equation (6.14) because, from Equation (6.8), we concluded that the flexibility matrix of a structure is symmetrical, or

$$[a]^T = [a] \qquad (6.18)$$

6.5. STIFFNESS AND FLEXIBILITY COEFFICIENTS IN TERMS OF STRAIN ENERGY

Stiffness Coefficients

Let us write Equation (6.13) in the following form:

$$
U = \tfrac{1}{2}
\begin{array}{c|c}
 & u_1\ u_2\ u_3\ \ldots u_l\ \ldots u_n \\
\hline
u_1 & k_{11}k_{12}k_{13}\ldots k_{1l}\ldots k_{1n} \\
u_2 & k_{21}k_{22}k_{23}\ldots k_{2l}\ldots k_{2n} \\
u_3 & k_{31}k_{32}k_{33}\ldots k_{3l}\ldots k_{3n} \\
\vdots & \qquad\qquad\quad\vdots \\
u_l & k_{l1}\ k_{l2}\ k_{l3}\ \ldots\ k_{ll}\ \ldots\ k_{ln} \\
\vdots & \qquad\qquad\quad\vdots \\
u_n & k_{n1}\ k_{n2}\ k_{n3}\ \ldots\ k_{nl}\ \ldots\ k_{nn}
\end{array}
\qquad (6.19)
$$

In this equation, each element k_{ij} multiplies u_i of the left column and u_j of the top row, then all the products are added and the sum multiplied by $\tfrac{1}{2}$.

If we take a partial derivative of the strain energy, U, with respect to any displacement u_l in Equation (6.13), then on the right-hand side of the equation only terms in which u_l appear will contribute to this partial derivative (all u_i are considered to be independent measurements). From Equation (6.19) it is seen that the terms in which u_l appears are associated with row l and column l of the stiffness coefficients k_{ij}. Because of the symmetry property, $k_{lj} = k_{jl}$, the sum of these terms is given by

$$
\tfrac{1}{2}(2k_{l1}u_l u_1 + 2k_{l2}u_l u_2 + \cdots + k_{ll}u_l^2 + \cdots + 2k_{ln}u_l u_n)
$$

Taking a partial derivative with respect to u_l, this sum becomes

$$
k_{l1}u_1 + k_{l2}u_2 + \cdots + k_{ll}u_l + \cdots + k_{ln}u_n = \sum_{j=1}^{n} k_{lj}u_j
$$

or

$$
\frac{\partial U}{\partial u_l} = \sum_{j=1}^{n} k_{lj}u_j \qquad (6.20)
$$

The right-hand side of this equation is equal to the force F_l at coordinate l [see Equation (3.13)]; hence,

$$
\frac{\partial U}{\partial u_l} = F_l \qquad (6.21)
$$

Equation (6.21) is *Castigliano's first theorem.*†

If we now take a partial derivative with respect to any u_s in Equation (6.20), we have

$$k_{ls} = \frac{\partial^2 U}{\partial u_l \, \partial u_s} \qquad (6.22)$$

$$l = 1, 2, \ldots, n \qquad s = 1, 2, \ldots, n$$

Hence, in general, the stiffness coefficient k_{ls} is equal to the second partial derivative of the strain energy with respect to the displacements at co-ordinates l and s.

Flexibility Coefficients

Starting with Equation (6.14) and proceeding as we did in deriving Equation (6.22), we obtain the following: Taking a partial derivative of Equation (6.14) with respect to any force F_l (with all the F_i considered to be independent) and using the reciprocity relation, $a_{lj} = a_{jl}$, we obtain

$$\frac{\partial U}{\partial F_l} = \sum_{j=1}^{n} a_{lj} F_j \qquad (6.23)$$

The right-hand side of this equation is equal to displacement, u_l, at co-ordinate l [see Equation (3.12)]; hence,

$$\frac{\partial U}{\partial F_l} = u_l \qquad (6.24)$$

This is *Castigliano's second theorem.*

If we take a partial derivative with respect to any F_s in Equation (6.23), we have

$$a_{ls} = \frac{\partial^2 U}{\partial F_l \, \partial F_s} \qquad (6.25)$$

$$l = 1, 2, \ldots, n \qquad s = 1, 2, \ldots, n$$

Or stated in words, Equation (6.25) reads: The flexibility coefficient a_{ls} is equal to the second partial derivative of the strain energy with respect to the forces at coordinates l and s.

---

† This theorem can also be derived without stipulating a linear force displacement relationship[19].

Equations (6.22) and (6.25) for Constrained Measurements

It is interesting to note the following in connection with Equations (6.22) and (6.25):

When the displacements u_i are dependent measurements, we cannot take a partial derivative with respect to any u_l and u_s because this implies that all other u_i are held constant[24]; hence Equation (6.22) cannot be applied, or the stiffness matrix does not exist. On the other hand, as long as the forces F_i are independent, Equation (6.25) applies, and the flexibility matrix can be constructed despite the dependence among the u_i.

When the forces F_i are dependent measurements Equation (6.25) does not apply; hence, the flexibility matrix does not exist. As long as the displacements u_i are independent, however, Equation (6.22) applies, and the stiffness matrix can be constructed despite the dependence amongst the F_i.

These conclusions agree again with the discussion in Sections 3.6 and 2.4.

6.6. ADDITIONAL PROPERTIES OF [*a*] AND [*k*]

Positive Definite Property

Equations (6.13) and (6.14) can be written as double summations in the following form

$$U = \tfrac{1}{2} \sum_{i=1}^{n} \sum_{j=1}^{n} k_{ij} u_i u_j \tag{6.26}$$

and

$$U = \tfrac{1}{2} \sum_{i=1}^{n} \sum_{j=1}^{n} a_{ij} F_i F_j \tag{6.27}$$

The double summation of Equations (6.26) and (6.27) is called a *quadratic form*[28] in variables u_i and F_i, respectively, provided that the coefficients a_{ij} and k_{ij} are symmetric.

A quadratic form is said to be *positive definite* if it assumes only positive values for any arbitrary values of the variables, except that when all the variables are zero it is zero.

The quadratic form in Equation (6.26) is positive definite, because the strain energy can assume only positive values for any arbitrary values of u_i except that it will be zero when $u_i = 0$ for all i. That is,

$$\sum_i \sum_j k_{ij} u_i u_j > 0, \qquad \text{for any arbitrary } u_i \text{ when not all } u_i = 0$$

$$= 0, \qquad \text{when all } u_i = 0 \tag{6.28}$$

Similarly, the quadratic form in Equation (6.27) is positive definite,

$$\sum_i \sum_j a_{ij} F_i F_j > 0, \qquad \text{for any arbitrary } F_i \text{ when not all } F_i = 0$$

$$= 0, \qquad \text{when all } F_i = 0 \tag{6.29}$$

The matrix of coefficients, $[k]$ in Equation (6.28) and $[a]$ in Equation (6.29), which makes the positive definite property possible, is referred to as *a positive definite matrix*. Hence the stiffness and flexibility matrices of a structure are positive definite.

Elements of the Principal Diagonal in [a] and [k]

In a stable structure, the elements k_{ii} and a_{ii} on the principal diagonal of a stiffness and flexibility matrix must always be positive.

This property follows from the definition of k_{ii} and a_{ii}. k_{ii} is the force required at coordinate i to produce a unit displacement at i; we therefore expect the force k_{ii} to be in the same direction as the unit displacement at i. Similarly for a_{ii}; we expect the displacement, a_{ii}, at coordinate i to be in the same direction as the unit force applied at i.

When an element k_{ii} on the principal diagonal of matrix $[k]$ is negative, the structure is unstable. We demonstrate this by the following example:

In Figure 6.6(a) we define two coordinates i and j as shown. The stiffness k_{ii} is given by $4EI/l$ when the member is prismatic (see Section 2.8). In Figure 6.6(b), we have a tensile force F applied to the member. The presence

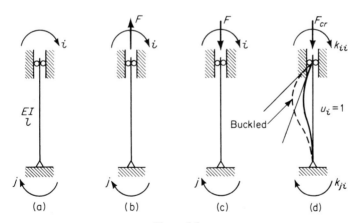

Figure 6.6.

of this force will cause the coefficient k_{ii} to be larger than $4EI/l$, because the force required at i to cause a unit displacement at i must overcome the effect of force F which tends to straighten the member. In Figure 6.6(c) a compressive force F is applied. This will cause the coefficient k_{ii} to become smaller than $4EI/l$, because F will assist in the effort to produce a unit displacement at i. In each part of Figure 6.6(a, b, c), k_{ii} is applied in the direction of coordinate i and is positive.

Let us suppose, now, that the force F in Figure 6.6(c) is increased to the value of the critical buckling force, F_{cr}, as shown in Figure 6.6(d). In this case, large rotations will be produced at coordinates i and j under the slightest distortion of the perfectly straight position of the member. If we try to generate column i of $[k]$ for the structure in Figure 6.6(d), the rotation at i will proceed to increase very rapidly as we produce the slightest movement at i in the positive direction of the coordinate. To keep $u_i = 1$, we must, therefore, apply at i a force k_{ii} in a direction which is opposite to the direction of the desired unit displacement; hence, k_{ii} is negative. This example serves to indicate that a negative element on the principal diagonal signifies a condition of instability.

(For discussion of the effects of compressive forces on the bending stiffness of a beam–column see References [14, 41, 42].)

6.7. ANOTHER INTERPRETATION OF COEFFICIENTS a_{ij} AND k_{ij}

We can use the concepts of virtual work discussed in Section 3.8 to give the following general interpretation to the elements of the stiffness and flexibility matrix.

Element k_{ij} of a stiffness matrix $[k]$ is equal in magnitude to the work done by the forces at the coordinates in the displaced configuration when column j of $[k]$ is generated, on the corresponding displacements at the coordinates in the displaced configuration when column i of $[k]$ is generated. This is seen from Figure 6.7. In Figure 6.7(a) we show n coordinates, Figures 6.7 (b and c) show, respectively, the configurations associated with columns j and i of $[k]$. For clarity, we show only k_{ij} in Figure 6.7(b). If we now multiply the forces at the coordinates in Figure 6.7(b) by the corresponding displacements in Figure 6.7(c), we obtain k_{ij} because all displacements at the coordinates in Figure 6.7(c) are zero except for $u_i = 1$.

If we consider the forces in Figure 6.7(b) to be real, and the displacements in Figure 6.7(c) to be virtual, then from Section 3.8 we can write

$$k_{ij}(u_i = 1) = \text{(internal stresses } \sigma_{sj} \text{ for } u_j = 1)(\text{internal strains } \varepsilon_{si} \text{ for } u_i = 1)$$

or

$$k_{ij} = \sum_{s=1}^{d} \int_V \sigma_{sj} \varepsilon_{si} \, dV \tag{6.30}$$

with all terms interpreted as in Equation (6.3).† Similarly,

$$k_{ji} = \sum_{s=1}^{4} \int_{V} \sigma_{si} \varepsilon_{sj} \, dV$$

and since $k_{ij} = k_{ji}$, we can rewrite Equation (6.30) with subscripts i and j interchanged on the right-hand side

$$k_{ij} = \sum_{s=1}^{4} \int_{V} \sigma_{si} \varepsilon_{sj} \, dV \qquad (6.31)$$

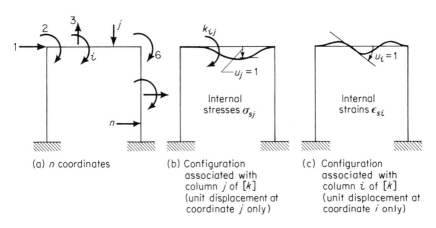

(a) n coordinates

(b) Configuration associated with column j of $[k]$ (unit displacement at coordinate j only)

(c) Configuration associated with column i of $[k]$ (unit displacement at coordinate i only)

Figure 6.7.

Following an analogous development for the elements of the flexibility matrix, we find that element a_{ij} is equal in magnitude to the work done by the forces at the coordinates in the displaced configuration when column i of $[a]$ is generated, on the corresponding displacements at the coordinates in the displaced configuration when column j of $[a]$ is generated. This is seen in Figure 6.8. In Figure 6.8(b) the only force acting at the coordinates of the structure is $F_i = 1$. If we multiply the forces at the coordinates in Figure 6.8(b) by the corresponding displacements in Figure 6.8(c) we have a_{ij}.

Again considering forces in Figure 6.8(b) as real and the displacements in Figure 6.8(c) as virtual, then, from Section 3.8, we have

$$a_{ij} = \sum_{s=1}^{4} \int_{V} \sigma_{si} \varepsilon_{sj} \, dV \qquad (6.32)$$

---

† The subscript j in σ_{sj} indicates that these stresses correspond to a unit displacement @j (the configuration associated with column j of $[k]$). Similarly, the strains ε_{si} correspond to a unit displacement @i (the configuration associated with column i of $[k]$).

in which σ_{si} represents the stresses due to a unit force @ i (the configuration corresponding to column i of $[a]$) and ε_{sj} represents the strains due to a unit force @ j (the configuration corresponding to column j of $[a]$).

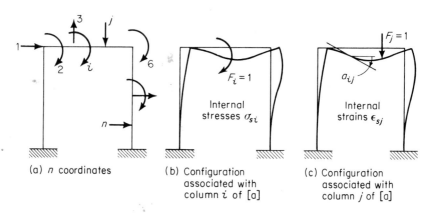

(a) n coordinates   (b) Configuration associated with column i of $[a]$ (c) Configuration associated with column j of $[a]$

Figure 6.8.

6.8. BETTI'S LAW

The Maxwell reciprocity relationship as expressed by Equations (6.8) and (6.9), or Equations (6.16) and (6.18), can be used to derive *Betti's law* also known as the *Maxwell–Betti theorem*[19] or the *Rayleigh–Betti Reciprocal theorem*[25].

The interesting feature of Betti's law is that it is easier to prove it, using the tools of matrix algebra, than to state it in words. Let us therefore reserve the statement of the law to the end of the section.

Consider the two identical linear elastic structures of Figures 6.9(a) and 6.9(b). The applied forces in Figures 6.9(a) and (b) are selected arbitrarily and will be referred to as loading systems I and II, respectively. Let us define a coordinate where each force is acting in Figures 6.9(a) and (b), as shown in Figure 6.9(c), and let $[a]$ be the flexibility matrix corresponding to these coordinates of the structure. For ease of reference, we designate the forces and displacements in Figure 6.9(a) as $\{F\}_I$ and $\{u\}_I$, and in Figure 6.9(b) as $\{F\}_{II}$ and $\{u\}_{II}$. For system I, Figure 6.9(a), we can write

$$\{u\}_I = [a]\{F\}_I \tag{6.33}$$

and for system II, Figure 6.9(b), we write

$$\{u\}_{II} = [a]\{F\}_{II} \tag{6.34}$$

If we now take the product

$$\{F\}_{\mathrm{I}}^{T}\{u\}_{\mathrm{II}}$$

of the forces in system I and the displacements in system II and substitute from Equation (6.34), we have

$$\{F\}_{\mathrm{I}}^{T}\{u\}_{\mathrm{II}} = \{F\}_{\mathrm{I}}^{T}[a]\{F\}_{\mathrm{II}} \qquad (6.35)$$

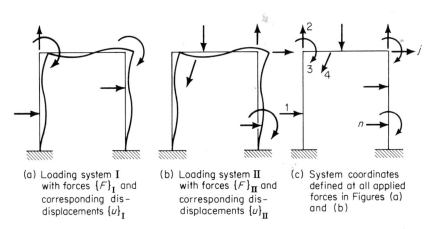

(a) Loading system I
with forces $\{F\}_{\mathrm{I}}$ and
corresponding dis-
displacements $\{u\}_{\mathrm{I}}$

(b) Loading system II
with forces $\{F\}_{\mathrm{II}}$ and
corresponding dis-
displacements $\{u\}_{\mathrm{II}}$

(c) System coordinates
defined at all applied
forces in Figures (a)
and (b)

Figure 6.9.

Similarly using Equation (6.33), the product

$$\{F\}_{\mathrm{II}}^{T}\{u\}_{\mathrm{I}}$$

of the forces in system II and the displacements in system I becomes

$$\{F\}_{\mathrm{II}}^{T}\{u\}_{\mathrm{I}} = \{F\}_{\mathrm{II}}^{T}[a]\{F\}_{\mathrm{I}} \qquad (6.36)$$

Each side of this equation is a scalar, so that transposing each side does not alter the value of the scalar. Therefore, using the reversal law and the symmetry of $[a]$, the right-hand side of Equation (6.36) can be written as

$$\{F\}_{\mathrm{I}}^{T}[a]\{F\}_{\mathrm{II}}$$

This is identical with the right-hand side of Equation (6.35). Hence we conclude that

$$\{F\}_{\mathrm{I}}^{T}\{u\}_{\mathrm{II}} = \{F\}_{\mathrm{II}}^{T}\{u\}_{\mathrm{I}} \qquad (6.37)$$

The relationship expressed by Equation (6.37) is known as *Betti's law*. Stated in words this law reads as follows: For a linear elastic structure subjected to two different loading systems I and II, the work done by the forces in system I acting through the corresponding displacements (virtual) in system II is equal to the work done by the forces in system II acting through the corresponding displacements (virtual) in system I.

6.9. APPLICATIONS OF BETTI'S LAW: FORCES NOT AT THE COORDINATES

We shall now demonstrate, by examples, how Betti's law can be used to deal with structures in which forces are not acting at the coordinates.

Example 1

Consider the structure of Figure 6.10(a) in which two coordinates are defined as shown. Considering only bending energy, the stiffness matrix for these coordinates is

$$[k] = \frac{EI}{l}\begin{bmatrix} 4 & 2 \\ 2 & 4 \end{bmatrix}$$

and we can write the equations

$$\{F\} = [k]\{u\} \quad \text{or} \quad \{u\} = [k]^{-1}\{F\} \tag{6.38}$$

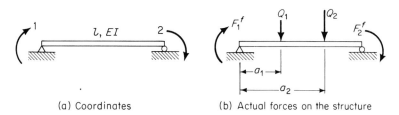

(a) Coordinates   (b) Actual forces on the structure

Figure 6.10.

These equations, however, are defined only for forces acting at the co-ordinates, but we wish to use them to compute the displacements u_1 and u_2 caused by the forces in Figure 6.10(b) (which are not all at the coordinates), without changing the stiffness matrix which has already been generated. To do so we proceed as follows:

Using a superposition of forces, we can apply the forces acting at the coordinates, which are designated as F_i^f, and the forces not at the co-ordinates, (designated as Q_i), separately as shown in Figure 6.11, so that the displacements and all internal stresses in Figure 6.11(a) are obtained by adding the corresponding values in (b) and (c).

In Figure 6.11(b), Equation (6.38) can be applied because the forces F_i^f are acting only at the coordinates, but Figure 6.11(c) requires further reduction. In Figure 6.12 we apply a superposition of displacements to the structure of Figure 6.11(c) as follows: In Figure 6.12(b), we represent the *fixed coordinate state* in which no displacements are permitted at the coordinates, whereas in Figure 6.12(c) we produce displacements $\{u\}^Q$ at the coordinates which are equal to the corresponding displacements caused by forces Q_i in Figure 6.12(a). The forces in Figures 6.12(b) and (c) are shown in the positive direction of the coordinates. In Figure 6.12(b), we designate the forces as F_i^0 in which the superscript zero reminds us that

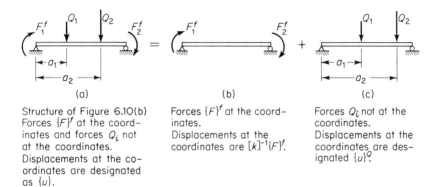

Structure of Figure 6.10(b) Forces $\{F\}^f$ at the coordinates and forces Q_i not at the coordinates. Displacements at the coordinates are designated as $\{u\}$.	Forces $\{F\}^f$ at the coordinates. Displacements at the coordinates are $[k]^{-1}\{F\}^f$.	Forces Q_i not at the coordinates. Displacements at the coordinates are designated $\{u\}^Q$.
(a)	(b)	(c)

Figure 6.11. Superposition of forces.

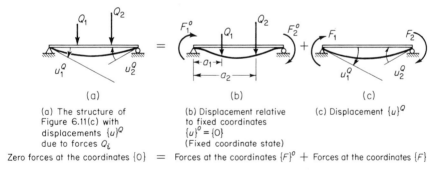

(a)	(b)	(c)
(a) The structure of Figure 6.11(c) with displacements $\{u\}^Q$ due to forces Q_i	(b) Displacement relative to fixed coordinates $\{u\}^0 = \{0\}$ (Fixed coordinate state)	(c) Displacement $\{u\}^Q$
Zero forces at the coordinates $\{0\}$	= Forces at the coordinates $\{F\}^0$	+ Forces at the coordinates $\{F\}$

Figure 6.12. Superposition of displacements.

these are the forces required to set the displacements at the coordinates to zero. The forces at the coordinates in Figure (c) are designated as F_i. Since the forces at the coordinates in Figure 6.12(a) are zero, it therefore follows that the sum of the corresponding forces in Figures 6.12(b) and (c) is also zero, or

$$\{F\}^0 + \{F\} = \{0\}$$

hence,

$$\{F\} = -\{F\}^0 \tag{6.39}$$

The reader who is familiar with moment distribution [12,14,47] will recognize the forces F_i^0 in Figure 6.12(b) as the fixed end moments. Equation (6.39) has the following interpretation: When forces, Q_i, are not applied at the coordinates but produce at the coordinates displacements u_i^Q, then the same displacements will be produced by forces F_i applied at the coordinates only, provided that these forces are equal in magnitude but opposite in direction to the forces F_i^0 required to stop the original forces Q_i from producing these displacements; that is, *the forces F_i in Figure 6.12(c) are equal in magnitude and opposite in sign to the forces at the coordinates, F_i^0, in the fixed coordinate state (Figure 6.12b).*

To find the forces F_i^0 in Figure 6.12(b) we can use Betti's law as follows:

Consider the shape $\phi_1(x)$ associated with a unit displacement at co-ordinate 1 only in Figure 6.10(a). Considering bending energy only, then this shape is given by

$$\phi_1(x) = x\left(\frac{l - x}{l}\right)^2 \tag{6.40}$$

and is shown in Figure 6.13. The expression of Equation (6.40) can be verified by applying the method of moment area to compute the displacement at any point x in Figure 6.13. We leave this as an exercise to the reader (Problem 4).

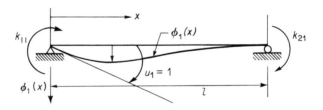

Figure 6.13. Shape $\phi_1(x)$ associated with a unit displacement at coordinate 1 only.

To compute F_1^0 in Figure 6.12(b), we apply now Betti's law to the loading systems of Figures 6.12(b) and 6.13. The forces in Figure 6.13 do zero work on the corresponding displacements in Figure 6.12(b) because these displacements are zero. Therefore, the forces in Figure 6.12(b) must do zero work on the corresponding displacements in Figure 6.13, or

$$F_1^0 + Q_1\phi_1(a_1) + Q_2\phi_1(a_2) = 0$$

hence,

$$F_1^0 = -Q_1\phi_1(a_1) - Q_2\phi_1(a_2)$$

Substituting for $\phi_1(a_1)$ and $\phi_1(a_2)$ from Equation (6.40), we have

$$F_1^0 = -\sum_{i=1}^{2} Q_i \frac{a_i(l - a_i)^2}{l^2} \tag{6.41}$$

This is the familiar expression for the fixed end moment due to concentrated loads[12, 13, 14].

To compute F_2^0 we apply Betti's law to Figures 6.12(b) and 6.14 which yields

$$F_2^0 - Q_1\phi_2(l - a_1) - Q_2\phi_2(l - a_2) = 0$$

or

$$F_2^0 = Q_1\phi_2(l - a_1) + Q_2\phi_2(l - a_2)$$

Substituting for $\phi_2(l - a_1)$ and $\phi_2(l - a_2)$ from Equation (6.40), we have

$$F_2^0 = \sum_{i=1}^{2} Q_i \frac{a_i^2(l - a_i)}{l^2} \tag{6.42}$$

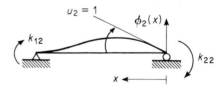

Figure 6.14. Shape $\phi_2(x)$ associated with a unit displacement at coordinate 2 only.

Using Equation (6.39), we write for the forces F_i in Figure 6.12(c)

$$\{F\} = -\{F\}^0 = \frac{1}{l^2} \left\{ \begin{array}{c} \sum_i Q_i a_i(l - a_i)^2 \\ -\sum_i Q_i a_i^2(l - a_i) \end{array} \right\} \tag{6.43}$$

To obtain the displacements, u_i, due to the loads in Figure 6.10(b) or 6.11(a), we add the results in Figures 6.11(b), 6.12(b), and 6.12(c) which are, respectively, given by

$$[k]^{-1}\{F\}^f, \quad \{0\}, \quad \text{and} \quad -[k]^{-1}\{F\}^0$$

The final displacements u_i are therefore

$$\{u\} = [k]^{-1}(\{F\}^f - \{F\}^0) \tag{6.44}$$

Substituting for $\{F\}^0$ from Equation (6.43), we have, in the present example,

$$\{u\} = [k]^{-1}\left(\{F\}^f + \frac{1}{l^2} \left\{ \begin{array}{c} \sum_i Q_i a_i(l - a_i)^2 \\ -\sum_i Q_i a_i^2(l - a_i) \end{array} \right\} \right)$$

To obtain the stresses, strains, or displacements at any point in the structure of Figure 6.11(a), we add the corresponding values from Figures 6.11(b), 6.12(b), and 6.12(c).

When forces Q_1 and Q_2 in Figure 6.10(b) are replaced by a distributed force with intensity $p(x)$ per unit length, then forces F_i^0 become

$$F_i^0 = -\int_0^l p(x)\phi_i(x)\,dx \qquad i = 1, 2$$

and for an applied moment $M(x)$ at point x

$$F_i^0 = -M(x)\frac{d\phi_i(x)}{dx} \qquad i = 1, 2$$

Verify these results using the procedures of this section.

Suggested Exercises: Do problems 1, 2, 3, 4, and 5.

Example 2

As a second example which will serve to generalize the procedures of the preceding example we consider the structure of Figure 6.15. The stiffness matrix associated with the three coordinates which are defined for the structure is given by (see Example 2, Section 3.5),

$$[k] = \begin{bmatrix} 24 & -6 & -6 \\ -6 & 8 & 2 \\ -6 & 2 & 8 \end{bmatrix}$$

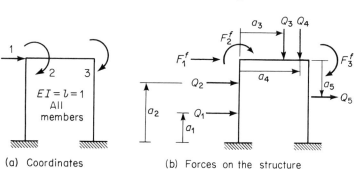

(a) Coordinates   (b) Forces on the structure

Figure 6.15.

To find the internal forces and the displacement of any point on the structure of Figure 6.15(b) we proceed in two steps. First we apply a superposition of forces as shown in Figure 6.16 so that we separate the forces, F_i^f, at the coordinates from the other forces Q_i. Next we apply a superposition of displacements to the structure in Figure 6.16(c) as shown in Figure 6.17 in which the displacements, u_i^Q, at the coordinates are separated from the displacement relative to fixed coordinates.

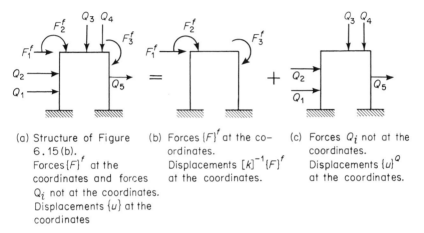

(a) Structure of Figure 6.15(b).
Forces $\{F\}^f$ at the coordinates and forces Q_i not at the coordinates. Displacements $\{u\}$ at the coordinates

(b) Forces $\{F\}^f$ at the coordinates.
Displacements $[k]^{-1}\{F\}^f$ at the coordinates.

(c) Forces Q_i not at the coordinates.
Displacements $\{u\}^Q$ at the coordinates.

Figure 6.16. Superposition of forces applied to the structure of Fig. 6.15(b).

The internal forces and displacements at any point on the structure in Figure 6.15(b) are obtained by adding the corresponding quantities in Figures 6.16(b), 6.17(b), and 6.17(c). To be able to do so we must first find the forces F_i^0 and F_i in Figures 6.17(b) and (c), respectively. From Figure 6.17 we have

$$\{F\}^0 = -\{F\}$$

That is, the forces, F_i, in Figure 6.17(c) are equal in magnitude and opposite in direction to the forces at the coordinates, F_i^0, in the fixed coordinate state, Figure 6.17(b).

To compute the jth fixed coordinate force, F_j^0, in Figure 6.17(b) we apply Betti's law to the structure of Figure 6.17(b) (considered as system I, for example) in which all $u_i = 0$, and to the displaced configuration, $\Phi_j(x)$, of the same structure in which $u_j = 1$ and $u_i = 0$ for all $i \neq j$ (considered as system II). The forces in system II are applied only at the coordinates. The displaced configurations $\Phi_i(x)$ for the structure of Figure 6.15 are shown in Figures 6.18(a, b, c).

For example, applying Betti's law to Figures 6.17(b) and 6.18(a) we have

$$F_1^0 + Q_1\Phi_1(a_1) + Q_2\Phi_1(a_2) + Q_5\Phi_1(a_5) = 0$$

in which $\Phi_1(a_1)$, $\Phi_1(a_2)$, and $\Phi_1(a_5)$ are the displacements shown in Figure

6.18(a). Similarly, from Figures 6.17(b) and 6.18(b),

$$F_2^0 - Q_1\Phi_2(a_1) - Q_2\Phi_2(a_2) + Q_3\Phi_2(a_3) + Q_4\Phi_2(a_4) = 0$$

and from Figures 6.17(b) and 6.18(c),

$$F_3^0 - Q_3\Phi_3(a_3) - Q_4\Phi_3(a_4) - Q_5\Phi_3(a_5) = 0$$

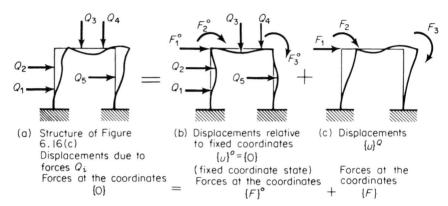

(a) Structure of Figure 6.16(c) Displacements due to forces Q_i Forces at the coordinates $\{0\}$	(b) Displacements relative to fixed coordinates $\{u\}^0 = \{0\}$ (fixed coordinate state) Forces at the coordinates $\{F\}^0$	(c) Displacements $\{u\}^Q$ Forces at the coordinates $\{F\}$

Figure 6.17. Superposition of displacements applied to the structure of Fig. 6.16(c).

The last three equations lead to the values of the fixed coordinate forces $F_i^0 (i = 1, 2, 3)$, which are actually obtained by summing at the coordinates the fixed moments or shears of the elements in the structure. The final displacements u_i in Figure 6.15(b) are obtained by substituting into Equation (6.44) $\{F\}^f$ which is known, [Figure 6.16(b)] and $\{F\}^0$ which was just evaluated.

The displacement functions $\Phi_2(x)$ and $\Phi_3(x)$ in Figures 6.18(b, c) can be identified and expressed by means of Figure 6.13 and Equation (6.40). The

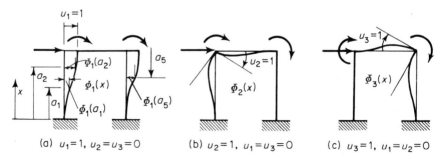

(a) $u_1 = 1$, $u_2 = u_3 = 0$ (b) $u_2 = 1$, $u_1 = u_3 = 0$ (c) $u_3 = 1$, $u_1 = u_2 = 0$

Figure 6.18. Displaced configurations $\Phi_i(x)$ with a unit displacement at one coordinate at a time.

function $\Phi_1(x)$ is derived from the equation

$$\phi(x) = 3\left(\frac{x}{l}\right)^2 - 2\left(\frac{x}{l}\right)^3$$

which expresses the deflected shape of the member shown in Figure 6.19.

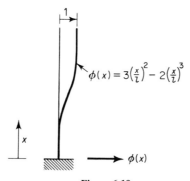

Figure 6.19.

Suggested Exercises: Do problems 6, 7, 8, and 9.

Example 3

In the structure of Figure 6.20 three coordinates are defined and forces
are applied as shown. It is desired to compute the displacements u_i at the
coordinates. Proceeding as in the last example we apply first a superposition

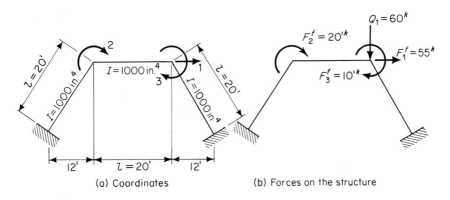

(a) Coordinates   (b) Forces on the structure

Figure 6.20.

of forces as shown in Figure 6.21, and then a superposition of displacements as shown in Figure 6.22. The fixed coordinate forces F_i^0 in Figure 6.22(b) are computed by applying Betti's law to Figure 6.22(b) and Figures 6.23(a, b, c).

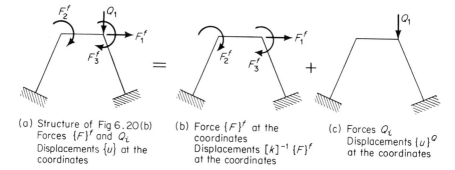

(a) Structure of Fig 6.20(b)
 Forces $\{F\}^f$ and Q_i
 Displacements $\{u\}$ at the
 coordinates

(b) Force $\{F\}^f$ at the
 coordinates
 Displacements $[k]^{-1}\{F\}^f$
 at the coordinates

(c) Forces Q_i
 Displacements $\{u\}^Q$
 at the coordinates

Figure 6.21. Superposition of forces applied to structure of Fig. 6.20(b).

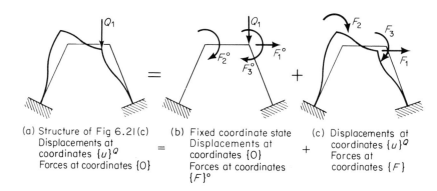

(a) Structure of Fig 6.21(c)
 Displacements at
 coordinates $\{u\}^Q$
 Forces at coordinates $\{0\}$

(b) Fixed coordinate state
 Displacements at
 coordinates $\{0\}$
 Forces at coordinates
 $\{F\}^o$

(c) Displacements at
 coordinates $\{u\}^Q$
 Forces at
 coordinates $\{F\}$

Figure 6.22. Superposition of displacements applied to structure of Fig. 6.21(c).

For example, from Figures 6.22(b) and 6.23(a), we have

$$F_1^0 - \tfrac{3}{4}Q_1 = 0$$

$$F_1^0 = \tfrac{3}{4}Q_1$$

Similarly using Figure 6.22(b) with Figures 6.23(b) and 6.23(c), we obtain, respectively,

$$F_2^0 = 0$$

and

$$F_3^0 = 0$$

so that

$$\{F\}^0 = \begin{Bmatrix} 45 \\ 0 \\ 0 \end{Bmatrix}$$

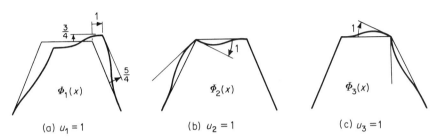

Figure 6.23. Displacement configurations $\Phi_i(x)$ with a unit displacement at one coordinate at a time.

The same result can be obtained directly by resolving Q_1 into components along the inclined and horizontal members, and considering only the horizontal component which does work on the displacements of the structure. (Why doesn't the other component do work on the structure?)

Using the stiffness matrix for the coordinates in Figure 6.20(a) which is given by

$$[k] = \frac{EI}{2l^3} \begin{bmatrix} 129 & 3l & 3l \\ 3l & 16l^2 & 4l^2 \\ 3l & 4l^2 & 16l^2 \end{bmatrix} \tag{6.45}$$

and the values for $\{F\}^f$ and $\{F\}^0$ in Equation (6.44), we have

$$\{u\} = [k]^{-1}\left(\begin{Bmatrix} 55 \\ 20 \\ 10 \end{Bmatrix} - \begin{Bmatrix} 45 \\ 0 \\ 0 \end{Bmatrix} \right)$$

$$= \frac{2l}{30,744EI} \begin{bmatrix} 240l^2 & -36l & -36l \\ -36l & 2055 & -507 \\ -36l & -507 & 2055 \end{bmatrix} \begin{Bmatrix} 10 \\ 20 \\ 10 \end{Bmatrix}$$

Suggested Exercises: Do problems 10 and 11.

6.10. **STRAIN ENERGY IN SYSTEMS AND IN ELEMENTS**

Strain Energy in Elements

In Section 6.4, we showed how the strain energy in a structure can be expressed in terms of its stiffness and flexibility matrices when the forces are applied at the coordinates. The expressions were given by Equation (6.13) and (6.14). Similar expressions can be written for the strain energy in any element *when the forces are applied at the coordinates only.* Whether we use the stiffness or flexibility matrix of the element to express the strain energy will depend on the existence of these matrices for the coordinates defined for the element.† We demonstrate this in the following development.

Consider the element of Figure 6.24 with forces P_i and displacements δ_i at the four coordinates as shown. Since this element may be one of many in a structure we identify it as element *s*. The strain energy, U_s, in this element, which is represented by its deformed configuration, is equal to the work done by the forces P_i (applied gradually), on the corresponding displacements δ_i (the initial rest position is shown in the Figure 6.24). That is,

$$U_s = \tfrac{1}{2}\{\delta\}_s^T\{P\}_s \qquad (6.46)$$

or

$$U_s = \tfrac{1}{2}\{P\}_s^T\{\delta\}_s \qquad (6.47)$$

in which $\{P\}_s$ and $\{\delta\}_s$ are, respectively, the vector of forces and displacements at the coordinates of element *s*. For the coordinates shown in Figure 6.24 there exists no flexibility matrix, but there exists a singular stiffness matrix $[\kappa]_s$ given by

$$[\kappa]_s = \frac{EI}{l}\begin{bmatrix} 4 & 2 & -6/l & 6/l \\ 2 & 4 & -6/l & 6/l \\ -6/l & -6/l & 12/l^2 & -12/l^2 \\ 6/l & 6/l & -12/l^2 & 12/l^2 \end{bmatrix}$$

We can, therefore, write

$$\{P\}_s = [\kappa]_s\{\delta\}_s \qquad (6.48)$$

Substituting Equation (6.48) into Equation (6.46), we obtain

$$U_s = \tfrac{1}{2}\{\delta\}_s^T[\kappa]_s\{\delta\}_s \qquad (6.49)$$

---

† The same considerations apply to the complete structure.

The forces P_i in Figure 6.24 are dependent measurements with two equations of constraint existing among them (the sum of forces in the horizontal direction is zero and the sum of moments is zero). We can, therefore, select two independent forces and find their corresponding

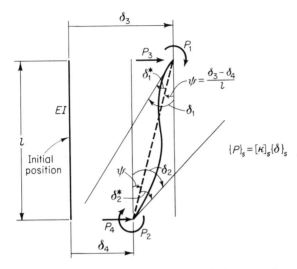

Figure 6.24. Element s with forces P_i and displacements δ_i at four coordinates for which $[\kappa]_s$ exists and $[\alpha]_s$ does not exist.

displacements. If we define coordinates to identify only these independent forces and displacements, then there exists a flexibility matrix as well as a stiffness matrix; hence, the strain energy can be expressed in terms of either matrix. We demonstrate this for the element of Figure 6.24.

The deformed configuration of element s in Figure 6.24, which represents its strain energy, can be obtained in two steps. In the first step, the element is transported as a rigid body from the initial position to the position shown by the dashed line. In the second step the beam is simply supported at the ends of the dashed line, Figure 6.25(a), and rotations δ_1^* and δ_2^* relative to the dashed line are produced at the ends by forces P_1 and P_2. The first step involves no strain energy, and in the second step only forces P_1 and P_2 do work because no displacements take place at coordinates 3 and 4 in this step. Consequently the strain energy, U_s, in the member of Figure 6.24 is equal to the work done by forces P_1 and P_2 on displacements δ_1^* and δ_2^*, respectively, or

$$U_s = \tfrac{1}{2}(P_1\delta_1^* + P_2\delta_2^*) \tag{6.50}$$

If we define only the coordinates 1 and 2 in Figure 6.24 with the beam simply supported at the ends of the dashed line as shown in Figure 6.25(a), then the flexibility matrix and stiffness matrix are given by

$$[\alpha]_s = \frac{l}{6EI}\begin{bmatrix} 2 & -1 \\ -1 & 2 \end{bmatrix}, \quad [\kappa]_s = \frac{EI}{l}\begin{bmatrix} 4 & 2 \\ 2 & 4 \end{bmatrix}$$

so that

$$\{P\}_s = [\kappa]_s\{\delta^*\}_s \quad \text{and} \quad \{\delta^*\}_s = [\alpha]_s\{P\}_s$$

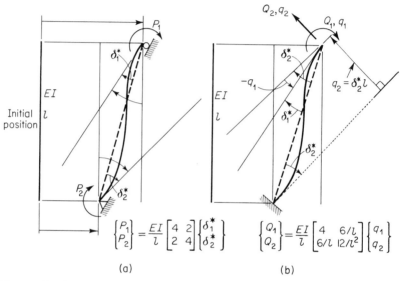

$$\begin{Bmatrix} P_1 \\ P_2 \end{Bmatrix} = \frac{EI}{l}\begin{bmatrix} 4 & 2 \\ 2 & 4 \end{bmatrix}\begin{Bmatrix} \delta_1^* \\ \delta_2^* \end{Bmatrix} \qquad \begin{Bmatrix} Q_1 \\ Q_2 \end{Bmatrix} = \frac{EI}{l}\begin{bmatrix} 4 & 6/l \\ 6/l & 12/l^2 \end{bmatrix}\begin{Bmatrix} q_1 \\ q_2 \end{Bmatrix}$$

(a)   (b)

Figure 6.25. Element s with only 2 coordinates defined for which both $[\alpha]_s$ and $[\kappa]_s$ exist.

in which $\{P\}_s = \begin{Bmatrix} P_1 \\ P_2 \end{Bmatrix}_s$ and $\{\delta^*\}_s = \begin{Bmatrix} \delta_1^* \\ \delta_2^* \end{Bmatrix}_s$

From Equation (6.50), we have

$$U_s = \tfrac{1}{2}\{\delta^*\}_s^T\{P\}_s$$

or

$$U_s = \tfrac{1}{2}\{P\}_s^T\{\delta^*\}_s$$

Substituting for $\{P\}_s$ in the first expression for U_s and for $\{\delta^*\}_s$ in the second, yields

$$U_s = \tfrac{1}{2}\{\delta^*\}_s^T[\kappa]_s\{\delta^*\}_s$$

and   (6.51)

$$U_s = \tfrac{1}{2}\{P\}_s^T[\alpha]_s\{P\}_s$$

It is instructive to show that the right-hand sides of Equations (6.50) and (6.46) or (6.47) are identical. Equations (6.46) or (6.47) can be written as

$$U_s = \tfrac{1}{2}(P_1\delta_1 + P_2\delta_2 + P_3\delta_3 + P_4\delta_4)$$

Substituting the conditions of equilibrium

$$P_3 = -P_4$$

and

$$P_3 l = -(P_1 + P_2)$$

and using the notation (see Figure 6.24)

$$\psi = \frac{\delta_3 - \delta_4}{l}$$

we obtain Equation 6.50

$$U_s = \tfrac{1}{2}(P_1\delta_1 + P_2\delta_2 - P_1\psi - P_2\psi)$$
$$= \tfrac{1}{2}(P_1\delta_1^* + P_2\delta_2^*)$$

in which (see Figure 6.24)

$$\delta_1^* = \delta_1 - \psi$$

and

$$\delta_2^* = \delta_2 - \psi$$

An alternate procedure for expressing the strain energy, U_s, of the element in Figure 6.24 is shown in Figure 6.25(b). First the beam is transported as a rigid body to the position shown by the dotted line in Figure 6.25(b), then it is constrained at the lower end as a cantilever beam and forces Q_1 and Q_2 are applied to produce the final displaced configuration. The strain energy, U_s, is equal to the work done by the forces Q_i on the corresponding displacements q_i,

$$U_s = \tfrac{1}{2}(Q_1 q_1 + Q_2 q_2)$$

in which q_1 is the rotation of the tangent to the tip of the cantilever with respect to the dotted line in Figure 6.25b, and q_2 is the displacement of the tip. The right-hand sides of this expression and Equation (6.50) are, of course, identical. To verify this we compare Figures 6.24 and 6.25(b) and note that

$$Q_1 = P_1, \qquad Q_2 = -P_3$$
$$q_1 = \delta_1^* - \delta_2^*, \qquad q_2 = \delta_2^* l$$

Substituting these relations and the condition of equilibrium,

$$P_3 l = -(P_1 + P_2)$$

into the last expression for U_s, we obtain Equation 6.50

$$U_s = \tfrac{1}{2}(Q_1 q_1 + Q_2 q_2)$$
$$= \tfrac{1}{2}(P_1 \delta_1^* + P_2 \delta_2^*)$$

Suggested Exercise: Do problem 12.

Strain Energy in a System in Terms of the Strain Energy in Elements

Consider the structure of Figure 6.26 with forces F_i producing displacements, u_i, at the coordinates as shown. The total strain energy, U, in the structure can be expressed in terms of the forces F_i and displacements u_i, Equations (6.11–6.14), or in terms of the strain energy in the individual elements,

$$U = \sum_{s=1}^{m} U_s$$

in which U_s is the strain energy in element s, and m is the total number of elements ($m = 6$ in Figure 6.26).

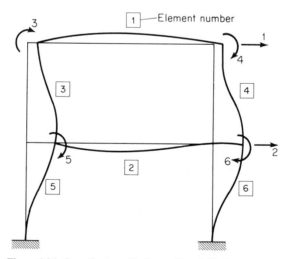

Figure 6.26. Coordinates with forces F_i and displacements u_i.

Figure 6.27 shows the internal forces and corresponding displacements at the ends of each element in the structure of Figure 6.26. Four coordinates are defined for each element to identify forces and displacements as in Figure 6.24. The forces F_i are not shown for clarity. The strain energy U_s in any element s can be expressed in terms of Equation (6.49). The total strain energy in the structure can then be written as

$$U = \sum_{s=1}^{m} U_s = \frac{1}{2} \sum_{s=1}^{m} \{\delta\}_s^T [\kappa]_s \{\delta\}_s \tag{6.52}$$

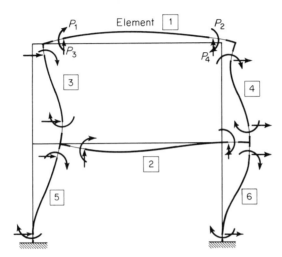

Figure 6.27. Internal forces P_i at ends of elements in the structure of Fig. 6.26.

This equation can also be written in the form

$$U = \frac{1}{2}\{\delta\}^T[\kappa]\{\delta\} \tag{6.53}$$

in which

$$\{\delta\} = \begin{Bmatrix} \{\delta\}_1 \\ \hline \{\delta\}_2 \\ \hline \vdots \\ \hline \{\delta\}_s \\ \hline \vdots \\ \hline \{\delta\}_m \end{Bmatrix} \quad \text{and} \quad [\kappa] = \begin{bmatrix} [\kappa]_1 & & & & \\ & [\kappa]_2 & & & \\ & & \ddots & & \\ & \text{elements} & & [\kappa]_s & \\ & \text{not shown} & & & \ddots \\ & \text{are zero} & & & & [\kappa]_m \end{bmatrix} \tag{6.54}$$

Matrix $[\kappa]$ contains the stiffness matrices of the unassembled elements and is referred to as the *uncoupled stiffness matrix* of the elements.

Verify the equality of the right-hand sides of Equations (6.52) and (6.53) by carrying out the multiplication on the right-hand side of Equation (6.53) using the partitioned matrices given in the identities (6.54).

If instead of four coordinates per element in Figure 6.27, we define only two coordinates for which the forces are independent (say P_1 and P_2), then the total strain energy U in the structure of Figure 6.26 or 6.27 can also be written in terms of the flexibility matrices $[\alpha]_s$ of the elements,† that is,

$$U = \tfrac{1}{2} \sum_{s=1}^{m} \{P\}_s^T [\alpha]_s \{P\}_s \tag{6.55}$$

or

$$U = \tfrac{1}{2} \{P\}^T [\alpha] \{P\} \tag{6.56}$$

in which

$$\{P\} = \begin{Bmatrix} \{P\}_1 \\ \hline \{P\}_2 \\ \hline \vdots \\ \hline \{P\}_s \\ \hline \vdots \\ \hline \{P\}_m \end{Bmatrix} \quad \text{and} \quad [\alpha] = \begin{bmatrix} [\alpha]_1 & & & & & \\ & [\alpha]_2 & & & & \\ & & \ddots & & & \\ & & & [\alpha]_s & & \\ \text{elements} & & & & \ddots & \\ \text{not shown} & & & & & \\ \text{are zero} & & & & & \\ & & & & & [\alpha]_m \end{bmatrix} \tag{6.57}$$

Verify the equality of the right-hand sides of Equations (6.55) and (6.56).

Equations (6.52) and (6.55) or (6.53) and (6.56) are the key equations in developing the stiffness and flexibility methods of structural analysis which are discussed in Chapters 8 and 9. We therefore suggest the reader make an effort to master these equations and their physical significance.

Stiffness and Flexibility Matrix for Beamlike Element in Space

So far we considered an element of a plane frame and derived expressions for its strain energy. The same expressions apply to an element of a space frame except that the stiffness and flexibility matrices are different. For instance, the stiffness matrix for a beamlike element which is part of a space frame, such as that of Figure 6.28, is defined for 12 coordinates as shown in Figure 6.29 and is given by the 12×12 matrix of Equation (6.58). In constructing this matrix shear energy was not included, and the shape factor was taken as unity when the torsional stiffness was computed;

---

† The same strain energy in terms of the stiffness matrices $[\kappa]_s$ (with two coordinates only per element, identifying P_1 and P_2 in Figure 6.27) can be obtained by summing the first of Eqs. 6.51 for all elements s. Note that in this equation $[\kappa]_s$ is of order 2×2 and δ_i^* are rotations relative to a straight line connecting the ends of an element [See Figure 6.25(a)].

$$
\begin{Bmatrix} P_1 \\ P_2 \\ P_3 \\ P_4 \\ P_5 \\ P_6 \\ P_7 \\ P_8 \\ P_9 \\ P_{10} \\ P_{11} \\ P_{12} \end{Bmatrix}_s =
\begin{bmatrix}
[\kappa]_s^{(1)} & & & \text{Submatrices not} \\
 & & & \text{shown are null} \\
 & & & \text{matrices} \\
 & [\kappa]_s^{(2)} & & \\
 & & [\kappa]_s^{(3)} & \\
 & & & [\kappa]_s^{(4)}
\end{bmatrix}
\begin{Bmatrix} \delta_1 \\ \delta_2 \\ \delta_3 \\ \delta_4 \\ \delta_5 \\ \delta_6 \\ \delta_7 \\ \delta_8 \\ \delta_9 \\ \delta_{10} \\ \delta_{11} \\ \delta_{12} \end{Bmatrix}_s \qquad (6.58)
$$

$$
[\kappa]_s^{(1)} = \frac{EI_y}{l}
\begin{bmatrix}
4 & 2 & -6/l & 6/l \\
2 & 4 & -6/l & 6/l \\
-6/l & -6/l & 12/l^2 & -12/l^2 \\
6/l & 6/l & -12/l^2 & 12/l^2
\end{bmatrix}
\qquad
[\kappa]_s^{(2)} = \frac{EA}{l}
\begin{bmatrix}
1 & 1 \\
1 & 1
\end{bmatrix}
$$

$$
[\kappa]_s^{(3)} = \frac{EI_x}{l}
\begin{bmatrix}
4 & 2 & -6/l & 6/l \\
2 & 4 & -6/l & 6/l \\
-6/l & -6/l & 12/l^2 & -12/l^2 \\
6/l & 6/l & -12/l^2 & 12/l^2
\end{bmatrix}
\qquad
[\kappa]_s^{(4)} = \frac{GI_z}{l}
\begin{bmatrix}
1 & 1 \\
1 & 1
\end{bmatrix}
$$

hence $\kappa_{11,11} = GI_z/l$. The member is considered to be uniform in section with I_x and I_y designating, respectively, the moments of inertia with respect to the x and y axis as shown in Figure 6.29, and I_z designating the polar moment of inertia with respect to the z axis. A is the area of the cross section. Submatrices $[\kappa]_s^{(1)}$ and $[\kappa]_s^{(3)}$ are identical in form. This can be seen from Figure 6.29(b) where the member and its coordinates are projected on the xy, xz, and yz planes.

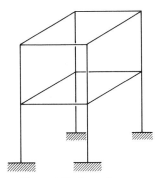

Figure 6.28. Space frame.

The flexibility matrix for an element in the space frame of Figure 6.28 is of order 6. The six coordinates may be any six for which the corresponding force measurements are independent. One such set of coordinates can be

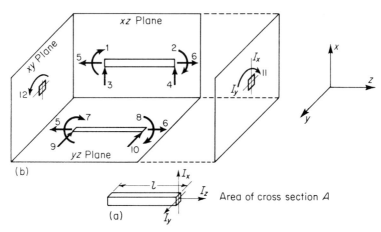

Figure 6.29. (a) Moments of inertia of element. (b) 12 coordinates for beam-like element in space shown by projecting beam and coordinates on *xy*, *xz* and *yz* planes.

obtained by fixing in space one end of the member and defining six co-ordinates at the other end. Another set is obtained by simply supporting the beam in space and defining coordinates at each end as suggested in problem 14.

Suggested Exercises: Do problems 13 and 14.

PROBLEMS

Problem 1: Use Betti's law to show that

$$F_1^0 = \frac{Q_1}{l^2} b(2a - b)$$

in the figure shown.

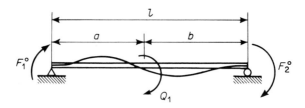

Problem 2: Using the coordinates in Figure 6.10 and the corresponding stiffness matrix, find the displacements u_1 and u_2 for the following loading systems.

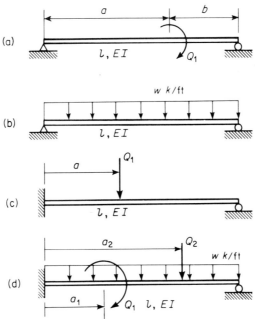

Problem 3: Generate the 2 × 2 stiffness matrix for the structure of Figure (a) using the coordinates as shown. Use this matrix to compute u_1 and u_2 for the loads shown in Figure (b). Find the bending moment and shear at the fixed end of the beam and the force in the spring.

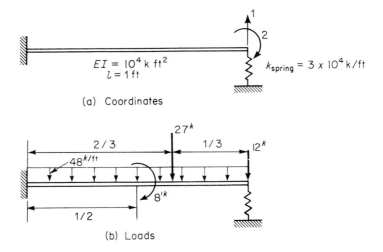

Suggested procedure for solution

1. Generate $[k]$
2. Compute $\{F\}^0$
3. Apply Equation (6.44) to compute u_1 and u_2
4. Compute spring force which is equal to $k_{spring}u_1$
5. Use a free body diagram of the beam to compute the shear and bending moment at the fixed end of the beam.

Problem 4: Derive the expression of Equation (6.40).

Problem 5: Compute the fixed coordinate forces F_1^0 and F_2^0 for the beam of Figure 6.12(b) if forces Q_i are replaced by a distributed force with intensity $p(x) = (x/l)b$ per unit length. b is a constant and x is measured from the left end of the beam.

Problem 6: Derive the expression $\phi(x)$ for the displaced configuration of the beam in Figure 6.19.

Problem 7: Let the forces Q_i and distances a_i in Figure 6.15(b) have the following values:

$$Q_1 = 10 \qquad Q_2 = 12 \qquad Q_3 = 6 \qquad Q_4 = 4 \qquad Q_5 = 8$$

$$a_1 = 0.4 \qquad a_2 = 0.7 \qquad a_3 = 0.5 \qquad a_4 = 0.9 \qquad a_5 = 0.5$$

Compute the fixed coordinate quantities F_i^0 of Figure 6.17(b). You may use Betti's law, or apply to each member directly the formula for the fixed end moments due to concentrated loads [Equations (6.41) and (6.42)] and sum corresponding values at the coordinates.

Problem 8: Generate the stiffness matrix for the four coordinates shown and use it to formulate the equations from which the displacement u_i at the coordinates can be computed.

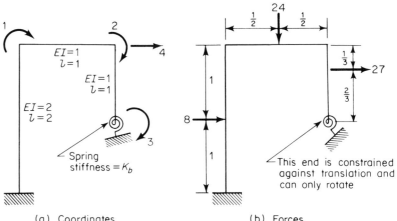

(a) Coordinates (b) Forces

FIGURE FOR PROBLEM 9

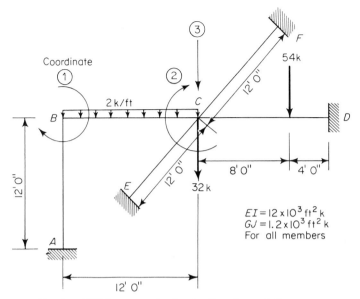

$EI = 12 \times 10^3 \, ft^2 \, k$
$GJ = 1.2 \times 10^3 \, ft^2 \, k$
For all members

Member *ECF* is perpendicular to the plane of the paper
all other members are in the plane of the paper

FIGURE FOR PROBLEM 10

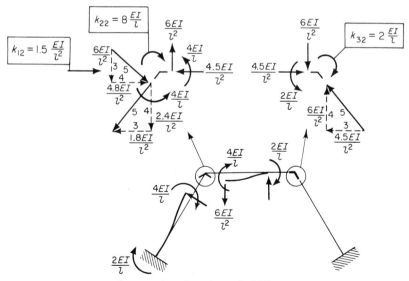

Computations for column 2 of $[k]$.

Problem 9: Construct the stiffness matrix for the three coordinates shown†
and compute the displacements at the coordinates, the shear and bending
moments at ends A and D, and the torsion at ends E and F. For the torsional
stiffness of member EC or CF at coordinate 2 take GJ/l (l is the length of
member EC or CF).

Problem 10: Generate the stiffness matrix $[k]$ for the structure in Figure
6.20(a) and compare your results with Equation (6.45). The free body diagrams
and computations to generate column 2 of $[k]$ are shown on page 175.

Problem 11: Generate the stiffness matrix for the three coordinates shown and
compute the displacements u_i at the coordinates due to a single force $Q_1 = 30^k$
applied as shown.

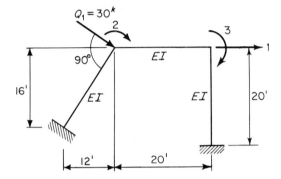

Problem 12: Construct the stiffness and flexibility matrices for the beam in
Figure 6.25(b) with coordinates 1 and 2 identifying the measurements q_1, q_2,
and Q_1, Q_2. Write the strain energy, U_s, in the beam in terms of these matrices.

Problem 13: Generate the 6×6 flexibility matrix for a cantilever beam in
space (include axial displacement and torsion).

Problem 14: Generate the 6×6 flexibility matrix for the beam in Figure 6.29
constrained so that the displacements at coordinates 3, 4, 5, 9, 10 and 12 are
always zero.

_____

† Figure for Problem 9 is on page 175.

CHAPTER 7

TRANSFORMATION OF INFORMATION IN STRUCTURES

7.1. INTRODUCTION

The analysis of structures is a process in which information given in one form is transformed into another form. For example, in Equation (3.12) the flexibility matrix of a structure is used to transform forces into corresponding displacements at the coordinates, and in Equation (3.13) the stiffness matrix of a structure is used to transform displacements to corresponding forces.

A common objective in the analysis of structures is finding the internal forces which result from the application of external forces. If, for simplicity and clarity, we consider the internal forces to be the forces P_i, defined at the element coordinates, and the external forces—the forces F_i at the coordinates of the system (total structure)—then the objective is fulfilled when we find the matrix $[b]$ in the equation

$$\{P\} = [b]\{F\} \tag{7.1}$$

where $\{P\}$ consists of all the element forces [see Equation (6.57)]. Equation (7.1) transforms system forces F_i to element forces P_i and constitutes an *equation of equilibrium* in which internal forces P_i are in equilibrium with the external forces F_i. $[b]$ can be easily generated for a statically determinate structure because the internal forces can be computed from conditions of equilibrium alone. Generating matrix $[b]$ in connection with statically indeterminate structures is discussed in Section 8.2.

To compute the element displacements δ_i which correspond to system displacements u_i, we find the matrix $[\beta]$ in the equation

$$\{\delta\} = [\beta]\{u\} \tag{7.2}$$

where $\{\delta\}$ consists of all the element displacements [see Equation (6.54)]. Equation (7.2) transforms system displacements u_i to element displacements δ_i and constitutes an *equation of displacement compatibility* which insures the connectivity of the structure. It is easy to generate $[\beta]$ for statically determinate as well as indeterminate structures.

An intermediate objective in analysis of structures is the construction of the stiffness and flexibility matrices of a system. This objective is also accomplished by a transformation of information; that is, information given in the form of element stiffness and flexibility matrices is transformed to corresponding system stiffness and flexibility matrices respectively. To a certain extent this was demonstrated in Section 3.7.

Much of the rest of this book is devoted to developing systematic and efficient methods of transforming information of the type discussed here. Two fundamental methods of structural analysis, the *flexibility* (*force*) and *stiffness* (*displacement*), are treated in Chapters 8 and 9, respectively. In this chapter we develop important transformations used in these methods. In the first section we discuss determinacy, indeterminacy and instability which must be examined before an analysis is undertaken.

7.2. DETERMINATE AND INDETERMINATE STRUCTURES

The procedures employed to determine the degree of indeterminacy of trusses and frames are treated by a number of writers[12, 15, 19]. Here we introduce a procedure, which we shall call the *tree construction*, to establish the degree of indeterminacy as well as the degree of instability of frames.

Consider the tree-shaped structure of Figure 7.1 in the plane of the paper. The base of the tree is constrained as a cantilever; that is, it cannot translate in the horizontal or vertical direction and it cannot rotate. Now, as long as the tree is "open" (that is, all the branches of the tree are open and no closed rings are formed by any of them), then, for any externally applied loads, we can compute the corresponding internal forces (shear, axial force, and bending moment) at any section of the tree and its branches from three equations of equilibrium which must be satisfied in the plane of the paper. Knowing all the internal forces, we can compute the displacements at any point on the tree (see Section 3.8). An open tree structure (such as that of Figure 7.1) is a *statically determinate structure*.

When a structure, such as the plane frame of Figure 7.2, is not an "open tree," we reduce it to an open tree by the following procedure: First we

Figure 7.1. "The Tree."

select a single base for the tree and remove the constraints at all other boundaries of the structure. In Figure 7.2 we select the left support as the single base, and therefore, three constraints are removed from the base of the right-hand column. Next we open all closed rings by removing three constraints at a section of each ring. In Figure 7.2, we do this by cutting the right-hand column of the ring, thus relaxing the three constraints which

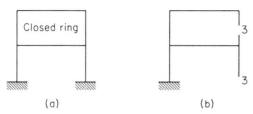

Figure 7.2. (a) Frame. (b) Frame reduced to an open tree.

force the two sections at the cut to move together in the vertical and horizontal directions, and to maintain continuity of slope by rotating an equal amount in the plane of the paper. The frame of Figure 7.2(a) is shown reduced to an open tree in Figure 7.2(b), with the numbers indicating the number of constraints removed in the process. The total number of constraints removed in the process of reducing a structure to an open tree corresponds to the degree of indeterminacy (or redundancy) of the structure. Therefore, the structure of Figure 7.2 is redundant to the sixth degree.

A second example is shown in Figure 7.3. Here again we select the left-hand column as the tree base and therefore, we must add a constraint to prevent its rotation. Added constraints are indicated by negative numbers, as indicated by the -1 in Figure 7.3(b). On the right-hand column, we remove two constraints which inhibit the displacements in the horizontal and vertical direction. The net number of constraints removed is $2 - 1 = 1$ and therefore, the degree of redundancy is 1.

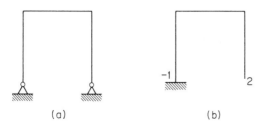

Figure 7.3. (a) Frame. (b) Frame reduced to open tree.

In the third example, Figure 7.4, we first add a rotation constraint to the base of the left-hand column and then remove two constraints at the base of the right-hand column and two at pin connection 1 (no rotation constraint at pin 1). At this point the right-hand portion can rotate about pin connection 2. This creates a condition of local instability (a mechanism) which must be avoided in a stable structure. Therefore, we add a rotation constraint at pin connection 2. The net number of constraints removed is $4 - 2 = 2$; hence the degree of redundancy of the structure in Figure 7.4(a) is 2.

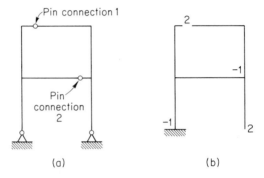

(a)   (b)

Figure 7.4. (a) Frame. (b) Frame reduced to open tree.

We summarize the foregoing procedure as follows:

1. Reduce the structure to an open tree (a cantilever structure with no unstable branches) and count the number of constraints removed and added.
2. The structure is statically indeterminate, determinate or unstable according to the following conditions (NCR stands for Number of Constraints Removed; and NCA for Number of Constraints Added).

    NCR > NCA   Indeterminate

    NCR = NCA   Determinate

    NCR < NCA   Unstable

3. The degree of indeterminacy of an indeterminate structure is given by

    degree of indeterminacy = NCR − NCA

    (NCR > NCA)

4. The degree of instability is defined as

$$\text{degree of instability} = \text{NCA} - \text{NCR}$$

$$(\text{NCA} > \text{NCR})$$

The degree of instability indicates the number of constraints that must be added to a structure in order to make it stable in a statically determinate fashion. For example, the structure of Figure 7.5 is unstable to the second degree because NCA − NCR = 2. The addition of two constraints will yield a statically determinate stable structure.

In applying the *tree construction* procedure to establish the degree of indeterminacy or stability of a structure, we must be careful not to overlook conditions of local instability which the procedure will fail to detect. For example, in Figure 7.6 NCR > NCA, but there is a definite condition of local instability (mechanism) at the second story of the frame which cannot be prevented by the first story although it is highly indeterminate.

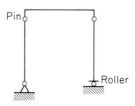

Figure 7.5.

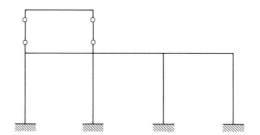

Figure 7.6. Local instability although NCR > NCA

The discussion in this section applies also to space frames. The open tree in space will have a base with six constraints, and to open a closed ring will require the removal of six constraints: three translations and three rotations.

Suggested Exercises: Do problems 1, 2, 3 and 4.

7.3. TRANSFORMATION OF SYSTEM FORCES TO ELEMENT FORCES

Let us show now how the forces F_i at the coordinates of a structural system are transformed to forces P_i at the coordinates of the elements in the structure. This requires that we generate matrix $[b]$ of Equation (7.1) for the structure. As an example we consider the frame of Figure 7.7. The system and element coordinates are shown in Figures 7.7(a) and 7.7(b), respectively. One way to generate matrix $[b]$ in the equation

$$\{P\} = [b]\{F\}$$

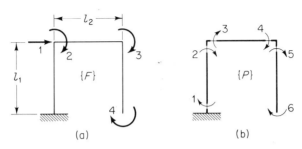

Figure 7.7. (a) System coordinates. (b) Element coordinates.

is to apply arbitrary forces† $F_i(i = 1, 2, 3, 4)$ and use the conditions of equilibrium to find the corresponding internal element forces $P_i(i = 1, 2, \ldots, 6)$‡. An alternate approach which will generate any column j of matrix $[b]$ is as follows: Apply a unit force @ system coordinate j only† and compute the corresponding element forces $P_i(i = 1, 2, \ldots, 6)$ from equilibrium.‡ The computed column $\{P\}$ is then the jth column of matrix $[b]$, as can be verified from Equation (7.1). Let us apply this procedure to generate the first column of $[b]$ in the structure of Figure 7.7. Applying in Figure 7.7(a), $F_1 = 1$ and $F_i = 0$ for all $i \neq 1$, we compute the internal forces P_i from equilibrium

$$P_1 = -l_1 \qquad P_i = 0 \qquad \text{for all } i \neq 1$$

hence the first column of $[b]$ is

$$\begin{Bmatrix} -l_1 \\ 0 \\ 0 \\ 0 \\ 0 \\ 0 \end{Bmatrix}$$

---

† Note that this can be done only when the forces F_i are independent; hence $[b]$ exists only when the F_i are independent.

‡ This can be done for a statically determinate structure only. Constructing $[b]$ in connection with statically indeterminate structures is treated in Section 8.2.

Applying next a unit force @ 2 only in Figure 7.7(a) and computing the corresponding $P_i(i = 1, 2, \ldots, 6)$ we have

$$\begin{Bmatrix} -1 \\ 1 \\ 0 \\ 0 \\ 0 \\ 0 \end{Bmatrix}$$

which is the second column of $[b]$. Proceeding in the same manner with unit forces at system coordinates 3 and 4, we finally obtain

$$[b] = \begin{bmatrix} -l_1 & -1 & -1 & -1 \\ 0 & 1 & 1 & 1 \\ 0 & 0 & -1 & -1 \\ 0 & 0 & 1 & 1 \\ 0 & 0 & 0 & -1 \\ 0 & 0 & 0 & 1 \end{bmatrix}$$

Suggested Exercises: Do problems 5, 6 and 7.

7.4. TRANSFORMATION OF ELEMENT FLEXIBILITY MATRICES TO SYSTEM FLEXIBILITY MATRIX

Using matrix $[b]$ which transforms system forces $\{F\}$ to element forces $\{P\}$, we can synthesize the flexibility matrix of a system from the flexibility matrices of its elements. Let us do this for the structure of Figure 7.7(a).

Consider any deformed configuration assumed by the structure of Figure 7.7(a) under the action of forces $F_i(i = 1, 2, 3, 4)$. The total strain energy U in the structure is equal to the work done by forces F_i on displacements u_i at the coordinates and can be written in terms of the flexibility matrix $[a]$ of the system as [see Equation (6.14)]

$$U = \tfrac{1}{2}\{F\}^T[a]\{F\} \tag{7.3}$$

This same strain energy can also be expressed as the sum of the strain energies, U_s, in the elements in Figure 7.7(b) [see Equations (6.55, 6.56)]:

$$U = \tfrac{1}{2}\{P\}^T[\alpha]\{P\} \tag{7.4}$$

Substituting

$$\{P\} = [b]\{F\}$$

and

$$\{P\}^T = \{F\}^T[b]^T$$

into Equation (7.4) and comparing Equations (7.3) and (7.4), we have

$$\{F\}^T[a]\{F\} = \{F\}^T[b]^T[\alpha][b]\{F\}$$

Since the F_i are independent (otherwise $[a]$ does not exist) and both $[a]$ and the matrix product $[b]^T[\alpha][b]$ (which we designate, for convenience, as $[\bar{a}]$) are symmetrical matrices, we can use the last equation to show that $[a]$ and $[\bar{a}]$ are identical matrices. If we set, in the last equation, any force $F_k = 1$ with all other forces $F_i = 0$ for $i \neq k$, then

$$a_{kk} = \bar{a}_{kk} \qquad \text{for all } k$$

that is, the elements on the principal diagonal of $[a]$ and $[\bar{a}]$ are identical. If we now set any two forces $F_k = 1$ and $F_l = 1$ ($k \neq l$), with all other forces $F_i = 0$ for $i \neq k$ and $i \neq l$, then

$$a_{kk} + 2a_{kl} + a_{ll} = \bar{a}_{kk} + 2\bar{a}_{kl} + \bar{a}_{ll}$$

Since $a_{kk} = \bar{a}_{kk}$ and $a_{ll} = \bar{a}_{ll}$, we conclude that

$$a_{kl} = \bar{a}_{kl}$$

Therefore,

$$[a] = [\bar{a}]$$

or

$$[a] = [b]^T[\alpha][b] \tag{7.5}$$

Hence the system flexibility matrix $[a]$ is synthesized from the element flexibility matrices $[\alpha]_s$ which are recorded as submatrices in $[\alpha]$, as shown in Equation (6.57). We note again that the proof which led to Eq. (7.5) depended both on the symmetry of matrices $[a]$ and $[\bar{a}]$ and on the independence of forces F_i. Verify that $[\bar{a}]$ is symmetrical.

For the structure of Figure 7.7,

$$[\alpha] = \begin{bmatrix} \dfrac{l_1}{6EI_1}\begin{bmatrix} 2 & -1 \\ -1 & 2 \end{bmatrix} & & \\[2em] & \dfrac{l_2}{6EI_2}\begin{bmatrix} 2 & -1 \\ -1 & 2 \end{bmatrix} & \\[2em] & & \dfrac{l_1}{6EI_1}\begin{bmatrix} 2 & -1 \\ -1 & 2 \end{bmatrix} \end{bmatrix}$$

Or setting, for simplicity, $EI_1 = EI_2 = l_1 = l_2 = 1$

$$[\alpha] = \tfrac{1}{6} \begin{bmatrix} \begin{bmatrix} 2 & -1 \\ -1 & 2 \end{bmatrix} & & \\ & \begin{bmatrix} 2 & -1 \\ -1 & 2 \end{bmatrix} & \\ & & \begin{bmatrix} 2 & -1 \\ -1 & 2 \end{bmatrix} \end{bmatrix}$$

Using $[b]$ from the last section (with $l = 1$) and $[\alpha]$ above in Equation (7.5) gives

$$[a] = \tfrac{1}{6} \begin{bmatrix} 2 & 3 & 3 & 3 \\ 3 & 6 & 6 & 6 \\ 3 & 6 & 12 & 12 \\ 3 & 6 & 12 & 18 \end{bmatrix}$$

The first three rows and columns of this matrix agree with the result obtained from Example 4, Section 3.5.

Equation (7.5) can also be derived from virtual work. Considering a virtual displacement with components $\{u\}$ at the system coordinates [Figure 7.7(a)] and corresponding (compatible) internal element displacements $\{\delta\}$ [Figure 7.7(b)], then from Equation (3.21), we write

$$\{F\}^T\{u\} = \{P\}^T\{\delta\}$$

Substituting from

$$\{u\} = [a]\{F\}$$
$$\{\delta\} = [\alpha]\{P\}$$

and

$$\{P\} = [b]\{F\}$$

leads to Equation (7.5).

Equation (7.5) can be written in a more convenient form for computer applications† as

$$[a] = \sum_{s=1}^{m} [b]_s^T [\alpha]_s [b]_s \qquad (7.6)$$

---

† The form of Equation (7.6) avoids recording the zeros which appear in $[\alpha]$ of Equation (7.5).

in which $[b]_s$ represents the submatrix of $[b]$ corresponding to element s and $[\alpha]_s$ is its flexibility matrix. That is,

$$
\left\{
\begin{array}{c}
\{P\}_1 \\
\hline
\{P\}_2 \\
\hline
\vdots \\
\vdots \\
\hline
\{P\}_s \\
\hline
\vdots \\
\hline
\{P\}_m
\end{array}
\right\}
=
\left[
\begin{array}{c}
[b]_1 \\
\hline
[b]_2 \\
\hline
\vdots \\
\vdots \\
\hline
[b]_s \\
\hline
\vdots \\
\hline
[b]_m
\end{array}
\right]
\{F\}
\tag{7.7}
$$

or

$$\{P\}_s = [b]_s\{F\} \qquad s = 1, 2, \ldots, m$$

and

$$\{\delta\}_s = [\alpha]_s\{P\}_s \qquad s = 1, 2, \ldots, m$$

Equation (7.7) is identical to Equation (7.1), except that it is written in a partitioned form which identifies the internal forces, $\{P\}_s$, and the corresponding $[b]_s$ of each element.

Suggested Exercises: Do problems 8, 9, 10 and 11.

7.5. TRANSFORMATION OF SYSTEM DISPLACEMENTS TO ELEMENT DISPLACEMENTS

Let us follow the procedure of Section 7.3 to transform displacements u_i at the coordinates of a system to displacements δ_i at the coordinates of its elements. This requires that we generate matrix $[\beta]$ of Equation (7.2). To

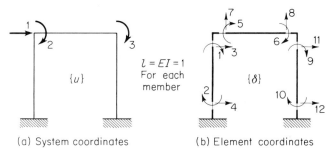

$l = EI = 1$
For each
member

(a) System coordinates   (b) Element coordinates

Figure 7.8.

do so, we consider the coordinates in the frame of Figure 7.8. One way to generate matrix $[\beta]$ in the equation

$$\{\delta\} = [\beta]\{u\}$$

is to apply arbitrary displacements† u_i $(i = 1, 2, 3)$ and use the conditions of compatibility (which insure the connection of the elements to form the system) to find the corresponding element displacements $\delta_i (i = 1, 2, \ldots, 12)$. An alternate approach which will generate any column j of $[\beta]$ is as follows: Apply a unit displacement at system coordinate j only† and find the corresponding compatible element displacements δ_i. These displacements δ_i form column j of $[\beta]$ as can be verified from Equation (7.2). Following this procedure for the structure of Figure 7.8 we obtain

$$[\beta] = \begin{bmatrix} 0 & 1 & 0 \\ 0 & 0 & 0 \\ 1 & 0 & 0 \\ 0 & 0 & 0 \\ \hline 0 & 1 & 0 \\ 0 & 0 & 1 \\ 0 & 0 & 0 \\ 0 & 0 & 0 \\ \hline 0 & 0 & 1 \\ 0 & 0 & 0 \\ 1 & 0 & 0 \\ 0 & 0 & 0 \end{bmatrix}$$

Note that if we delete, for instance, element coordinates 11 and 12 in Figure 7.8(b), then remaining coordinates 9 and 10 represent rotations relative to a straight line connecting the ends of the member (see Figure 6.25). In the new $[\beta]$ matrix rows 11 and 12 will be deleted and rows 9 and 10 will become

$$-\frac{1}{l} \quad 0 \quad 1$$

$$-\frac{1}{l} \quad 0 \quad 0$$

Suggested Exercises: Do problems 12 and 13.

---

† Note that this can be done only when the u_i are independent; hence $[\beta]$ exists only when the u_i are independent.

7.6. TRANSFORMATION OF ELEMENT STIFFNESS MATRICES TO SYSTEM STIFFNESS MATRIX

Following a development similar to that of Section 7.4, we can use $[\beta]$ to synthesize the stiffness matrix $[k]$ of a system from the stiffness matrices of its elements.

Consider the frame of Figure 7.8 under the action of forces F_i at the system coordinates. The strain energy U in the system can be written in terms of the stiffness matrix $[k]$ of the system as [see Equation (6.13)]

$$U = \tfrac{1}{2}\{u\}^T[k]\{u\} \tag{7.8}$$

This same strain energy can also be written as the sum of the strain energies U_s in the elements of the system [see Equations (6.52) and (6.53)]

$$U = \tfrac{1}{2}\{\delta\}^T[\kappa]\{\delta\} \tag{7.9}$$

Substituting

$$\{\delta\} = [\beta]\{u\}$$

and

$$\{\delta\}^T = \{u\}^T[\beta]^T$$

into Equation (7.9) and comparing Equations (7.8) and (7.9), we have

$$\{u\}^T[k]\{u\} = \{u\}^T[\beta]^T[\kappa][\beta]\{u\}$$

Since the u_i are independent (otherwise $[k]$ does not exist) and both $[k]$ and the matrix product $[\beta]^T[\kappa][\beta]$ are symmetrical matrices, then, following the reasoning which led to Equation (7.5), we conclude that

$$[k] = [\beta]^T[\kappa][\beta] \tag{7.10}$$

Hence, the system stiffness matrix $[k]$ is synthesized from the element stiffness matrices $[\kappa]_s$ which are recorded as submatrices in $[\kappa]$, as shown in Equation (6.54).

For the structure of Figure 7.8,

$$[\kappa] = \begin{bmatrix} [\kappa]_1 & & \\ & [\kappa]_2 & \\ & & [\kappa]_3 \end{bmatrix}$$

in which [see Equation (6.58)]

$$[\kappa]_s = \frac{EI}{l} \begin{bmatrix} 4 & 2 & -6/l & 6/l \\ 2 & 4 & -6/l & 6/l \\ -6/l & -6/l & 12/l^2 & -12/l^2 \\ 6/l & 6/l & -12/l^2 & 12/l^2 \end{bmatrix}$$

$$s = 1, 2, 3$$

Using $[\beta]$ computed in the last section and $[\kappa]$ in the foregoing in Equation (7.10) gives

$$[k] = \frac{EI}{l} \begin{bmatrix} 24/l^2 & -6/l & -6/l \\ -6/l & 8 & 2 \\ -6/l & 2 & 8 \end{bmatrix}$$

which agrees with the results generated in Example 2, Section 3.5.

Equation (7.10) can also be derived from virtual work. Considering virtual forces F_i at the system coordinates and corresponding internal element forces P_i which are in equilibrium with forces F_i, then from Equation (3.19), we write

$$\{u\}^T\{F\} = \{\delta\}^T\{P\}$$

Substituting from

$$\{F\} = [k]\{u\}$$
$$\{P\} = [\kappa]\{\delta\}$$

and

$$\{\delta\} = [\beta]\{u\}$$

leads to Equation (7.10).

As was done in the case of Equation (7.5), Equation (7.10) can also be written in a more convenient form for computer applications as

$$[k] = \sum_{s=1}^{m} [\beta]_s^T [\kappa]_s [\beta]_s \tag{7.11}$$

in which $[\beta]_s$ is the submatrix of $[\beta]$ corresponding to element s, and $[\kappa]_s$ is its stiffness matrix. That is,

$$\left\{ \begin{array}{c} \{\delta\}_1 \\ \hline \{\delta\}_2 \\ \hline \vdots \\ \hline \{\delta\}_s \\ \hline \vdots \\ \hline \{\delta\}_m \end{array} \right\} = \left[\begin{array}{c} [\beta]_1 \\ \hline [\beta]_2 \\ \hline \vdots \\ \hline [\beta]_s \\ \hline \vdots \\ \hline [\beta]_m \end{array} \right] \{u\} \tag{7.12}$$

or

$$\{\delta\}_s = [\beta]_s \{u\} \qquad s = 1, 2, \ldots, m$$

and

$$\{P\}_s = [\kappa]_s \{\delta\}_s \qquad s = 1, 2, \ldots, m$$

Equation (7.12) is identical to Equation (7.2), except that it is written in a partitioned form which identifies the internal displacements, $\{\delta\}_s$, and corresponding $[\beta]_s$ of each element.

Suggested Exercises: Do problems 14, 15 and 16.

7.7. TRANSFORMATIONS OF FORCES AND DISPLACEMENTS IN GENERAL

The transformations of forces and displacements in Sections 7.3 and 7.5 represent transformation of measurements from a set of dependent coordinates to a set of generalized coordinates. The complete set of element coordinates are dependent; the system coordinates are generalized (independent). For instance, in Figure 7.7(b), P_2 and P_3 are dependent and can be related by the equation of moment equilibrium around the upper left joint. The externally applied forces in Figure 7.7(a) are independent. Similarly in Figure 7.8(b), the displacements δ_i are dependent, and can be related by applying the conditions of compatibility. For instance, $\delta_1 = \delta_5$ is compatible with the 90° angle maintained at the upper left corner of the frame. The system displacements u_i in Figure 7.8(a), however, are independent.

When the same element coordinates are used to identify both the forces P_i and displacements δ_i, then there exists a relationship between the transformations of forces and displacements. To show the nature of this relationship, we consider the frame of Figure 7.8. From the conditions of compatibility, we have

$$\{\delta\} = [\beta]\{u\} \tag{7.13}$$

in which $[\beta]$ is given in Section 7.5. When the frame of Figure 7.8(a) is acted upon by forces F_i which produce displacements, u_i, the total energy stored in the structure is

$$\tfrac{1}{2}\{u\}^T\{F\}$$

The same strain energy can be obtained by summing the strain energy in the elements, which can be written as

$$\tfrac{1}{2}\sum_{s=1}^{m}\{\delta\}_s^T\{P\}_s = \tfrac{1}{2}\{\delta\}^T\{P\}$$

in which

$$\{\delta\} = \left\{ \begin{array}{c} \{\delta\}_1 \\ \hline \{\delta\}_2 \\ \hline \vdots \\ \hline \{\delta\}_m \end{array} \right\} \quad \text{and} \quad \{P\} = \left\{ \begin{array}{c} \{P\}_1 \\ \hline \{P\}_2 \\ \hline \vdots \\ \hline \{P\}_m \end{array} \right\}$$

Equating the two expressions for energy, we have

$$\{u\}^T\{F\} = \{\delta\}^T\{P\} \tag{7.14}$$

Substituting $\{u\}^T[\beta]^T$ for $\{\delta\}^T$ from Equation (7.13) gives

$$\{u\}^T\{F\} = \{u\}^T[\beta]^T\{P\}$$

or

$$\{u\}^T(\{F\} - [\beta]^T\{P\}) = 0$$

Since the displacements $\{u\}$ are independent and can be assigned arbitrary values (otherwise $[\beta]$ cannot be constructed), it follows that the last equation can be satisfied only if the expression in the parentheses vanishes, or

$$\{F\} = [\beta]^T\{P\} \tag{7.15}$$

Forces $\{F\}$ are the *generalized forces* in the u coordinates.

Equation (7.15) can also be generated from virtual work by considering the structure to undergo a virtual displacement with components u_i and corresponding compatible internal displacements δ_i. Equating the virtual work $\{u\}^T\{F\}$ done by forces F_i to the virtual work $\{\delta\}^T\{P\}$ done by the internal forces P_i, we have Equation (7.14) which then leads to Equation (7.15).

Equations (7.13) and (7.15) show the relationship that exists between the transformation of displacements and forces from coordinates δ (which identify δ_i and P_i) to generalized coordinates u (which identify u_i and F_i).

If instead of starting in Equation (7.13) with a transformation of displacements, we start with a transformation of forces

$$\{P\} = [b]\{F\}$$

in which forces F_i are independent (otherwise $[b]$ cannot be constructed), then from Equation (7.14) the corresponding transformation of displacements is given by

$$\{u\} = [b]^T\{\delta\}$$

We leave it as an exercise to the reader to verify this result.

To verify Equation (7.15) for the structure of Figure 7.8, we write the equations of equilibrium for shear across the top portion of the frame and for moment about the two joints (identified by system coordinates 2 and 3) as follows:

$$F_1 = P_3 + P_{11} \qquad\qquad F_2 = P_1 + P_5 \qquad\qquad F_3 = P_6 + P_9$$

In matrix form, we write

$$\begin{Bmatrix} F_1 \\ F_2 \\ F_3 \end{Bmatrix} = \begin{bmatrix} 0 & 0 & 1 & 0 & 0 & 0 & 0 & 0 & 0 & 0 & 1 & 0 \\ 1 & 0 & 0 & 0 & 1 & 0 & 0 & 0 & 0 & 0 & 0 & 0 \\ 0 & 0 & 0 & 0 & 0 & 1 & 0 & 0 & 1 & 0 & 0 & 0 \end{bmatrix} \begin{Bmatrix} \{P\}_1 \\ \{P\}_2 \\ \{P\}_3 \end{Bmatrix}$$

$$\underset{[\beta]^T}{\uparrow}$$

The foregoing 3×12 matrix is the transpose of matrix $[\beta]$ derived in Section 7.5 from the conditions of compatibility.

Transforming System Coordinates to Generalized Coordinates

The preceding discussion applies to transformation of coordinates in general. Suppose that we are given a set of coordinates u, which may be constrained,† in which measurements u_i and F_i are identified. If we now define a new set of generalized coordinates q, which identify generalized displacement q_i and generalized forces Q_i, for which the transformation of displacements is given by

$$\{u\} = [C]\{q\} \tag{7.16}$$

then the transformation of forces is given by

$$\{Q\} = [C]^T\{F\} \tag{7.17}$$

Equation (7.17) is derived from the same considerations which led to Equation (7.15). Considering a virtual displacement with components $\{q\}$, the same displacements can be expressed by vector $\{u\}$. The virtual work done by the real forces $\{F\}$ on the displacements $\{u\}$ is $\{u\}^T\{F\}$. The same

---

† We shall refer to coordinates as *constrained* when either the forces or displacements which are identified by the coordinates are constrained.

virtual work expressed in the q coordinates is

$$\{q\}^T\{Q\}$$

Equating the last two expressions and substituting for $\{u\}^T$ from Equation (7.16), we are led to

$$\{q\}^T(\{Q\} - [C]^T\{F\}) = 0$$

Since the q_i are independent,† the expression in the parentheses must vanish, or

$$\{Q\} = [C]^T\{F\}$$

Computing Generalized Forces by Betti's Law

It is interesting to generate Equation (7.17) using Betti's law. Consider the structure of Figure 7.9 in which the members are infinitely stiff axially,

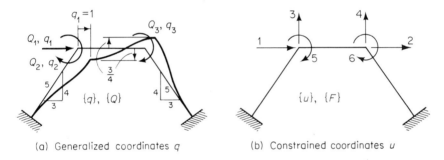

(a) Generalized coordinates q (b) Constrained coordinates u

Figure 7.9.

so that the coordinates in Figure 7.9(b) are constrained and those of Figure 7.9(a) are generalized. The transformation of displacements is given by

$$\{u\} = \begin{bmatrix} 1 & 0 & 0 \\ 1 & 0 & 0 \\ -\frac{3}{4} & 0 & 0 \\ \frac{3}{4} & 0 & 0 \\ 0 & 1 & 0 \\ 0 & 0 & 1 \end{bmatrix} \{q\}$$

To generate the generalized forces $\{Q\}$ which correspond to forces $\{F\}$,

---

† Otherwise matrix $[C]$ of Equation (7.16) cannot be constructed.

we apply at the generalized coordinates of Figure 7.9(a) forces Q_i which produce the same displacement at these coordinates as those produced there by forces F_i in Figure 7.9(b). Now, applying Betti's law, we multiply the forces Q_i in Figure 7.9(a) by the corresponding displacements in Figure 7.9(b) which are actually the generalized displacements q_i. The forces F_i of Figure 7.9(b) are multiplied by corresponding displacements u_i in Figure 7.9(a) which are given by $[C]\{q\}$. Hence,

$$\{q\}^T\{Q\} = \{q\}^T[C]^T\{F\}$$

which leads to Equation (7.17).

It can also be seen from Betti's law, as discussed in Section 6.9, that *the magnitude of any generalized force Q_j is equal to the virtual work done by forces F_i on the displacements which correspond to virtual displacement $q_j = 1$ with all other $q_i = 0(i \neq j)$.* For instance, in Figure 7.9

$$Q_1 = F_1 + F_2 - \tfrac{3}{4}F_3 + \tfrac{3}{4}F_4$$

Suggested Exercise: Do problem 17.

Transformation to Symmetrical and Antisymmetrical Generalized Coordinates

When a structure is symmetrical it is convenient to define a set of generalized coordinates which identify symmetrical and antisymmetrical displacement configurations. This reduces the computations in the analysis of such structures (see Section 9.7). The generalized forces corresponding to such coordinates are computed from Equation (7.17). Let us illustrate this by an example.

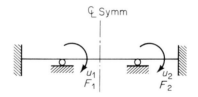

(a) Coordinates u

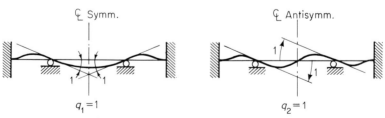

(b) Generalized coordinates q with a symmetrical and antisymmetrical shape

Figure 7.10.

The structure of Figure 7.10 is symmetrical and has coordinates u as shown in Figure 7.10(a). Figure 7.10(b) shows the coordinates q_1 and q_2 which define a symmetrical and antisymmetrical shape respectively. To derive any column j of matrix $[C]$ in Equation (7.16), we set $q_j = 1$ with all other $q_i = 0$ for $i \neq j$ and find the corresponding displacements u_i. Applying this procedure to Figure 7.10, we obtain

$$[C]$$
$$\downarrow$$
$$\begin{Bmatrix} u_1 \\ u_2 \end{Bmatrix} = \begin{bmatrix} 1 & 1 \\ -1 & 1 \end{bmatrix} \begin{Bmatrix} q_1 \\ q_2 \end{Bmatrix}$$

The generalized forces are computed from Equation (7.17)

$$[C]^T$$
$$\downarrow$$
$$\begin{Bmatrix} Q_1 \\ Q_2 \end{Bmatrix} = \begin{bmatrix} 1 & -1 \\ 1 & 1 \end{bmatrix} \begin{Bmatrix} F_1 \\ F_2 \end{Bmatrix}$$

To interpret this last equation we premultiply each side by the inverse of $[C]^T$

$$\begin{Bmatrix} F_1 \\ F_2 \end{Bmatrix} = \tfrac{1}{2} \begin{bmatrix} 1 & 1 \\ -1 & 1 \end{bmatrix} \begin{Bmatrix} Q_1 \\ Q_2 \end{Bmatrix}$$

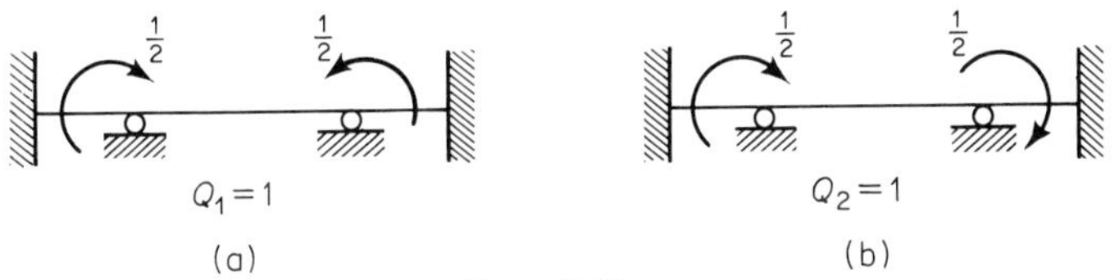

Figure 7.11.

Setting now $Q_1 = 1$ and $Q_2 = 0$, we find $F_1 = \tfrac{1}{2}$ and $F_2 = -\tfrac{1}{2}$, and setting $Q_2 = 1$, $Q_1 = 0$, we have $F_1 = \tfrac{1}{2}$, $F_2 = \tfrac{1}{2}$. Using these results on the structure of Figure 7.10, we obtain Figure 7.11 which shows the forces on the structure associated with generalized forces Q_1 and Q_2. Hence Q_1 and Q_2 represent, respectively, a symmetrical and antisymmetrical force group. When Q_1 and Q_2 are different from 1, we multiply the moments of $\tfrac{1}{2}$ shown in Figure 7.11 (a, b) by the values of Q_1 and Q_2, respectively. The values of Q_1 and Q_2 are computed from Equation (7.17). In the present example of Figure 7.10,

$$Q_1 = F_1 - F_2$$

and

$$Q_2 = F_1 + F_2$$

For example, when $F_1 = 30^{'k}$ and $F_2 = 18^{'k}$, then the generalized forces Q_1 and Q_2 of Figure 7.11 appear as shown in Figure 7.12.

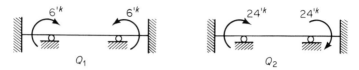

Figure 7.12.

Suggested Exercise: Do problem 18.

7.8. TRANSFORMATION OF STIFFNESS AND FLEXIBILITY MATRIX IN GENERAL

The transformations expressed by Equations (7.5) and (7.10) can be shown to apply to coordinate transformations in general.

Transformation of Flexibility Matrix

Consider a system with coordinates u in which a flexibility matrix $[a]_u$ exists (forces F_i are independent). If we apply a coordinates transformation from coordinates u to generalized coordinates q, in which the generalized forces Q_i are related to forces F_i in the u coordinates by

$$\{F\} = [b]\{Q\} \tag{7.18}$$

then the flexibility matrix $[a]_q$ of the system in the q coordinates is given by

$$[a]_q = [b]^T[a]_u[b] \tag{7.19}$$

This result can be generated as follows: Write in each coordinate system the expression for virtual work associated with a virtual displacement $\{q\}$ and equate the two expressions

$$\{F\}^T\{u\} = \{Q\}^T\{q\} \tag{7.20}$$

Substituting

$$\{u\} = [a]_u\{F\}$$

and

$$\{q\} = [a]_q\{Q\}$$

we have

$$\{F\}^T[a]_u\{F\} = \{Q\}^T[a]_q\{Q\}$$

Substituting for $\{F\}$ and $\{F\}^T$ from Equation (7.18), this becomes

$$\{Q\}^T[b]^T[a]_u[b]\{Q\} = \{Q\}^T[a]_q\{Q\}$$

which leads to Equation (7.19).

Transformation of Stiffness Matrix

Consider a system with coordinates u in which a stiffness matrix $[k]_u$ exists (u_i are independent). If we apply a coordinates transformation to generalized coordinates q, in which the generalized displacements q_i are related to displacements u_i by

$$\{u\} = [\beta]\{q\} \tag{7.21}$$

then the stiffness matrix, $[k]_q$, of the system in the q coordinates is given by

$$[k]_q = [\beta]^T[k]_u[\beta] \tag{7.22}$$

To generate this result we write Equation (7.20) in the form

$$\{u\}^T\{F\} = \{q\}^T\{Q\}$$

and substitute

$$\{F\} = [k]_u\{u\}$$

$$\{Q\} = [k]_q\{q\}$$

to give

$$\{u\}^T[k]_u\{u\} = \{q\}^T[k]_q\{q\}$$

Substituting for $\{u\}$ and $\{u\}^T$ from Equation (7.21), the last equation becomes

$$\{q\}^T[\beta]^T[k]_u[\beta]\{q\} = \{q\}^T[k]_q\{q\}$$

which leads to Equation (7.22).

Suggested Exercise: Do problem 19.

7.9. NORMAL COORDINATES AND ORTHOGONAL TRANSFORMATIONS

Normal Coordinates

A transformation of coordinates which takes place frequently in dynamics of structures is the transformation of generalized coordinates q to *normal coordinates* η which are also generalized. The transformation has the form

$$\{q\} = [\Phi]\{\eta\} \tag{7.23}$$

in which $\{q\}$ and $\{\eta\}$ are the displacement vectors in coordinates q and η, respectively, and $[\Phi]$ is a square matrix.

Comparing Equation (7.23) with Equation (7.21), we can express the stiffness matrix $[k]_\eta$ associated with normal coordinates η in terms of $[k]_q$ through the use of Equation (7.22)

$$[k]_\eta = [\Phi]^T[k]_q[\Phi] \tag{7.24}$$

This transformation has the property of reducing $[k]_q$ to a diagonal matrix $[k]_\eta$. It is this property which makes the normal coordinates and the transformation of Equation (7.23) very useful in structural dynamics[39]. Each normal coordinate η_i represents the amplitude of a normal mode shape of vibration of the system. The normal mode shapes are represented by the columns of matrix $[\Phi]$ in Equation (7.23). The normal modes have a special property of orthogonality with respect to the mass matrix and stiffness matrix of the vibrating system[39]. It is this property which makes it possible to reduce $[k]_q$ to a diagonal matrix $[k]_\eta$ in Equation (7.24)[28, 32, 39].

Orthogonal Transformations

A transformation of coordinates

$$\{u\} = [\gamma]\{q\} \tag{7.25}$$

from one set of generalized coordinates u to another set q is *orthogonal* when the transformation matrix $[\gamma]$ has an inverse which is equal to its transpose, that is,

$$[\gamma]^T = [\gamma]^{-1}$$

or   (7.26)

$$[\gamma]^T[\gamma] = [I]$$

An orthogonal transformation is equivalent to a rotation about the origin of the coordinate system. In two-dimensional space we performed such a transformation in Section 5.9, by rotating the coordinates u_1, u_2 to new coordinates q_1, q_2. The transformation was given by

$$\{u\} = \begin{bmatrix} \cos\theta & \sin\theta \\ -\sin\theta & \cos\theta \end{bmatrix}\{q\} \tag{7.27}$$
$$\underset{[\gamma]}{\uparrow}$$

in which $[\gamma]$ has the properties of Equation (7.26) and therefore constitutes an orthogonal transformation.

Using matrix $[\gamma]$ to transform the forces, we write

$$\{Q\} = [\gamma]^T\{F\}$$

or

$$\{F\} = [\gamma]\{Q\} \tag{7.28}$$

because

$$([\gamma]^T)^{-1} = [\gamma]$$

(For an orthogonal transformation $[\gamma]^T = [\gamma]^{-1}$ and $([\gamma]^{-1})^{-1} = [\gamma]$.)

Comparing Equation (7.28) with Equation (7.18) we can express the flexibility matrix $[a]_q$ from Equation (7.19) as

$$[a]_q = [\gamma]^T[a]_u[\gamma] \tag{7.29}$$

Through the solution of an eigenvalue problem, $[\gamma]$ may be selected to make $[a]_q$ in Equation (7.29) a diagonal matrix. In Section 5.9, this was accomplished by finding the following $[\gamma]$:

$$[\gamma] = \begin{bmatrix} 0.882 & 0.472 \\ -0.472 & 0.882 \end{bmatrix}$$

Using this value of $[\gamma]$, together with

$$[a]_u = \begin{bmatrix} \frac{8}{3} & 3 \\ 3 & \frac{20}{3} \end{bmatrix}$$

for the structure of Figure 5.1, in Equation (7.29) yields the following diagonal matrix $[a]_q$ in the q coordinates

$$[a]_q = \begin{bmatrix} 1.06 & 0 \\ 0 & 8.28 \end{bmatrix}$$

This agrees with the results in Section 5.9.

Suggested Exercises: Do problems 20, 21, 22 and 23.

PROBLEMS

Problem 1: Show a number of possibilities of transforming the structure of Figure 7.5 into a statically determinate stable structure by adding two constraints. Show by sketches the welding or bolting that may be required to add the two constraints you select. (Consider the members to be WF sections.)

Problem 2: Add sufficient constraints to the second story in Figure 7.6 to make it indeterminate to the second degree, then establish the degree of indeterminacy of the complete stable frame.

Problem 3: Establish the degree of indeterminacy or instability of the plane structures shown.

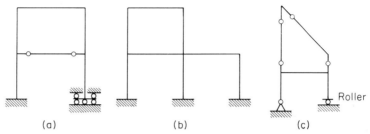

(a)   (b)   (c)

Roller

Problem 4: Determine the degree of indeterminacy or instability of the space frames shown.

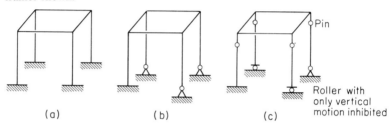

Pin

(a)   (b)   (c)

Roller with only vertical motion inhibited

Problem 5: Explain why Equations (7.1) and (7.2) express respectively the conditions of equilibrium and compatibility for a structure.

Problems 6, 7: Generate the [b] matrix for the following structures:

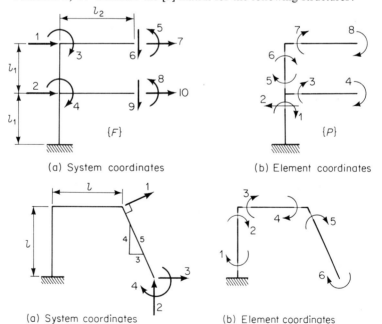

(a) System coordinates

(b) Element coordinates

(a) System coordinates

(b) Element coordinates

Problems 8, 9: Use Equation (7.6) to generate the system flexibility matrix for the structures of Problems 6 and 7. For simplicity set $l_1 = l_2 = EI = 1$ in the structure of Problem 6. In the structure of Problem 7, $EI = 1$ for each member.

Problem 10: How can you use Equation (7.5) or (7.6) to generate $[a]$ for the structure of Figure 6.26. Why is this difficult?

Problem 11: Verify that the right-hand sides of Equations (7.5) and (7.6) are identical.

Problem 12: Construct the matrix $[\beta]$ for the structure with system and element coordinates as shown.

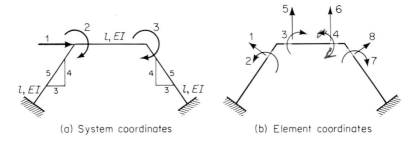

(a) System coordinates   (b) Element coordinates

Problem 13: Construct the matrix $[\beta]$ for the structure with coordinates as shown.

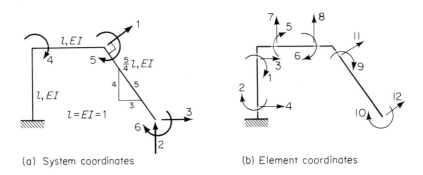

(a) System coordinates   (b) Element coordinates

Problems 14, 15: Use Equation (7.10) to generate $[k]$ for the structures of Problems 12 and 13.

Problem 16: Verify that the right-hand sides of Equations (7.10) and (7.11) are identical.

Problem 17: Show that Equations (6.41) and (6.42) represent an application of Equation (7.17) in which the forces F_i^0 are the generalized forces, and forces Q_i of Equations (6.41) and (6.42) correspond to forces F_i of Equation (7.17).

Problem 18: Find a transformation matrix $[C]$ which will transform displacements u of Figure 7.8(a) into generalized displacements with symmetrical and antisymmetrical configurations.

Problem 19: Let $[a]_u$ be the 2×2 flexibility matrix in coordinates u for the structure of Figure 7.10(a). Transform $[a]_u$ to flexibility matrix $[a]_q$ in coordinates q of Figure 7.10(b). Show that $[a]_q$ is a diagonal matrix. Repeat the foregoing for the corresponding stiffness matrices $[k]_u$ and $[k]_q$. Prove that $[a]_q[k]_q = [I]$.

Problem 20: In Figure 7.8(b) delete element coordinates 3, 4, 7, 8, 11, 12 and change coordinate numbers 5, 6, 9, 10 to 3, 4, 5, 6 respectively. Construct matrix $[\beta]$. Note that the new coordinates of each element represent relative rotations with respect to a straight line connecting its ends. [See Figure 6.25(a) and Equation 6.51.]

Problem 21: Use matrix $[\beta]$ of problem 20 to generate the stiffness matrix for the structure in Figure 7.8(a).

Problem 22: In problem 12 delete element coordinates 5, 6 and change coordinate numbers 7 and 8 to 5 and 6 respectively. Construct matrix $[\beta]$.

Problem 23: Use matrix $[\beta]$ of problem 22 to generate the stiffness matrix for the structure in Figure (a) of problem 12.

CHAPTER 8

THE FLEXIBILITY METHOD

8.1. FLEXIBILITY METHOD APPLIED TO STATICALLY DETERMINATE STRUCTURES

At this point we have all the necessary preparation to introduce the *flexibility method* in the matrix analysis of structures. This method is also known as the *force method*[20] because it begins with a superposition of forces as expressed by Equation (7.1) or as the *compatibility method* because it leads to equations of displacement compatibility. (See Section 2.10.) The basic steps in the flexibility method as applied to a statically determinate structure are as follows:

1. Select system coordinates where external forces are applied† and where displacement measurements are desired, and for which a flexibility matrix exists.
2. Select elements so that system coordinates occur only at their ends.‡ Select element coordinates for which the flexibility matrices exist so we can write $\{\delta\}_s = [\alpha]_s \{P\}_s$ for each element, and $\{\delta\} = [\alpha]\{P\}$ for all elements before they are connected to form the system. Use a sufficient number of element coordinates to account for all significant energy forms (see Sections 3.8 and 6.2).
3. Using the conditions of equilibrium transform the system forces in Step 1 to element forces in Step 2, [Equation (7.1)]

$$\{P\} = [b]\{F\}$$

---

† For distributed forces see end of Section 8.2.

‡ Otherwise Equations (6.46) and (6.47) (Section 6.10) are not valid and the development which led to Equations (7.5) and (7.6) does not hold true.

4. Synthesize the system flexibility matrix from the element flexibility matrices, [Equations (7.5) or (7.6)]

$$[a] = [b]^T[\alpha][b] = \sum_{s=1}^{m} [b]_s^T[\alpha]_s[b]_s$$

Given a set of forces F_i at the system coordinates compute the following:
5. Compute the corresponding displacements u_i

$$\{u\} = [a]\{F\}$$

6. Compute the internal forces P_i

$$\{P\} = [b]\{F\}$$

7. Compute the internal displacements δ_i

$$\{\delta\} = [\alpha]\{P\} = [\alpha][b]\{F\}$$

For a statically determinate structure the flexibility method can be used to compute displacements u_i at any desired number of coordinates.

As an example, let us outline the procedure for computing the displacements u_i due to forces F_i in Figure 8.1(a). We define system coordinates where forces are applied and where displacements are desired, as shown in Figure 8.1(a). Next we select elements so that system coordinates occur only at their ends, and choose element coordinates for which flexibility matrices exist. Elements and element coordinates are shown in Figure 8.1(b). Proceeding now with Steps 3, 4, and 5 we can obtain our desired objective.

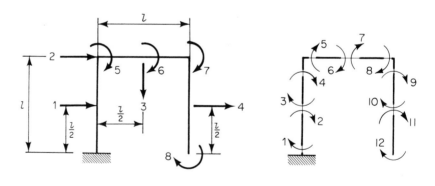

(a) System coordinates   (b) Element coordinates

Figure 8.1.

8.2. FLEXIBILITY METHOD APPLIED TO STATICALLY INDETERMINATE STRUCTURES

For statically determinate structures, matrix $[b]$ of Equation (7.1) is generated from the conditions of equilibrium. For statically indeterminate structures, the conditions of equilibrium are not sufficient to generate $[b]$ (see Problem 7.10). This is not surprising because once $[b]$ is generated we can compute the internal forces $\{P\}$ corresponding to externally applied forces $\{F\}$ and this is one of the main objectives in the solution of statically indeterminate structures.

We shall now show how the flexibility method is used to analyze statically indeterminate structures. Let us develop the steps in connection with the structure shown in Figure 8.2(a) in which only forces F_1^* and F_2^* are applied. First let us state our objectives:

1. Generate the 2×2 flexibility matrix $[a]^*$ which will transform any forces F_1^*, F_2^* to corresponding displacements u_1^*, u_2^* in the structure of Figure 8.2(a).
2. Generate a matrix which will transform the applied forces $\{F\}^*$ to corresponding internal forces $\{P\}$.

To fulfill these objectives we proceed in steps similar to those listed in Section 8.1 for a statically determinate structure, except that the choice of system coordinates involves also the reduction of the statically in-determinate structure to a stable statically determinate one. The steps are as follows:

1. (a) Reduce the indeterminate structure to a stable statically deter-minate structure by removing a number of constraints equal to the degree of indeterminacy. The reduced statically determinate structure is called the *primary structure*. The structure of Figure 8.2(a) is reduced to a primary structure in Figure 8.2(b).
   (b) Define system coordinates at the points of interest on the struc-ture (where external forces are applied† or where displacement measurements are desired), and extend the system coordinates to include coordinates at the constraints which are removed in the primary structure. The coordinates at the constraints identify internal forces which are referred to as *redundant forces*. The system coordinates are shown in Figure 8.2(b). For convenience we designate by $\{F\}^*$ and $\{u\}^*$ the external forces and correspond-ing displacements, and by $\{F\}^0$ and $\{u\}^0$ the redundant forces and corresponding displacements.

2. Select elements so that external system coordinates which are marked by an asterisk (not at the redundants) occur only at their ends‡ [see Figure 8.2(c)]. Select element coordinates for which flexibility

---

† For distributed forces see end of Section 8.2.

‡ Otherwise Equations (6.46) and (6.47) (Section 6.10) are not valid and the development which led to Equations (7.5) and (7.6) does not hold true.

matrices exist. Number the coordinates in sequence proceeding from element to element [see Figure 8.2(c)], so we can write $\{\delta\}_s = [\alpha]_s \{P\}_s$ for each element and

$$\{\delta\} = [\alpha]\{P\} \tag{8.1}$$

for all elements before they are connected to form the system. Use a sufficient number of element coordinates to account for all significant energy forms (see Sections 3.8 and 6.2).

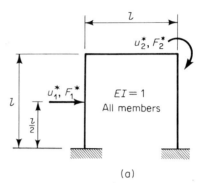

(a)

Applied forces $\{F\}^*$ on statically indeterminate structure

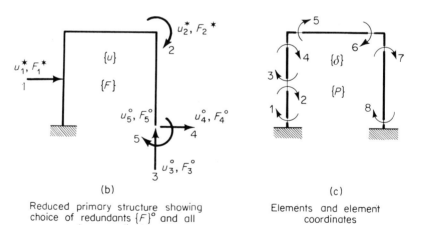

(b)

Reduced primary structure showing choice of redundants $\{F\}^\circ$ and all system coordinates

(c)

Elements and element coordinates

Figure 8.2.

3. Using the procedure of Section 7.3 construct the transformation matrix $[b]$ which transforms the system forces $\{F\}$ in the primary

structure to element forces $\{P\}$, that is,

$$\{P\} = [b]\{F\} \tag{8.2}$$

To distinguish between forces $\{F\}^*$ and $\{F\}^0$ it is convenient to partition the last equation and write it in the form

$$\{P\} = \left[[b]^* \;\middle|\; [b]^0\right]\left\{\frac{\{F\}^*}{\{F\}^0}\right\} \tag{8.3}$$

or

$$\{P\} = [b]^*\{F\}^* + [b]^0\{F\}^0 \tag{8.4}$$

Note that at this point the redundant forces $\{F\}^0$ are not known and hence $\{P\}$ cannot be computed. Using the coordinates of Figures 8.2(b) and 8.2(c) which identify $\{F\}$ and $\{P\}$, then for the structure of Figure 8.2, Equation (8.3) takes the form

$$\begin{Bmatrix} P_1 \\ P_2 \\ P_3 \\ P_4 \\ P_5 \\ P_6 \\ P_7 \\ P_8 \end{Bmatrix} = \begin{bmatrix} -\dfrac{l}{2} & -1 & l & 0 & -1 \\ 0 & 1 & -l & -\dfrac{l}{2} & 1 \\ 0 & -1 & l & \dfrac{l}{2} & -1 \\ 0 & 1 & -l & -l & 1 \\ 0 & -1 & l & l & -1 \\ 0 & 1 & 0 & -l & 1 \\ 0 & 0 & 0 & l & -1 \\ 0 & 0 & 0 & 0 & 1 \end{bmatrix} \begin{Bmatrix} F_1^* \\ F_2^* \\ \hline F_3^0 \\ F_4^0 \\ F_5^0 \end{Bmatrix} \tag{8.5}$$

$$\underset{[b]^*}{\uparrow} \qquad \underset{[b]^0}{\uparrow}$$

4. Synthesize the system flexibility matrix $[a]$ for the coordinates of the reduced primary structure using Equation (7.5) (or 7.6)

$$[a] = [b]^T[\alpha][b] \tag{8.6}$$

This equation can be written in partitioned form as follows: (in which the coordinates at the redundants(^{0}) are separated from the external system coordinates(*))

$$\begin{matrix} * \\ 0 \end{matrix}\begin{bmatrix} [a]_{11} & [a]_{12} \\ \hline [a]_{21} & [a]_{22} \end{bmatrix} = \begin{bmatrix} [b]^{*T} \\ \hline [b]^{0T} \end{bmatrix}[\alpha]\left[[b]^* \;\middle|\; [b]^0\right] \tag{8.7}$$

Using the rules of Chapter 4 for operating with partitioned matrices, we expand the right-hand side of Equation (8.7) and identify the resulting submatrices with the corresponding ones on the left-hand side of Equation (8.7). This gives the following results:

$$\left.\begin{aligned}
[a]_{11} &= [b]^{*\,T}[\alpha][b]^* \\
[a]_{12} &= [b]^{*\,T}[\alpha][b]^0 = [a]_{21}^T \\
[a]_{21} &= [b]^{0\,T}[\alpha][b]^* = [a]_{12}^T \\
[a]_{22} &= [b]^{0\,T}[\alpha][b]^0
\end{aligned}\right\} \tag{8.8}$$

5. To fulfill our first objective we write, for the reduced primary structure, the following force displacement relationship in partitioned form

$$\underset{\uparrow}{\left\{\begin{matrix}\{u\}^* \\ \hline \{u\}^0\end{matrix}\right\}} = \underset{\uparrow}{{}^*_0\begin{bmatrix}\overset{*}{[a]_{11}} & \overset{0}{[a]_{12}} \\ \hline [a]_{21} & [a]_{22}\end{bmatrix}} \underset{\uparrow}{\left\{\begin{matrix}\{F\}^* \\ \hline \{F\}^0\end{matrix}\right\}} \tag{8.9}$$
$$\{u\} [a] \{F\}$$

In this equation $\{F\}^*$ represents a vector of arbitrary forces which are applied to the system. Vector $\{F\}^0$ represents the redundant forces which are internal to the system and depend on $\{F\}^*$. The redundant forces $\{F\}^0$ must be such that the displacements $\{u\}^0$ at the redundants will be restored to their actual value in the original unreduced structure under the action of forces $\{F\}^*$. This is equivalent to saying that the values of F_i^0 must be such as to satisfy the *conditions of compatibility* where constraints were removed. These conditions of compatibility are satisfied when $\{u\}^0 = \{0\}$ [see Figures 8.2(a, b)]. From energy consideration we may say that the same energy must be stored in the system in Figures 8.2(a, b, c). This means that the same deformed configuration is obtained in each figure and, therefore, $\{u\}^0 = \{0\}$ must be satisfied when we compare Figures 8.2 (a, b).

It is now seen why we designated the forces and displacements at the redundants by a superscript zero; this will remind us that the displacements there are zero.

Substituting $\{u\}^0 = \{0\}$ in Equation (8.9), and writing it as two separate matrix equations, we have

$$\left.\begin{aligned}
\{u\}^* &= [a]_{11}\{F\}^* + [a]_{12}\{F\}^0 \\
\{0\} &= [a]_{21}\{F\}^* + [a]_{22}\{F\}^0
\end{aligned}\right\} \tag{8.10}$$

From the second equation we solve for the redundants $\{F\}^0$ in terms of the applied forces $\{F\}^*$

$$\{F\}^0 = -[a]_{22}^{-1}[a]_{21}\{F\}^* \tag{8.11}$$

Substituting this expression for $\{F\}^0$ in the first of Equations (8.10), we have

$$\{u\}^* = [a]^*\{F\}^* \tag{8.12}$$

in which

$$[a]^* = [a]_{11} - [a]_{12}[a]_{22}^{-1}[a]_{21} \tag{8.13}$$

This satisfies our first objective because all the submatrices $[a]_{ij}$ in Equation (8.13) can be computed from Equation (8.8).

6. To fulfill the second objective we substitute for $\{F\}^0$ from Equation (8.11) into Equation (8.4) and write

$$\{P\} = ([b]^* - [b]^0[a]_{22}^{-1}[a]_{21})\{F\}^* \tag{8.14}$$

7. If the displacements $\{\delta\}$ at the element coordinates are required they can also be expressed in terms of the applied forces $\{F\}^*$. Substituting for $\{P\}$ from Equation (8.14) into Equation (8.1)

$$\{\delta\} = [\alpha]([b]^* - [b]^0[a]_{22}^{-1}[a]_{21})\{F\}^* \tag{8.15}$$

To complete the solution to the example problem of Figure 8.2, we first write matrix $[\alpha]$ for the four elements shown in Figure 8.2(c).

$$[\alpha] = \frac{l}{12} \begin{bmatrix} \begin{bmatrix} 2 & -1 \\ -1 & 2 \end{bmatrix} & \text{All elements not shown are zero} \\ & \begin{bmatrix} 2 & -1 \\ -1 & 2 \end{bmatrix} \\ & & \begin{bmatrix} 4 & -2 \\ -2 & 4 \end{bmatrix} \\ & & & \begin{bmatrix} 4 & -2 \\ -2 & 4 \end{bmatrix} \end{bmatrix} \tag{8.16}$$

Next, we generate matrix $[a]$ by carrying out the multiplications of Equation (8.6), or Equation (8.7) or (8.8) which are identical to Equation

(8.6). Matrix $[b]$ is given in Equation (8.5).

$$[a] = \frac{l}{12} \begin{bmatrix} \frac{l^2}{2} & \frac{3}{2}l & -\frac{3}{2}l^2 & -\frac{l^2}{4} & \frac{3}{2}l \\[2mm] \frac{3}{2}l & 24 & -18l & -18l & 24 \\[2mm] -\frac{3}{2}l^2 & -18l & 16l^2 & 12l^2 & -18l \\[2mm] -\frac{l^2}{4} & -18l & 12l^2 & 20l^2 & -24l \\[2mm] \frac{3}{2}l & 24 & -18l & -24l & 36 \end{bmatrix} \tag{8.17}$$

with $[a]_{11} \rightarrow$, $\leftarrow [a]_{12}$, $[a]_{21} \rightarrow$, $\leftarrow [a]_{22}$ indicating the partitioning.

To simplify the arithmetic let us set $l = 1$ and proceed with the computations. Since $[a]_{22}^{-1}$ is required in both Equation (8.13) and (8.14), we perform this operation first.

$$[a]_{22}^{-1} = \frac{12}{7} \begin{bmatrix} 1 & 0 & \frac{1}{2} \\[2mm] 0 & \frac{7}{4} & \frac{7}{6} \\[2mm] \frac{1}{2} & \frac{7}{6} & \frac{11}{9} \end{bmatrix}$$

Next we evaluate the product

$$[a]_{22}^{-1}[a]_{21} = \frac{1}{7} \begin{bmatrix} -\frac{3}{4} & -6 \\[2mm] \frac{21}{16} & -\frac{7}{2} \\[2mm] \frac{19}{24} & -\frac{2}{3} \end{bmatrix}$$

Substituting this result in Equations (8.13) and (8.14) and carrying out the required matrix operations, we obtain

$$[a]^* = \frac{1}{12} \overset{[a]_{11}}{\begin{bmatrix} \frac{1}{2} & \frac{3}{2} \\[2mm] \frac{3}{2} & 24 \end{bmatrix}} - \frac{1}{84} \overset{[a]_{12}[a]_{22}^{-1}[a]_{21}}{\begin{bmatrix} \frac{127}{64} & \frac{71}{8} \\[2mm] \frac{71}{8} & 155 \end{bmatrix}}$$

$$= \frac{1}{12} \begin{bmatrix} \frac{97}{448} & \frac{13}{56} \\[2mm] \frac{13}{56} & \frac{13}{7} \end{bmatrix} \tag{8.18}$$

Chap. 8   THE FLEXIBILITY METHOD   **211**

$$\begin{Bmatrix} P_1 \\ P_2 \\ P_3 \\ P_4 \\ P_5 \\ P_6 \\ P_7 \\ P_8 \end{Bmatrix} = \left(\begin{bmatrix} -\frac{1}{2} & -1 \\ 0 & 1 \\ 0 & -1 \\ 0 & 1 \\ 0 & -1 \\ 0 & 1 \\ 0 & 0 \\ 0 & 0 \end{bmatrix} - \frac{1}{21} \begin{bmatrix} -\frac{37}{8} & -16 \\ \frac{85}{32} & \frac{85}{4} \\ -\frac{85}{32} & -\frac{85}{4} \\ \frac{11}{16} & \frac{53}{2} \\ -\frac{11}{16} & -\frac{53}{2} \\ -\frac{25}{16} & \frac{17}{2} \\ \frac{25}{16} & -\frac{17}{2} \\ \frac{19}{8} & -2 \end{bmatrix} \right) \begin{Bmatrix} F_1^* \\ F_2^* \end{Bmatrix}$$

$$= \frac{1}{21} \begin{bmatrix} -\frac{47}{8} & -5 \\ -\frac{85}{32} & -\frac{1}{4} \\ \frac{85}{32} & \frac{1}{4} \\ -\frac{11}{16} & -\frac{11}{2} \\ \frac{11}{16} & \frac{11}{2} \\ \frac{25}{16} & \frac{25}{2} \\ -\frac{25}{16} & \frac{17}{2} \\ -\frac{19}{8} & 2 \end{bmatrix} \begin{Bmatrix} F_1^* \\ F_2^* \end{Bmatrix} \tag{8.19}$$

Suggested Exercise: Do problem 12.

Structures with Distributed Forces

We note here that the flexibility method of this section can be used to analyze structures with distributed forces. The distributed forces as well as concentrated forces not at the coordinates are transformed by the method of Section 6.9 to equivalent generalized forces at the system coordinates marked by (*). System coordinates may be conveniently defined at the intersections of all elements and where displacements are desired. The final internal forces and displacements are obtained by adding the results of the fixed coordinate state (see Section 6.9) and the results computed from an analysis by the method of this section which involves forces at the coordinates only.

8.3. CHOICE OF REDUNDANTS

From Equations (8.13) and (8.14), we see that analysis of an indeterminate structure by the flexibility method requires the inversion of submatrix $[a]_{22}$

which corresponds to the redundant force vector $\{F\}^0$. Setting $\{F\}^* = \{0\}$ in Equation (8.9), we have

$$\{u\}^0 = [a]_{22}\{F\}^0 \tag{8.20}$$

This is the force-displacement relationship in the reduced primary structure when only the coordinates at the redundants are considered. Now since $[a]_{22}$ must be inverted, it becomes apparent that the choice of redundants is an important task. A poor choice may cause $[a]_{22}$ to be nearly singular and therefore make inversion very difficult. From Chapter 4 and from the discussion of ill-conditioned equations in Section 5.8, we recall that $[a]_{22}$ will be nearly singular, and Equation (8.20) will therefore be ill conditioned, when the rows or columns of $[a]_{22}$ are nearly dependent. We shall now show that this condition can often be avoided by appealing to physical considerations relating to the behavior of structures.

Consider the continuous beam of Figure 8.3 which has $n + 2$ supports, and therefore is indeterminate to the nth degree. To reduce this structure to a primary structure we must select n redundant forces and remove the corresponding constraints. We make two choices of redundants. In Figure

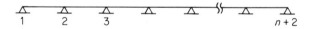

Figure 8.3. Indeterminate structure (nth degree).

8.4(a), the reactions at all n interior supports are selected as redundants. In Figure 8.4(b), the moments in the beam at the interior supports are selected as redundants. In the coordinates of Figure 8.4(b) the forces F_i^0 come in pairs (action and equal reaction), and the displacements u_i^0 are the generalized displacements on which the force pairs do work. These displacements are therefore relative displacements representing the change in angle between beam ends at each support (see Figure 8.5).

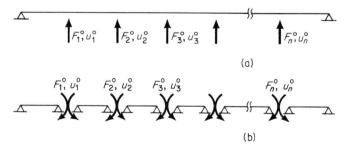

Figure 8.4. Choice of redundants.

Let us generate the flexibility matrix $[a]_{22}$ corresponding to each choice of redundants. In Figure 8.4(a) we generate the first column of $[a]_{22}$ from the elementary equation (Equation 8.20),

$$\{u\}^0 = [a]_{22}\{F\}^0$$

by applying $F_1^0 = 1$ with all other $F_i^0 = 0$ for $i \neq 1$ and measuring the displacements u_i^0. Similarly the second column of $[a]_{22}$ is generated by applying $F_2^0 = 1$ with all other $F_i^0 = 0$ for $i \neq 2$ and measuring the corresponding u_i^0. Now for a long beam with many forces F_i^0 there will be a very small difference in the displacement measurements which correspond to the first two columns of $[a]_{22}$. The same reasoning will apply to any two adjacent columns in $[a]_{22}$. This means then that in Figure 8.4(a) we expect the rows and columns of $[a]_{22}$ to be nearly equal which, of course, makes them nearly linearly dependent; hence the flexibility matrix will be nearly singular. The choice of redundants in Figure 8.4(a) is therefore a poor one.

Proceeding now in a similar manner in Figure 8.4(b) we find that the application of $F_1^0 = 1$ with all $F_i^0 = 0$ for $i \neq 1$ yields displacements u_i^0 at coordinates 1 and 2 only. When $F_2^0 = 1$ and all other $F_i^0 = 0$ for $i \neq 2$ displacements u_i^0 occur at coordinates 1, 2, and 3 only. The second column of $[a]_{22}$ is therefore different from the first because the third element is zero in the first column, and in addition the largest value of any column j of $[a]_{22}$ occurs at the jth row which is the coordinate where the unit force is applied. Similar reasoning will show that the other columns of $[a]_{22}$ for Figure 8.4(b) are also different.

To demonstrate this with actual numbers let us set $EI = l = 1$ for all spans of Figure 8.4(b) and develop matrix $[a]_{22}$. Using the equation

$$\begin{Bmatrix} \delta_1 \\ \delta_2 \end{Bmatrix} = \frac{1}{6} \begin{bmatrix} 2 & -1 \\ -1 & 2 \end{bmatrix} \begin{Bmatrix} P_1 \\ P_2 \end{Bmatrix}$$

for a simply supported beam [see Figure 3.12(a), Section 3.6], we obtain the results shown in Figure 8.5 for the first and second columns of $[a]_{22}$ in Figure 8.4(b).

The reader can easily verify that the following matrix $[a]_{22}$ will result

$$[a]_{22} = \begin{bmatrix} \frac{2}{3} & \frac{1}{6} & & & & \\ \frac{1}{6} & \frac{2}{3} & \frac{1}{6} & & & \\ & \frac{1}{6} & \frac{2}{3} & \frac{1}{6} & & \\ & & \ddots & & & \\ & & & \frac{1}{6} & \frac{2}{3} & \frac{1}{6} \\ & & & & \frac{1}{6} & \frac{2}{3} \end{bmatrix} \qquad (8.21)$$

in which each element on the principal diagonal is $\frac{2}{3}$, the elements on each side of the principal diagonal are $\frac{1}{6}$ each, and all other elements are zero. This matrix is clearly nonsingular; hence the choice of redundants in Figure 8.4(b) is a good one.

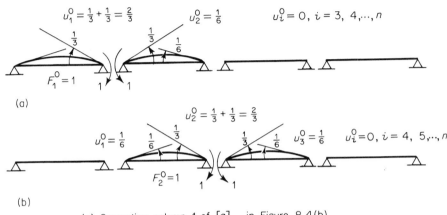

(a) Generating column 1 of $[a]_{22}$ in Figure 8.4(b)
(b) Generating column 2 of $[a]_{22}$ in Figure 8.4(b)

Figure 8.5.

A matrix of the form shown in Equation (8.21) is called a *band matrix* because of its nonzero elements being situated on a band along the direction of the principal diagonal. Band matrices can be inverted with greater ease and speed than ordinary matrices of the same order[43].

We have shown in the example of the structure of Figure 8.3 that, by reasoning on grounds of the physical interpretation of the columns of matrix $[a]_{22}$, singularity may be avoided. In general it is desirable to select redundants† so as to make the configurations associated with columns of $[a]_{22}$ different and also to minimize the strain energy which propagates the system in these configurations with the result of many zero displacements associated with each configuration. Such a choice is not always easy to make, in particular, in complex aircraft and spacecraft.

Suggested Exercises: Do problems 1–5.

---

† These redundants can also be in the form of generalized redundant force groups[20,21,71], such as the symmetrical and antisymmetrical force groups in Section 7.7.

8.4. TRANSFORMATION FROM ONE SET OF REDUNDANTS TO ANOTHER

The discussion of the last section shows that it may sometimes be desirable to change the choice of redundants. If however, some of the computations have already been performed when it is decided to change the choice of redundants, then the change can be effected without repeating all the calculations. Let us demonstrate this by considering the example of Section 8.2, Figure 8.2. Suppose that we decide to change our choice of redundants after we have completed the computations for matrix $[a]$ as given by Equation (8.17). The new choice of redundants is shown in Figure 8.6, in which the primary structure is formed by removing three continuity constraints at the center of the beam and reducing the structure to two cantilevers. Note that the forces F_3^0, F_4^0, F_5^0 come in pairs (action and

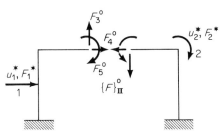

Figure 8.6.

reaction) and the corresponding displacements are the generalized displacements on which these force pairs do work. Hence u_3^0 is the relative displacement in the vertical direction of the two cut ends of the beam, u_4^0 is the relative displacement in the horizontal direction, and u_5^0 is the relative rotation. The coordinates for the external forces (marked by *) and the element coordinates remain unchanged as they are shown in Figures 8.2(a) and 8.2(c), respectively.

Let us denote the system forces corresponding to the first choice and new choice of redundants by subscripts I and II, respectively. Hence, we have for first choice

$$\{u\}_{\text{I}} = [a]_{\text{I}}\{F\}_{\text{I}} \tag{8.22}$$

where

$$\{u\}_{\text{I}} = \left\{ \begin{array}{c} \{u\}^* \\ \hline \{u\}_{\text{I}}^0 \end{array} \right\} \qquad [a]_{\text{I}} = \left[\begin{array}{c|c} [a]_{11}^{\text{I}} & [a]_{12}^{\text{I}} \\ \hline [a]_{21}^{\text{I}} & [a]_{22}^{\text{I}} \end{array} \right]$$

$$\{F\}_{\text{I}} = \left\{ \begin{array}{c} \{F\}^* \\ \hline \{F\}_{\text{I}}^0 \end{array} \right\}$$

For the new choice of redundants we have

$$\{u\}_{\text{II}} = [a]_{\text{II}}\{F\}_{\text{II}} \tag{8.23}$$

where

$$\{u\}_{\text{II}} = \left\{ \begin{array}{c} \{u\}^* \\ \hline \{u\}^0_{\text{II}} \end{array} \right\} \qquad [a]_{\text{II}} = \left[\begin{array}{c|c} [a]^{\text{II}}_{11} & [a]^{\text{II}}_{12} \\ \hline [a]^{\text{II}}_{21} & [a]^{\text{II}}_{22} \end{array} \right]$$

$$\{F\}_{\text{II}} = \left\{ \begin{array}{c} \{F\}^* \\ \hline \{F\}^0_{\text{II}} \end{array} \right\}$$

Setting $\{F\}^* = \{0\}$ in Equations (8.22) and (8.23) we obtain equations similar to Equation (8.20)

$$\{u\}^0_{\text{I}} = [a]^{\text{I}}_{22}\{F\}^0_{\text{I}} \tag{8.24}$$

$$\{u\}^0_{\text{II}} = [a]^{\text{II}}_{22}\{F\}^0_{\text{II}} \tag{8.25}$$

We shall show now how to transform $[a]^{\text{I}}_{22}$ of Equation (8.24) to $[a]^{\text{II}}_{22}$ of Equation (8.25) by the method of Section 7.8.

Using the equations of equilibrium, we can relate $\{F\}^0_{\text{I}}$ and $\{F\}^0_{\text{II}}$ and write

$$\{F\}^0_{\text{I}} = [B]\{F\}^0_{\text{II}} \tag{8.26}$$

in which the forces in the new coordinates are on the right-hand side. To generate matrix $[B]$ of Equation (8.26) for the redundant forces $\{F\}^0_{\text{I}}$ of Figure 8.2(b) and the forces $\{F\}^0_{\text{II}}$ of Figure 8.6, we compute in Figure 8.6 the forces at the constraints of choice I (the reactions at the base of the right-hand column) in terms of the redundant forces $\{F\}^0_{\text{II}}$. The first column of $[B]$ is obtained by setting $F^0_{3,\text{II}} = 1$, $F^0_{4,\text{II}} = F^0_{5,\text{II}} = 0$, and computing $\{F\}^0_{\text{I}}$ from equilibrium. Similarly the second column corresponds to $\{F\}^0_{\text{I}}$ which is in equilibrium with $F^0_{4,\text{II}} = 1$, $F^0_{3,\text{II}} = F^0_{5,\text{II}} = 0$, and the third column of $[B]$ corresponds to $\{F\}^0_{\text{I}}$ which is in equilibrium with $F^0_{5,\text{II}} = 1$, $F^0_{3,\text{II}} = F^0_{4,\text{II}} = 0$. The following result is obtained when this procedure is applied (see Figure 8.7):

$$\left\{ \begin{array}{c} F_3 \\ F_4 \\ F_5 \end{array} \right\}^0_{\text{I}} = \left[\begin{array}{ccc} 1 & 0 & 0 \\ 0 & 1 & 0 \\ 1/2 & l & 1 \end{array} \right] \left\{ \begin{array}{c} F_3 \\ F_4 \\ F_5 \end{array} \right\}^0_{\text{II}} \tag{8.27}$$

Equation (8.26) is similar to Equation (7.18). Following the results of Section 7.8, we can write [see Equation (7.19)]

$$[a]^{\text{II}}_{22} = [B]^T[a]^{\text{I}}_{22}[B] \tag{8.28}$$

Equation (8.28) transforms matrix $[a]^I_{22}$ computed for one choice of redundants (I) to matrix $[a]^{II}_{22}$ which corresponds to a new choice of redundants (II).

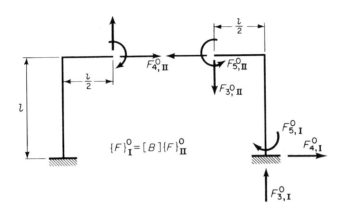

$$\{F\}^O_I = [B]\{F\}^O_{II}$$

Figure 8.7. Computing $[B]$ of Eq. (8.26) from equilibrium.

Suggested Exercises: Do problems 6, 7, 8, 9, 10, 11, 13, 14, 15, 16, 17, 18.

8.5. INTERNAL FORCES DUE TO THERMAL EXPANSION OR LACK OF FIT

When a statically determinate structure is subjected to a change in temperature, the element displacements δ_i will take place with no resulting internal forces P_i. If the structure is statically indeterminate, however, there will result internal forces P_i. We shall now show how to compute these forces by the flexibility method.

Let us designate by $\{\Delta\}_s$ the displacements due to temperature at the coordinates of element s before it is connected to the system, and let $\{\Delta\}$ designate the displacements at the coordinates of all the elements before they are connected together to form the system. If, in addition to the change in temperature, we subject each separate element s to forces $\{P\}_s$ at the coordinates, then an additional displacement $[\alpha]_s\{P\}_s$ will take place at the coordinates. The total displacement $\{\delta\}_s$ for any element s is then

$$\{\delta\}_s = [\alpha]_s\{P\}_s + \{\Delta\}_s \qquad (8.29)$$

Including all m elements of the unconnected system, we can write

$$\{\delta\} = [\alpha]\{P\} + \{\Delta\} \qquad (8.30)$$

From Equation (8.2) we write

$$\{P\} = [b]\{F\} \qquad (8.31)$$

Using the results of Section 7.7, then, corresponding to the force transformation of Equation (8.31), we have the following displacement transformation:

$$\{u\} = [b]^T\{\delta\} \tag{8.32}$$

Partitioning the matrices of Equation (8.32) to distinguish between coordinates at applied forces and redundants, we have

$$\left\{\begin{array}{c} \{u\}^* \\ \hline \{0\}^0 \end{array}\right\} = \left[\begin{array}{c} [b]^{*T} \\ \hline [b]^{0T} \end{array}\right]\{\delta\} \tag{8.33}$$

Written as two matrix equations, Equation (8.33) becomes

$$\{u\}^* = [b]^{*T}\{\delta\} \tag{8.34}$$

$$\{0\}^0 = [b]^{0T}\{\delta\} \tag{8.35}$$

Equation (8.35) is a restatement of the conditions of compatibility which must be satisfied in the analysis of indeterminate structures by the flexibility method. This equation may, therefore, also serve as a check on the solution.

We now substitute for $\{\delta\}$ from Equation (8.30) into Equation (8.35)

$$[b]^{0T}([\alpha]\{P\} + \{\Delta\}) = \{0\} \tag{8.36}$$

Substituting for $\{P\}$ from Equation (8.4) into Equation (8.36) and solving for $\{F\}^0$, we have

$$\{F\}^0 = -([b]^{0T}[\alpha][b]^0)^{-1}([b]^{0T}[\alpha][b]^*)\{F\}^*$$
$$-([b]^{0T}[\alpha][b]^0)^{-1}[b]^{0T}\{\Delta\}$$

Identifying the triple matrix products in parentheses from Equation (8.8), $\{F\}^0$ becomes

$$\{F\}^0 = -[a]_{22}^{-1}[a]_{21}\{F\}^* - [a]_{22}^{-1}[b]^{0T}\{\Delta\} \tag{8.37}$$

Substituting from Equation (8.37) into Equation (8.4) gives

$$\{P\} = ([b]^* - [b]^0[a]_{22}^{-1}[a]_{21})\{F\}^* - [b]^0[a]_{22}^{-1}[b]^{0T}\{\Delta\} \tag{8.38}$$

Equations (8.38) represent the expressions for internal forces due to applied forces and thermal expansion. When $\{\Delta\} = \{0\}$, Equations (8.37) and (8.38) reduce to Equations (8.11) and (8.14), respectively.

The development here and the resulting equations (8.37) and (8.38) apply also to redundant structures in which the elements do not fit the geometry called for by the design; namely, they are too long, too short, bent or twisted. In such cases, referred to as *lack of fit*, internal forces are induced when the structure is assembled from the nonfitting elements. In this case,

$\{\Delta\}$ of Equation (8.38) represents the initial lack of fit in the unconnected elements.

Suggested Exercises: Do problems 19, 20, 21 and 22.

PROBLEMS

Problem 1: Generate the 2×2 matrix $[a]^*$ and find the internal forces in terms of $\{F\}^*$ for the structure shown.

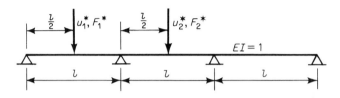

Applied forces

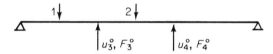

Primary structure with system coordinates
(choice of redundants)

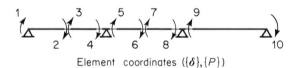

Element coordinates $(\{\delta\}, \{P\})$

Problem 2: Repeat Problem 1 using the following primary structure:

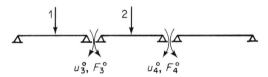

Primary structure with system coordinates
(choice of redundants)

Problem 3: Find one good choice and one poor choice of redundants for a multistory frame which consists of 2 column lines and n girders. Discuss your choices.

Problem 4: Generate $[a]^*$ and express $\{P\}$ in terms of $\{F\}^*$ for the structure shown.

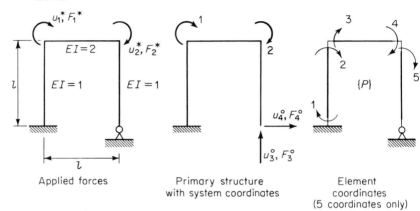

Applied forces   Primary structure   Element
                 with system coordinates   coordinates
                                       (5 coordinates only)

Problem 5: Repeat Problem 4 for the following choice of primary structure and element coordinates:

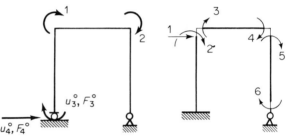

Primary structure with   Element coordinates
system coordinates

Problem 6: Generate $[a]^{II}_{22}$ for the structure of Figure 8.2, using the choice of redundants shown in Figure 8.6. Assume that $[a]^{I}_{22}$ given by Equation (8.17) is not known.

Problem 7: Repeat Problem 6 assuming $[a]^{I}_{22}$ is given. [Use Equation (8.28)]. Compare your results with those obtained in Problem 6.

Problem 8: Consider the redundant forces in Problem 1 as $\{F\}^0_{I}$ and those in Problem 2 as $\{F\}^0_{II}$. Find matrix $[B]$ in the equation

$$\{F\}^0_{I} = [B]\{F\}^0_{II}$$

Problem 9: Use the result of Problem 8 to compute $[a]^{II}_{22}$ of Problem 2 in terms of $[a]^{I}_{22}$ of Problem 1.

Problem 10: Consider the redundant forces in Problem 4 as $\{F\}^0_{II}$ and those in Problem 5 as $\{F\}^0_{I}$. Find matrix $[B]$ in the equation

$$\{F\}^0_{I} = [B]\{F\}^0_{II}$$

Problem 11: Use the result of Problem 10 to compute $[a]_{22}^{II}$ of Problem 4 in terms of the corresponding submatrix from Problem 5.

Problem 12: Compute the internal forces P_1, P_2, P_3, and P_4 shown in Figure (b) for the structure loaded as shown in Figure (a). Use the flexibility approach with the redundants shown in Figure (c).

Problem 13: Use the flexibility matrix corresponding to the redundants in Figure (c) to generate the flexibility matrix $[a]_{22}^{II}$ for the redundants in Figure (d).

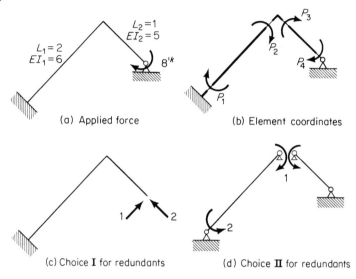

(a) Applied force   (b) Element coordinates

(c) Choice I for redundants   (d) Choice II for redundants

FIGURES FOR PROBLEMS 12 AND 13

Problem 14: Suppose that forces $\{F\}_1^0$ are applied to the primary structure of Figure 8.2(b) causing displacements $\{u\}_1^0$. How can these displacements be transformed to corresponding displacements $\{u\}_{II}^0$ in the primary structure of Figure 8.6? Use energy considerations to derive the result.

Problem 15: Compute $[a]^*$ and express $\{P\}$ in terms of $\{F\}^*$ for the structure shown. Make your own choice of redundant forces and element coordinates. All members are pin connected and EA is the same constant for each member.

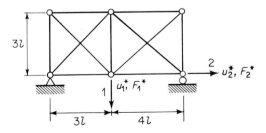

Problem 16: Compute [a]* and express {P} in terms of {F}* for the structure shown. Make your own choice of redundant forces and element coordinates. Consider only bending energy in the beam and columns and only axial energy in the diagonal brace.

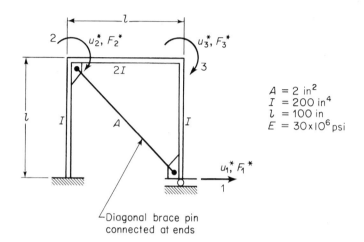

$A = 2$ in^2
$I = 200$ in^4
$l = 100$ in
$E = 30 \times 10^6$ psi

Diagonal brace pin connected at ends

Problem 17: Let the area of each column in Problem 16 be 8 in.^{2} and the area of the girder 12 in.^{2}. Repeat Problem 16 by selecting element coordinates to account also for the axial energy in the beam and columns.

Problem 18: Repeat Problem 4 accounting for axial energy in the elements. Redefine vector {P} and compute it in terms of {F}*. Consider the axial stiffness EA of each member to be $\frac{1}{4}$ of its bending stiffness EI.

Problem 19: Compute the axial bar forces in the truss of problem 15 due to an increase of 60°F in the temperature. Set $E = 30 \times 10^6$ psi and $EA = 30 \times 10^7$ lb. The coefficient of thermal expansion is 6×10^{-6} in/in °F.

Problem 20: Compute the internal forces in the structure of problem 16 due to an increase of 60°F in the temperature of the diagonal brace only. The coefficient of thermal expansion is 6×10^{-6} in/in°F.

Problem 21: Consider an initial lack of fit of

$$\Delta_4 = 1.5 \times 10^{-7}$$

$$\Delta_7 = 2.2 \times 10^{-7}$$

at element coordinates 4 and 7 respectively in the structure of Figure 8.2(c). Compute the internal forces P_i after the structure is assembled. Set $EI = (30 \times 10^6$ psi$)(10^3$ in$^4)$, $l = 12'$ $0''$.

Problem 22: Consider an initial lack of fit of

$$\Delta_1 = 2 \times 10^{-7}$$

$$\Delta_2 = 3 \times 10^{-7}$$

for the element with coordinates 1 and 2 in the structure of Problems 12, 13. Compute the internal forces P_i after the structure is assembled. Set

$$EI_1 = (30 \times 10^6 \text{ psi})(600 \text{ in}^4), L_1 = 24'\, 0''$$

$$EI_2 = (30 \times 10^6 \text{ psi})(500 \text{ in}^4), L_2 = 12'\, 0''$$

CHAPTER 9

THE STIFFNESS METHOD

9.1. INTRODUCTION

The *stiffness method* in structural analysis is analogous to the flexibility method presented in Chapter 8. It uses the stiffness matrix of the system and those of its elements in the same way that the flexibility method uses the flexibility matrix of the system and those of its elements. The stiffness method is also known as the *displacement method*[20] because it begins with a superposition of displacements as expressed by Equation (7.2) or as the *equilibrium method*[42] because it leads to equations of equilibrium. (See Section 2.10). In developing the stiffness method there is no need to distinguish between determinate and indeterminate structures because the steps are identical in each case. The method is, however, more useful in the analysis of indeterminate structures.

To develop the stiffness method so as to show its analogy to the flexibility method, we shall develop it twice: first in general, next applied to a structure where it is known that no forces will be applied at some of its coordinates.

9.2. DEVELOPMENT OF THE STIFFNESS METHOD

Let us relate the development of the method to the structure of Figure 9.1. The structure consists of inextensible elements with flexural rigidities $EI_1 = 1$ and $EI_2 = 2$ for the columns and beam, respectively. It is known from the outset that this frame will be subjected to a great number of different loading conditions. In each loading condition the beam and columns will be subjected to a number of concentrated loads at many points along their length as well as to uniform loads.

In Figure 9.2 the forces F_i at the coordinates and the forces Q_i not at the coordinates are applied separately. In Figure 9.3 the displacements due to forces Q_i between the coordinates are applied

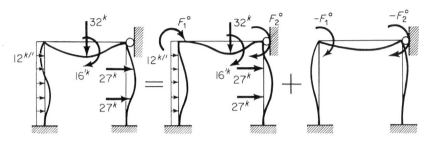

(a) Structure of Figure 9.2 (c)   (b) Fixed coordinate state   (c) Displacements under action of forces $-F_i^{\,o}$

Figure 9.3. Superposition of displacements.

with the system coordinates fixed (fixed coordinate state), and then forces F_i^0 at the coordinates in the fixed coordinate state are applied with their sign reversed.

The fixed coordinate forces $\{F\}^0$ are computed from the corresponding forces $\{P\}_s^0$ at the element coordinates. Using Equation (7.15), we can write

$$\{F\}^0 = [\beta]^T \{P\}^0$$

In the present example, Figure 9.3(b), we have [the minus sign indicates a force in a direction opposite to the coordinates in Figure 9.1(c)]

$$\begin{Bmatrix} P_1 \\ P_2 \end{Bmatrix}^0 = \begin{Bmatrix} -1 \\ 1 \end{Bmatrix}, \qquad \begin{Bmatrix} P_3 \\ P_4 \end{Bmatrix}^0 = \begin{Bmatrix} 0 \\ 8 \end{Bmatrix}, \qquad \begin{Bmatrix} P_5 \\ P_6 \end{Bmatrix}^0 = \begin{Bmatrix} 6 \\ -6 \end{Bmatrix}$$

or

$$\{P\}^0 = \begin{Bmatrix} -1 \\ 1 \\ 0 \\ 8 \\ 6 \\ -6 \end{Bmatrix}$$

The transformation matrix $[\beta]$ is

$$[\beta] = \begin{bmatrix} 0 & 0 \\ 1 & 0 \\ \hline 1 & 0 \\ 0 & 1 \\ \hline 0 & 1 \\ 0 & 0 \end{bmatrix}$$

Hence,

$$\{F\}^0 = [\beta]^T\{P\}^0 = \begin{Bmatrix} 1 \\ 14 \end{Bmatrix}$$

This equation is an expression of equilibrium at the joints of the frame in Figure 9.3(b).

6. From Figures 9.2(b) and 9.3(c) compute the displacements u_i at the system coordinates [see Equation (6.44)]

$$\{u\} = [k]^{-1}(\{F\}^f - \{F\}^0)$$

7. Using the results of Step 6 we can write

$$\{\delta\} = [\beta]\{u\}$$
$$= [\beta][k]^{-1}(\{F\}^f - \{F\}^0) \tag{9.1a}$$

and therefore the superposition of internal forces $\{P\}$ in Figures 9.2(b) and 9.3(c) is given by

$$\{P\} = [\kappa]\{\delta\}$$
$$= [\kappa][\beta][k]^{-1}(\{F\}^f - \{F\}^0) \tag{9.1b}$$

8. The superposition of forces and displacements of Figures 9.2(b), 9.3(b), and 9.3(c) gives the corresponding forces and displacements at any point in Figure 9.2(a) [or 9.1(d)] as desired. Therefore, using the results of Steps 5 and 7, we have for the final value of the forces $\{P\}^f$ at the element coordinates†

$$\{P\}^f = \{P\}^0 + [\kappa][\beta][k]^{-1}(\{F\}^f - \{F\}^0) \tag{9.1c}$$

---

† Note that when no forces $\{F\}^f$ are applied at the coordinates, then $\{F\}^f = \{0\}$ in Equation (9.1c) and only the superposition of displacements in Figure 9.3 applies.

If we substitute for $\{F\}^0$ in Equation (9.1c) its expression in terms of $\{P\}^0$ from Equation (7.15)

$$\{F\}^0 = [\beta]^T \{P\}^0$$

then Equation (9.1c) becomes

$$\{P\}^f = \{P\}^0 + [\kappa][\beta][k]^{-1}(\{F\}^f - [\beta]^T\{P\}^0)$$
$$= [\kappa][\beta][k]^{-1}\{F\}^f + ([I] - [\kappa][\beta][k]^{-1}[\beta]^T)\{P\}^0 \quad (9.1d)$$

in which $[I]$ is the identity matrix.

With forces $\{P\}^f$ known, each element can be analyzed as a statically determinate structure to compute the displacements and internal forces at any point in the structure. This fulfills our objectives. If the loading condition is changed, then a new vector $\{F\}^f$ is given for the forces at the coordinates, and vectors $\{P\}^0$ and $\{F\}^0$ must be computed from the forces Q_i not at the coordinates, but the product $[\kappa][\beta][k]^{-1}$ remains unchanged.

To complete the example of Figure 9.1, we write

$$[\kappa] = \begin{bmatrix} \begin{bmatrix} 4 & 2 \\ 2 & 4 \end{bmatrix} & & \\ & \begin{bmatrix} 8 & 4 \\ 4 & 8 \end{bmatrix} & \\ & & \begin{bmatrix} 4 & 2 \\ 2 & 4 \end{bmatrix} \end{bmatrix}$$

$$[k] = \begin{bmatrix} 12 & 4 \\ 4 & 12 \end{bmatrix}$$

$$[k]^{-1} = \tfrac{1}{128} \begin{bmatrix} 12 & -4 \\ -4 & 12 \end{bmatrix}$$

$$[\kappa][\beta][k]^{-1} = \tfrac{1}{128} \begin{bmatrix} 24 & -8 \\ 48 & -16 \\ 80 & 16 \\ 16 & 80 \\ -16 & 48 \\ -8 & 24 \end{bmatrix}$$

$$\{F\}^f - \{F\}^0 = \left\{\begin{array}{c} 8 \\ 0 \end{array}\right\} - \left\{\begin{array}{c} 1 \\ 14 \end{array}\right\} = \left\{\begin{array}{c} 7 \\ -14 \end{array}\right\}$$

Using these results and $\{P\}^0$ from Step 5 gives

$$\{P\}^f = \{P\}^0 + [\kappa][\beta][k]^{-1}(\{F\}^f - \{F\}^0)$$

$$= \left\{\begin{array}{c} -1 \\ 1 \\ 0 \\ 8 \\ 6 \\ -6 \end{array}\right\} + \frac{1}{128} \left[\begin{array}{cc} 24 & -8 \\ 48 & -16 \\ 80 & 16 \\ 16 & 80 \\ -16 & 48 \\ -8 & 24 \end{array}\right] \left\{\begin{array}{c} 7 \\ -14 \end{array}\right\}$$

$$= \left\{\begin{array}{c} 19/16 \\ 43/8 \\ 21/8 \\ 1/8 \\ -1/8 \\ -145/16 \end{array}\right\} = \frac{1}{16} \left\{\begin{array}{c} 19 \\ 86 \\ 42 \\ 2 \\ -2 \\ -145 \end{array}\right\}$$

These results satisfy the conditions of equilibrium at the joints where system coordinates 1 and 2 are marked.

Suggested Exercises: Do problems 1, 2, 3, 4, 5 and 6.

9.3. DEVELOPMENT OF THE STIFFNESS METHOD FOR STRUCTURES WITH ZERO FORCES AT SOME COORDINATES

Introduction

There are cases in which forces are applied at a fixed number of points on a structure and we wish to relate the forces and displacements at these points and find the corresponding internal forces. In such cases, it suffices to define system coordinates at only the points where external forces are applied. It turns out, however, that it may be easier to formulate the problem by defining more coordinates than the number required. The larger number of coordinates are selected so that a corresponding stiffness matrix can be synthesized from element stiffness matrices which are known. This larger stiffness matrix is then reduced to one which corresponds to the coordinates where the external forces are applied.

An example where this procedure was employed was discussed in Section 4.14, when a reduced stiffness matrix was generated for a stepped member. Another example, which arises frequently in structural dynamics,[39] is the two-story building frame of Figure 9.4(a) which is considered to move in the plane of the paper. The system is idealized by concentrating the mass in two rigid lumps at the floor levels and assuming that each lumped mass is mounted on rollers so that it can only translate laterally, along coordinates u_1^* and u_2^* in Figure 9.4(a). Rotation of the mass cannot take place because we also assume the frame members to be inextensible. The force-displacement properties of the massless frame are still distributed. As this idealized frame is vibrating, inertial forces are induced only at the coordinates identified by u_1^* and u_2^*. In order to write the equations of motion for the system, we must generate the stiffness matrix $[k]^*$ of the frame which corresponds to coordinates 1 and 2. The first column of $[k]^*$ can be generated by setting $u_1^* = 1$ and $u_2^* = 0$ and computing the forces at the coordinates as shown in Figure 9.4(b). This is a difficult task because the computations for k_{11}^* and k_{21}^* require the solution of an indeterminate structure. Similar reasoning will apply to the computations for the second column of $[k]^*$.

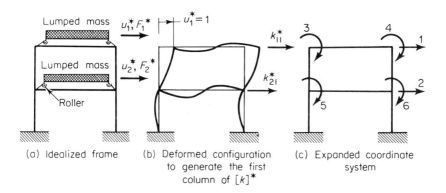

(a) Idealized frame

(b) Deformed configuration to generate the first column of $[k]^*$

(c) Expanded coordinate system

Figure 9.4.

To avoid this difficult task we expand the coordinate system by defining a coordinate at each moving joint of the frame as shown in Figure 9.4(c), and generate the corresponding 6×6 stiffness matrix $[k]$. We can now write the force-displacement relationship for the six coordinates in partitioned form

$$\left\{ \frac{\{F\}^*}{\{0\}} \right\} = \left[\begin{array}{c|c} [k]_{11} & [k]_{12} \\ \hline [k]_{21} & [k]_{22} \end{array} \right] \left\{ \frac{\{u\}^*}{\{u\}^0} \right\}$$

in which $\{u\}^*$ and $\{u\}^0$ are the displacements at the coordinates with nonzero forces and zero forces, respectively. Writing the last equation as two separate matrix equations and proceeding as in Section 4.14, we obtain the reduced stiffness matrix $[k]^*$

$$[k]^* = [k]_{11} - [k]_{12}[k]_{22}^{-1}[k]_{21}$$

Inverting $[k]^*$, we can write

$$\{u\}^* = [k]^{*-1}\{F\}^*$$

and from $\{u\}^*$ we can solve for all the element displacements $\{\delta\}$ and the corresponding internal forces $\{P\}$ in terms of $\{F\}^*$.

The procedure outlined here will now be developed in more detail and in a way analogous to the development of the flexibility method in Section 8.2.

Development of Method

Let us develop the basic steps in the *stiffness method* as presented here by referring to the structure of Figure 9.5(a) in which only forces F_1^* and F_2^* are applied. As in the flexibility method let us first state our objectives in the analysis.

Objectives

1. Generate a 2×2 stiffness matrix $[k]^*$ which will transform any desired displacements u_1^*, u_2^* in the structure of Figure 9.5(a) to the corresponding forces F_1^*, F_2^* which will cause them.
2. Generate a matrix which will transform displacements $\{u\}^*$ to corresponding internal element displacements $\{\delta\}$.

To fulfill these objectives we proceed in the following steps which form a complete parallel to the steps listed in Section 8.2 in the development of the flexibility method.

1. Select a sufficient number of system coordinates for which a stiffness matrix exists, and for which it will be easy to generate this matrix from known stiffness matrices of the elements.
2. Select elements so that system coordinates occur only at their ends.†
   Select element coordinates for which stiffness matrices exist and number the coordinates in sequence so we can write

$$\{P\}_s = [\kappa]_s \{\delta\}_s$$

---

† Otherwise Equations (6.46) and (6.47) are not valid and the development which led to Equations (7.10) and (7.11) does not hold true.

for each element s, and

$$\{P\} = [\kappa]\{\delta\} \qquad (9.1)$$

for all elements before they are connected to form the system. Use element coordinates to account for all significant energy forms (see Sections 3.8 and 6.2).

3. Using the procedure of Section 7.5, construct the transformation matrix $[\beta]$ which insures compatibility by relating the element displacements $\{\delta\}$ to system displacements $\{u\}$

$$\{\delta\} = [\beta]\{u\} \qquad (9.2)$$

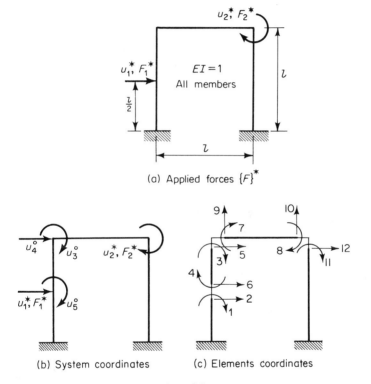

(a) Applied forces $\{F\}^*$

(b) System coordinates   (c) Elements coordinates

Figure 9.5.

To distinguish between system coordinates where the applied forces are zero, we denote the displacements at these coordinates as $\{u\}^o$. The displacements at system coordinates where the applied forces $\{F\}^*$ are nonzero are denoted by $\{u\}^*$. Using this notation, Equation

(9.2) can be partitioned and written in the form

$$\{\delta\} = \left[[\beta]^* \,\middle|\, [\beta]^0 \right] \left\{ \frac{\{u\}^*}{\{u\}^0} \right\} \tag{9.3}$$

or

$$\{\delta\} = [\beta]^*\{u\}^* + [\beta]^0\{u\}^0 \tag{9.4}$$

Note that at this point the displacements $\{u\}^0$ are not known; hence $\{\delta\}$ cannot be computed.

Using for example the coordinates of Figures 9.5(b) and (c) which identify $\{u\}$ and $\{\delta\}$, respectively, then Equation (9.3) takes the form

$$\begin{Bmatrix} \delta_1 \\ \delta_2 \\ \delta_3 \\ \delta_4 \\ \delta_5 \\ \delta_6 \\ \delta_7 \\ \delta_8 \\ \delta_9 \\ \delta_{10} \\ \delta_{11} \\ \delta_{12} \end{Bmatrix} = \begin{bmatrix} 0 & 0 & 0 & 0 & 1 \\ 1 & 0 & 0 & 0 & 0 \\ 0 & 0 & 1 & 0 & 0 \\ 0 & 0 & 0 & 0 & 1 \\ 0 & 0 & 0 & 1 & 0 \\ 1 & 0 & 0 & 0 & 0 \\ 0 & 0 & 1 & 0 & 0 \\ 0 & 1 & 0 & 0 & 0 \\ 0 & 0 & 0 & 0 & 0 \\ 0 & 0 & 0 & 0 & 0 \\ 0 & 1 & 0 & 0 & 0 \\ 0 & 0 & 0 & 1 & 0 \end{bmatrix} \begin{Bmatrix} u_1^* \\ u_2^* \\ u_3^0 \\ u_4^0 \\ u_5^0 \end{Bmatrix} \tag{9.5}$$

$$\underset{[\beta]^*}{\uparrow} \qquad \underset{[\beta]^0}{\uparrow}$$

4. Synthesize the system stiffness matrix $[k]$ using Equations (7.10) or (7.11)

$$[k] = [\beta]^T[\kappa][\beta] \tag{9.6}$$

This equation can be written in partitioned form as follows:

$$\begin{array}{c} {}^* \\ {}_0 \end{array} \left[\begin{array}{c|c} [k]_{11} & [k]_{12} \\ \hline [k]_{21} & [k]_{22} \end{array} \right] = \left[\begin{array}{c} [\beta]^{*T} \\ \hline [\beta]^{0T} \end{array} \right] [\kappa] \left[[\beta]^* \,\middle|\, [\beta]^0 \right] \tag{9.7}$$

in which the asterisk (*) designates system coordinates with nonzero forces and the zero (^{0}) designates system coordinates with zero forces.

Expanding the right-hand side of Equation (9.7) and identifying the resulting submatrices with the corresponding ones on the left-hand side, we obtain

$$[k]_{11} = [\beta]^{*T}[\kappa][\beta]^*$$
$$[k]_{12} = [\beta]^{*T}[\kappa][\beta]^0 = [k]_{21}^T$$
$$[k]_{21} = [\beta]^{0T}[\kappa][\beta]^* = [k]_{12}^T$$
$$[k]_{22} = [\beta]^{0T}[\kappa][\beta]^0$$

(9.8)

5. To fulfill our first objective we write for the system coordinates the following force displacement relationship in partitioned form

$$\left\{ \begin{array}{c} \{F\}^* \\ \hline \{F\}^0 \end{array} \right\} = \begin{array}{c} {}^* \\ {}_0 \end{array}\left[\begin{array}{c|c} [k]_{11} & [k]_{12} \\ \hline [k]_{21} & [k]_{22} \end{array} \right]\left\{ \begin{array}{c} \{u\}^* \\ \hline \{u\}^0 \end{array} \right\}$$

(9.9)

From our basic definition of system coordinates we recall that $\{F\}^0 = \{0\}$. Substituting this in Equation (9.9) and writing it as two separate matrix equations, we have

$$\{F\}^* = [k]_{11}\{u\}^* + [k]_{12}\{u\}^0$$
$$\{0\} = [k]_{21}\{u\}^* + [k]_{22}\{u\}^0$$

(9.10)

From the second equation, we solve for the displacements $\{u\}^0$ in terms of displacements $\{u\}^*$

$$\{u\}^0 = -[k]_{22}^{-1}[k]_{21}\{u\}^*$$

(9.11)

Substituting this expression for $\{u\}^0$ in the first of Equations (9.10), we have

$$\{F\}^* = [k]^*\{u\}^*$$

(9.12)

in which

$$[k]^* = [k]_{11} - [k]_{12}[k]_{22}^{-1}[k]_{21}$$

(9.13)

This satisfies our first objective because all the submatrices $[k]_{ij}$ in Equation (9.13) can be computed from Equation (9.8).

6. To fulfill the second objective, we substitute for $\{u\}^0$ from Equation (9.11) into Equation (9.4) and write

$$\{\delta\} = ([\beta]^* - [\beta]^0[k]_{22}^{-1}[k]_{21})\{u\}^*$$

(9.14)

7. If the internal forces $\{P\}$ at the element coordinates are required, they can also be expressed in terms of the displacements $\{u\}^*$. Substituting for $\{\delta\}$ from Equation (9.14) into Equation (9.1),

$$\{P\} = [\kappa]([\beta]^* - [\beta]^0[k]_{22}^{-1}[k]_{21})\{u\}^*$$

(9.15)

Of course $\{\delta\}$ and $\{P\}$ can be expressed in terms of the applied forces $\{F\}^*$ by solving for $\{u\}^*$ from Equation (9.12)

$$\{u\}^* = [k]^{*\,-1}\{F\}^*$$

and substituting into Equations (9.14) and (9.15), respectively.

To complete the solution to the example problem of Figure 9.5, we first write matrix $[\kappa]$ for the four elements shown in Figure 9.5(c). To simplify the arithmetic we set $l = 1$.

$$[\kappa] = \begin{bmatrix} [\kappa]_1 & & & \\ & [\kappa]_2 & & \\ & & [\kappa]_3 & \\ & & & [\kappa]_4 \end{bmatrix} \tag{9.16}$$

$$[\kappa]_1 = \begin{bmatrix} 8 & -24 \\ -24 & 96 \end{bmatrix} \qquad [\kappa]_4 = \begin{bmatrix} 4 & -6 \\ -6 & 12 \end{bmatrix}$$

$$[\kappa]_2 = \begin{bmatrix} 8 & 4 & -24 & 24 \\ 4 & 8 & -24 & 24 \\ -24 & -24 & 96 & -96 \\ 24 & 24 & -96 & 96 \end{bmatrix}$$

$$[\kappa]_3 = \begin{bmatrix} 4 & 2 & -6 & 6 \\ 2 & 4 & -6 & 6 \\ -6 & -6 & 12 & -12 \\ 6 & 6 & -12 & 12 \end{bmatrix}$$

Next we generate matrix $[k]$ using Equation (9.6), or Equations (9.7) or (9.8) which are identical to Equation (9.6)†

$$[k] = \begin{bmatrix} 192 & 0 & 24 & -96 & 0 \\ 0 & 8 & 2 & -6 & 0 \\ 24 & 2 & 12 & -24 & 4 \\ -96 & -6 & -24 & 108 & -24 \\ 0 & 0 & 4 & -24 & 16 \end{bmatrix} \tag{9.17}$$

---

† A more direct approach to generate $[k]$ is discussed in Section 9.8.

Since $[k]_{22}^{-1}$ is required in both Equation (9.13) and Equation (9.14), we perform this operation first

$$[k]_{22}^{-1} = \frac{3}{13 \times 12} \begin{bmatrix} 8 & 2 & 1 \\ 2 & \frac{11}{9} & \frac{4}{3} \\ 1 & \frac{4}{3} & 5 \end{bmatrix}$$

Next we evaluate the product

$$[k]_{22}^{-1}[k]_{21} = \tfrac{3}{13} \begin{bmatrix} 0 & \dfrac{1}{3} \\ \dfrac{-52}{9} & \dfrac{-5}{18} \\ \dfrac{-26}{3} & \dfrac{-1}{2} \end{bmatrix}$$

Substituting this result in Equations (9.13) and (9.14) and carrying out the indicated matrix operations, we obtain

$$[k]^* = \begin{bmatrix} 192 & 0 \\ 0 & 8 \end{bmatrix} - \tfrac{1}{13} \begin{bmatrix} 1664 & 104 \\ 104 & 7 \end{bmatrix}$$

$$= \tfrac{1}{13} \begin{bmatrix} 832 & -104 \\ -104 & 97 \end{bmatrix} \tag{9.18}$$

$$\begin{Bmatrix} \delta_1 \\ \delta_2 \\ \delta_3 \\ \delta_4 \\ \delta_5 \\ \delta_6 \\ \delta_7 \\ \delta_8 \\ \delta_9 \\ \delta_{10} \\ \delta_{11} \\ \delta_{12} \end{Bmatrix} = \left(\overset{[\beta]^*}{\begin{bmatrix} 0 & 0 \\ 1 & 0 \\ 0 & 0 \\ 0 & 0 \\ 0 & 0 \\ 1 & 0 \\ 0 & 0 \\ 0 & 1 \\ 0 & 0 \\ 0 & 0 \\ 0 & 1 \\ 0 & 0 \end{bmatrix}} - \tfrac{3}{13} \overset{[\beta]^0[k]_{22}^{-1}[k]_{21}}{\begin{bmatrix} -26/3 & -1/2 \\ 0 & 0 \\ 0 & 1/3 \\ -26/3 & -1/2 \\ -52/9 & -5/18 \\ 0 & 0 \\ 0 & 1/3 \\ 0 & 0 \\ 0 & 0 \\ 0 & 0 \\ 0 & 0 \\ -52/9 & -5/18 \end{bmatrix}} \right) \begin{Bmatrix} u_1^* \\ u_2^* \end{Bmatrix}$$

$$\{\delta\} = \tfrac{3}{13}
\begin{bmatrix}
26/3 & 1/2 \\
13/3 & 0 \\
0 & -1/3 \\
26/3 & 1/2 \\
52/9 & 5/18 \\
13/3 & 0 \\
0 & -1/3 \\
0 & 13/3 \\
0 & 0 \\
0 & 0 \\
0 & 13/3 \\
52/9 & 5/18
\end{bmatrix}
\begin{Bmatrix} u_1^* \\ u_2^* \end{Bmatrix}
\tag{9.19}$$

As a check note that $[a]^*$ of Equation (8.18) and $[k]^*$ of Equation (9.18) are the inverse of each other, as should be expected because the structure of Figures 8.2(a) and 9.5(a) is the same and has the identical system coordinates designated by an asterisk.

$$
\begin{array}{c}
[k]^* \\
\downarrow \\
\tfrac{1}{13}\begin{bmatrix} 832 & -104 \\ -104 & 97 \end{bmatrix}
\end{array}
$$

$$
\begin{array}{c}
[a]^* \\
\downarrow \\
\tfrac{1}{12}\begin{bmatrix} \frac{97}{448} & \frac{13}{56} \\ \frac{13}{56} & \frac{13}{7} \end{bmatrix}
\end{array}
\qquad
\begin{bmatrix} 1 & 0 \\ 0 & 1 \end{bmatrix} \leftarrow [I]
$$

Suggested Exercises: Do problems 7 and 8.

9.4. ANALOGY BETWEEN THE FLEXIBILITY AND STIFFNESS METHODS

A comparison of the equations of Section 8.2 with corresponding equations, of the same number, of Section 9.3 shows the complete analogy between the stiffness and flexibility methods.

The correspondence of symbols in the equations of these two sections is shown in Table 9.1. It is seen, for instance, that the redundant forces $\{F\}^0$ in the flexibility method† correspond to the displacements $\{u\}^0$ in the stiffness method. Forces $\{F\}^0$ occur where the displacements are zero and displacements $\{u\}^0$ occur where the forces are zero. Because of this analogy,

---

† These forces should not be confused with the fixed coordinate forces $\{F\}^0$ of Section 9.2.

the displacements $\{u\}^0$ in the stiffness method are sometimes referred to as *redundant displacements*.† A complete description of the analogy between the two methods can be found in the literature[20, 21].

TABLE 9.1

CORRESPONDENCE OF SYMBOLS IN THE STIFFNESS
AND FLEXIBILITY METHODS

Symbols in the Flexibility Method (equations of Section 8.2)	Corresponding Symbols in the Stiffness Method (equations of Section 9.3)
$\{\delta\}$	$\{P\}$
$[\alpha]$	$[\kappa]$
$\{P\}$	$\{\delta\}$
$[b]$	$[\beta]$
$[b]^*$	$[\beta]^*$
$[b]^0$	$[\beta]^0$
$\{F\}$	$\{u\}$
$\{F\}^*$	$\{u\}^*$
$\{F\}^0$	$\{u\}^0$
$[a]$	$[k]$
$[a]_{ij}$	$[k]_{ij}$
$[a]^*$	$[k]^*$
$\{u\}^*$	$\{F\}^*$
$\{u\}^0$	$\{F\}^0$

9.5. INTERNAL FORCES DUE TO THERMAL EXPANSION OR LACK OF FIT

In Section 8.5 we used the flexibility method to compute the internal forces due to thermal expansion or lack of fit. We shall now show how the stiffness method as developed in Section 9.2 can be used to compute these forces. Let us again denote by $\{\Delta\}$ the thermal displacements‡ at the coordinates of the elements before they are connected to form the system. The solution for the final internal forces $\{P\}^f$ expressed by Equation (9.1d) applies here too, except that the forces $\{P\}^0$ in the fixed coordinate state are due to the thermal expansion or lack of fit, whereas in Section 9.2 they were caused by forces not at the coordinates.

To compute the forces $\{P\}^0$ in the present case we consider the structure of Figure 9.6 in which the members are extensible. The system coordinates are shown in Figure 9.6(a) and the element coordinates as well as displacements $\{\Delta\}$ are shown in Figure 9.6(b). In Figure (9.7) we show a

---

† Argyris[20] refers to them as *kinematic redundants* and Pestel[21] as *kinematic deficiencies*.

‡ Or displacements which represent a lack of fit.

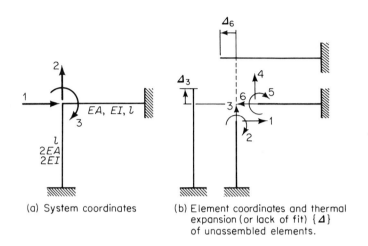

(a) System coordinates   (b) Element coordinates and thermal
                                    expansion (or lack of fit) $\{\Delta\}$
                                    of unassembled elements.

Figure 9.6.

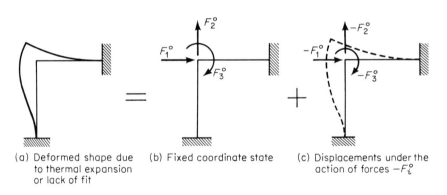

(a) Deformed shape due   (b) Fixed coordinate state   (c) Displacements under the
    to thermal expansion   action of forces $-F_i^o$
    or lack of fit

Figure 9.7. Superposition of displacements.

superposition of displacements which is analogous to the one shown in
Figure 9.3. In the fixed coordinate state (Figure 9.7b), the element forces are

$$\{P\}^0 = -[\kappa]\{\Delta\} \qquad (9.20)$$

The minus sign in this equation is needed because forces $\{P\}^0$ must be
applied in a direction opposite to displacements $\{\Delta\}$. This can be verified
by examining Figures 9.6(b) and 9.7(b).

If the structure is subjected only to a thermal expansion or lack of fit
represented by displacements $\{\Delta\}$ of the unassembled elements, then we

set $\{F\}^f = \{0\}$ in Equation (9.1d) and substitute $\{P\}^0$ from Equation (9.20) to give

$$\{P\}^f = ([\kappa][\beta][k]^{-1}[\beta]^T - [I])[\kappa]\{\Delta\} \tag{9.21}$$

If there also exist forces $\{F\}^f$ at the coordinates, then

$$\{P\}^f = [\kappa][\beta][k]^{-1}\{F\}^f + ([\kappa][\beta][k]^{-1}[\beta]^T - [I])[\kappa]\{\Delta\} \tag{9.22}$$

Suggested Exercises: Do problems 9 and 10.

9.6. EXPANDING A STIFFNESS MATRIX TO INCLUDE RIGID BODY DEGREES OF FREEDOM

From the discussion in Section 3.6 and Section 4.11, we recall that when the forces at the coordinates of a system are dependent, then the stiffness matrix is singular. The dependency among the forces expresses the conditions of equilibrium, and the number of dependent forces represents the number of degrees of freedom of rigid body motion.

If a structure is constrained so that it cannot undergo rigid body motion and it has a nonsingular stiffness matrix, then we can expand this matrix to include rigid body displacements by removing the physical constraints and defining new coordinates in their place.

Let us demonstrate this for the simple beam of Figure 9.8. The beam of Figure 9.8(a) is constrained against rigid body motion and has the following nonsingular stiffness matrix $[k]_1$ for the two coordinates shown

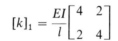

$$[k]_1 = \frac{EI}{l}\begin{bmatrix} 4 & 2 \\ 2 & 4 \end{bmatrix}$$

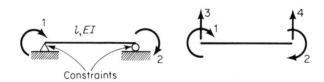

(a) Constrained beam   (b) Unconstrained beam

Figure 9.8.

In Figure 9.8(b) the physical constraints are removed and coordinates 3 and 4 are introduced in their place. The beam is now free to translate as a rigid body in a vertical direction and rotate about one end (horizontal translation is not considered here). We wish to expand the 2×2 stiffness matrix $[k]_1$ for the structure of Figure 9.8(a) to a 4×4 stiffness matrix for the same

structure (unconstrained) as shown in Figure 9.8(b). To do so we write
from equilibrium

$$\{F\}_2 = [B]\{F\}_1$$

or

$$\{F\} = [b]\{F\}_1 \tag{9.23}$$

in which

$\{F\}_1 \equiv$ force vector at the original coordinates for which $[k]_1$ is nonsingular

$\{F\}_2 \equiv$ force vector at added coordinates

$$\{F\} = \left\{ \begin{array}{c} \{F\}_1 \\ \hline \{F\}_2 \end{array} \right\} \equiv \text{ expanded force vector}$$

$$[b] = \left[\begin{array}{c} [I] \\ \hline [B] \end{array} \right]$$

From Equations (7.16) and (7.17), we can write the following displacements transformation, which corresponds to the force transformation of Equation (9.23):

$$\{u\}_1 = [b]^T\{u\} \tag{9.24}$$

in which

$\{u\}_1 \equiv$ displacement vector at original coordinates
$\{u\} \equiv$ expanded displacement vector corresponding to $\{F\}$

Comparing this equation to Equation (7.21) and using Equation (7.22), we have for the expanded matrix $[k]$

$$[k] = [b]\,[k]_1[b]^T$$

$$= \left[\begin{array}{c} [I] \\ \hline [B] \end{array} \right] [k]_1 \left[[I] \mid [B]^T \right] \tag{9.25}$$

$$= \left[\begin{array}{c|c} [k]_1 & [k]_1\,[B]^T \\ \hline [B]\,[k]_1 & [B]\,[k]_1[B]^T \end{array} \right]$$

In the beam of Figure 9.8

$$\left\{ \begin{array}{c} F_3 \\ F_4 \end{array} \right\} = \frac{1}{l} \left[\begin{array}{cc} -1 & -1 \\ 1 & 1 \end{array} \right] \left\{ \begin{array}{c} F_1 \\ F_2 \end{array} \right\}$$

or

$$[B] = \frac{1}{l} \left[\begin{array}{cc} -1 & -1 \\ 1 & 1 \end{array} \right]$$

Using Equation (9.25), $[k]_1$ is expanded into the following singular matrix:

$$\begin{array}{c} [k]_1 \rightarrow \\ \\ \frac{EI}{l} \\ [B][k]_1 \rightarrow \end{array} \left[\begin{array}{cc|cc} 4 & 2 & -6/l & 6/l \\ 2 & 4 & -6/l & 6/l \\ \hline -6/l & -6/l & 12/l^2 & -12/l^2 \\ 6/l & 6/l & -12/l^2 & 12/l^2 \end{array} \right] \begin{array}{l} \leftarrow [k]_1[B]^T \\ \\ \leftarrow [B][k]_1[B]^T \end{array}$$

Suggested Exercises: Do problems 11 and 12.

9.7. STIFFNESS METHOD APPLIED TO SYMMETRICAL STRUCTURES

When the stiffness method is applied to a symmetrical structure, then the order of its stiffness matrix, which must be inverted in the computations, can be reduced. The reduction is to one-half for a single axis of symmetry and to one-fourth for two axes of symmetry. The reduction of the stiffness matrix is effected by a transformation to symmetrical and antisymmetrical coordinates as discussed in Section 7.7. Let us demonstrate this, first, for a structure with a single axis of symmetry; then, for a structure with two axes of symmetry.

Structure with One Axis of Symmetry

The structure of Figure 9.9 is symmetrical about a vertical axis and has four coordinates which identify the forces F_i and displacements u_i at the four joints. The members are considered inextensible. The displacements u_i are arbitrary but can always be synthesized from symmetrical and antisymmetrical displacement configurations. For the structure of Figure 9.9, four such displacement configurations are shown in Figures 9.10(a, b, c, d) and are designated as *generalized displacements* q_1, q_2, q_3, and q_4,

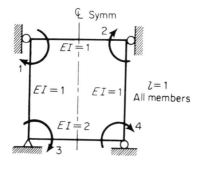

Figure 9.9.

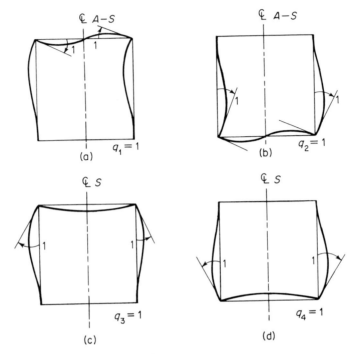

All corner rotations are 1 unit

Figure 9.10.

respectively. The corresponding generalized forces are designated by Q_i $(i = 1, 2, 3, 4)$. Applying Equations (7.16) and (7.17), we have

$$\{u\} = [C]\{q\} \qquad (9.26)$$

and

$$\{Q\} = [C]^T\{F\} \qquad (9.27)$$

in which

$$[C] = \begin{bmatrix} 1 & 0 & 1 & 0 \\ 1 & 0 & -1 & 0 \\ 0 & 1 & 0 & -1 \\ 0 & 1 & 0 & 1 \end{bmatrix}$$

From Equation (7.22), we have ([C] replaces [β] in Equation 7.22)

$$[k]_q = [C]^T[k]_u[C] \qquad (9.28)$$

in which $[k]_q$ and $[k]_u$ designate the stiffness matrix in the q and u coordinates, respectively. From Figure 9.9

$$[k]_u = \begin{bmatrix} 8 & 2 & 2 & 0 \\ 2 & 8 & 0 & 2 \\ 2 & 0 & 12 & 4 \\ 0 & 2 & 4 & 12 \end{bmatrix}$$

and therefore

$$[k]_q = \begin{bmatrix} 20 & 4 & 0 & 0 \\ 4 & 32 & 0 & 0 \\ \hline 0 & 0 & 12 & -4 \\ 0 & 0 & -4 & 16 \end{bmatrix} = \begin{bmatrix} [k]_{AS} & [0] \\ \hline [0] & [k]_S \end{bmatrix} \tag{9.29}$$

(Subscripts AS and S designate antisymmetrical and symmetrical coordinates, respectively.) Hence the original 4×4 stiffness matrix in coordinates u has been reduced to two 2×2 uncoupled matrices $[k]_{AS}$ and $[k]_S$, in which $[k]_{AS}$ corresponds to the antisymmetrical configurations q_1 and q_2, and $[k]_S$ corresponds to the symmetrical configurations q_3 and q_4. The analysis of the structure of Figure 9.9 will therefore require the inversion of two 2×2 matrices in the q coordinates instead of a 4×4 matrix in the u coordinates as shown by the following:

Using matrix $[k]_q$ of Equation (9.29) we can write

$$\left\{ \frac{\{Q\}_{AS}}{\{Q\}_S} \right\} = \begin{bmatrix} [k]_{AS} & [0] \\ \hline [0] & [k]_S \end{bmatrix} \left\{ \frac{\{q\}_{AS}}{\{q\}_S} \right\} \tag{9.30}$$

in which

$$\left\{ \frac{\{Q\}_{AS}}{\{Q\}_S} \right\} = \{Q\} \quad \text{and} \quad \left\{ \frac{\{q\}_{AS}}{\{q\}_S} \right\} = \{q\}$$

Equation (9.30) can be written as two separate matrix equations for the antisymmetrical (AS) and symmetrical (S) coordinates

$$\{Q\}_{AS} = [k]_{AS}\{q\}_{AS}$$
$$\{Q\}_S = [k]_S\{q\}_S \tag{9.31}$$

or

$$\{q\}_{AS} = [k]_{AS}^{-1}\{Q\}_{AS}$$
$$\{q\}_S = [k]_S^{-1}\{Q\}_S \tag{9.32}$$

To solve for displacements u_i caused by forces F_i we proceed as follows: We compute forces Q_i from Equation (9.27), substitute their values in Equation (9.32), and solve for q_i. Next we substitute the q_i values in Equation (9.26) and obtain the desired displacements u_i.

The fact that matrix $[k]_q$ in Equation (9.29) has zero elements at positions which correspond to coupling between symmetrical and antisymmetrical configurations follows *in general* from Equation (6.30), Section 6.7. This is so because the work done by the forces on the structure in a symmetrical configuration (q_3 or q_4 in Figure 9.10) on the displacements in any antisymmetrical configuration (q_1 or q_2 in Figure 9.10) is zero. This will become more evident when we describe the symmetrical and antisymmetrical force groups on the structure which correspond to a unit value of each generalized force Q_i.

From Equation (9.27)

$$\{F\} = ([C]^T)^{-1}\{Q\} \tag{9.33}$$

In our example, this equation becomes

$$
\begin{Bmatrix} F_1 \\ F_2 \\ F_3 \\ F_4 \end{Bmatrix} = \frac{1}{2}
\begin{bmatrix}
1 & 0 & 1 & 0 \\
1 & 0 & -1 & 0 \\
0 & 1 & 0 & -1 \\
0 & 1 & 0 & 1
\end{bmatrix}
\begin{Bmatrix} Q_1 \\ Q_2 \\ Q_3 \\ Q_4 \end{Bmatrix}
$$

From this last equation, we can describe the generalized forces Q_i by setting one of them at a time equal to unity. This leads to the force groups shown in Figure 9.11. We now see that Q_1 and Q_2 of Figure 9.11 do zero work on q_3 and q_4 of Figure 9.10 and similarly Q_3 and Q_4 do zero work on q_1 and q_2.

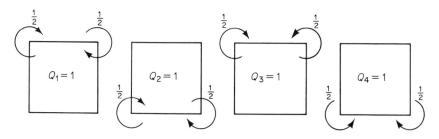

Figure 9.11. Generalized forces Q_i corresponding to the displacements q_i of Fig. 9.10.

Structure with Two Axes of Symmetry

Consider the structure of Figure 9.12 with two axes of symmetry. The symmetrical and antisymmetrical displacement configurations are shown in Figures 9.12(b, c, d, e). Matrix $[C]$ of Equation (9.26) has now the form

$$[C] = \begin{bmatrix} 1 & 1 & 1 & 1 \\ 1 & -1 & 1 & -1 \\ 1 & -1 & -1 & 1 \\ 1 & 1 & -1 & -1 \end{bmatrix}$$

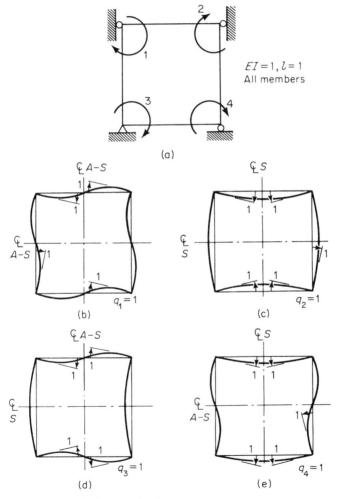

$EI = 1, l = 1$
All members

(a)

(b)   (c)

(d)   (e)

All corner rotations are 1 unit

Figure 9.12. Stiffness matrix applied to symmetrical structures.

Using this matrix in Equation (9.28), $[k]_u$ corresponding to the u coordinates of Figure 9.12(a) reduces to a diagonal matrix $[k]_q$ in the q coordinates

$$[k]_q = \begin{bmatrix} 48 & & & \\ & 16 & & \\ & & 32 & \\ & & & 32 \end{bmatrix}$$

Hence the symmetry about two axes reduces the task of inverting a 4×4 matrix to that of inverting four 1×1 matrices (that is, solving four independent equations in one unknown each).

Suggested Exercises: Do problems 13, 14, 15 and 16.

9.8. THE CODE SYSTEM IN THE STIFFNESS METHOD

From Section 9.2, we realize that the main task in formulating a problem by the stiffness method is to synthesize the system stiffness matrix from those of its elements. This is accomplished through the use of Equations (7.10) or (7.11). The *code system* which will now be described accomplishes the same objective in a much more efficient way for computer applications[44, 45]. Before we present the code system let us rewrite here Equations (7.2) and (7.10)

$$\{\delta\} = [\beta]\{u\} \tag{7.2}$$

$$[k] = [\beta]^T[\kappa][\beta] \tag{7.10}$$

and examine their physical significance. Equation (7.2) *identifies the element coordinates* with system coordinates through matrix $[\beta]$, and in Equation (7.10) the same matrix $[\beta]$ is used to take element stiffness matrices $[\kappa]_s$ and place them in the appropriate position in the system stiffness matrix $[k]$. We can accomplish these operations more directly by the following procedure.

Code Number for Each Element

Consider the frame of Figure 9.13(a) with three system coordinates as shown. For simplicity we set $l = 1$ for all members but the EI are different as shown. Let us number each element coordinate in a fixed sequence as shown in Figure 9.13(b). Let us suppose now that we have in a shop the three unconnected elements of the frame in Figure 9.13(a) and that each element has the four numbered arrows as shown in Figure 9.13(b). We wish to instruct a team of workers to build the frame. To do so we write on each element a code of four numbers. For example, on the element which will

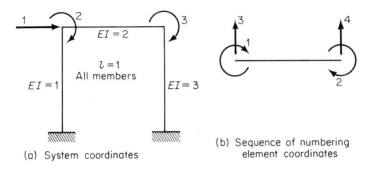

(a) System coordinates

(b) Sequence of numbering element coordinates

Figure 9.13.

become the left-hand column of the frame we write the following code of numbers shown enclosed in four boxes:

1   2   3   4 ←——— Position of box corresponds to element coordinate.

Code ——→ $\boxed{2}$ $\boxed{0}$ $\boxed{1}$ $\boxed{0}$ ←——— Number inside box is a system coordinate.

The position (1, 2, 3, 4) of each box in this code (counting from the left) represents the element coordinate number and may be considered as the address of the box. The number inside each box designates the system coordinate which corresponds to the element coordinate signified by the position of the box. Hence, in the foregoing code, element coordinate 1 corresponds to system coordinate 2, and element coordinate 3 corresponds to system coordinate 1. No system coordinates correspond to element coordinates 2 and 4 and therefore a zero, 0, is placed in their boxes. Using the code $\boxed{2}$ $\boxed{0}$ $\boxed{1}$ $\boxed{0}$, the left-hand column is erected so that its coordinates 1 and 3—arrows 1, 3 in Figure 9.13(b)—match system co-ordinates 2 and 1, respectively—arrows 2 and 1 in Figure 9.13(a). No system coordinates correspond to element coordinates 2 and 4, hence the zeros in their boxes.

Proceeding in a similar manner, the code for the beam in the frame of Figure 9.13(a) is

$\boxed{2}$ $\boxed{3}$ $\boxed{0}$ $\boxed{0}$

and for the right-hand column

$\boxed{3}$ $\boxed{0}$ $\boxed{1}$ $\boxed{0}$

These codes can be written by inspection by placing each element with its sequentially numbered coordinates in its position on the structure and matching system and element coordinates.

The code of numbers contains the following information:

1. It identifies each element of the system by a name,† which is its sequence of code numbers, and tells us where the element is connected in the structure.
2. It gives us essentially the coordinate transformation $[\beta]$ of Equation (7.2)
3. It tells us how to construct the stiffness matrix of the system from the stiffness matrices of its elements.

Item 1 of this list has been discussed. We shall now verify items 2 and 3.

If we write the code of element $\boxed{2}$ $\boxed{0}$ $\boxed{1}$ $\boxed{0}$ as a column in the form

$$
\begin{array}{cc}
1 & \boxed{2} \\
2 & \boxed{0} \\
3 & \boxed{1} \\
4 & \boxed{0}
\end{array}
$$

this gives us $[\beta]$ for the left-hand column of the frame. The position of each box (counting from the top) represents the row number of $[\beta]$, and the number in a box is the column number of $[\beta]$ in which the number 1 must be inserted (all the other elements of the row are zero). A zero in a box signifies all zeros in that row. The preceding code gives then

$$
\begin{array}{c}
\boxed{2} \\
\boxed{0} \\
\boxed{1} \\
\boxed{0}
\end{array}
\begin{bmatrix}
0 & 1 & 0 \\
0 & 0 & 0 \\
1 & 0 & 0 \\
0 & 0 & 0
\end{bmatrix}
$$

Listing the codes of all three elements we obtain the complete matrix $[\beta]$ as given in Section 7.5.

To construct the system stiffness matrix we proceed as follows: We prepare room for the 3×3 system stiffness matrix as shown in Table 9.2. Above and on the left of each element stiffness matrix we write its code as shown. Beginning with any member, say $\boxed{2}$ $\boxed{0}$ $\boxed{1}$ $\boxed{0}$, we place each element of its stiffness matrix in the system stiffness matrix in a row number and column number specified by the number in the box to the left

---

† No two elements can have the same code unless they are both connected to the same points in the structure.

and above the element, respectively. A zero code, $\boxed{0}$, signifies that the corresponding row and column of the element stiffness matrix does not contribute to the system stiffness and is not considered. For example, in the stiffness matrix of member $\boxed{2}\ \boxed{0}\ \boxed{1}\ \boxed{0}$ the 4 goes to position (2, 2) in the system, the -6 goes to (2, 1) and (1, 2), and the 12 goes to (1, 1). Similarly in the stiffness matrix of element $\boxed{2}\ \boxed{3}\ \boxed{0}\ \boxed{0}$ the 8 goes to (2, 2) and (3, 3), 4 goes to (2, 3) and (3, 2). Finally, in the stiffness matrix of element $\boxed{3}\ \boxed{0}\ \boxed{1}\ \boxed{0}$ the 12 goes to (3, 3), -18 to (3, 1) and to (1, 3), and 36 to (1, 1). The system stiffness matrix is obtained by adding the contributions from all the elements (see Table 9.2).

TABLE 9.2

SYNTHESIS OF STIFFNESS MATRIX FOR FRAME OF FIGURE 9.13

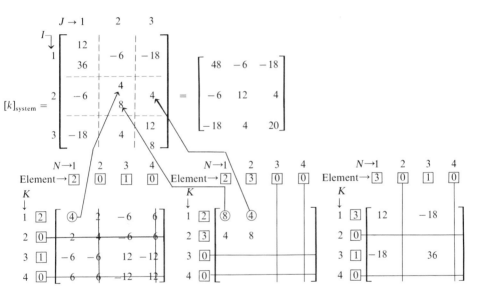

Cases Where There is No One-to-One Correspondence Between Element Coordinates and System Coordinates

When the elements of the system do not intersect at right angles, the $[\beta]$ matrix does not consist of zeros and ones and the code system cannot be applied unless we first transform the element coordinates shown in Figure 9.13(b) to a new set of element coordinates which have the desired one-to-one correspondence to the system coordinates. Let us show how this is done by an example. Consider the frame of Figure 9.14(a). In Figure 9.14(b) we show the desired "new" element coordinates q and the code numbers for the elements. In Figure 9.14(c) we show the "old" element coordinates δ for which we have stiffness matrices.

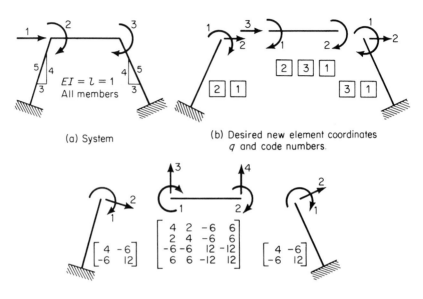

(a) System

(b) Desired new element coordinates q and code numbers.

(c) Old element coordinates δ and corresponding stiffness matrices

Figure 9.14.

From the way the elements are connected in the frame, we can write for each column

$$\begin{Bmatrix} \delta_1 \\ \delta_2 \end{Bmatrix}_O = \begin{bmatrix} 1 & 0 \\ 0 & \frac{5}{4} \end{bmatrix} \begin{Bmatrix} q_1 \\ q_2 \end{Bmatrix}_N$$

where O and N designate old and new coordinates, respectively. For the beam we have†

$$\begin{Bmatrix} \delta_1 \\ \delta_2 \\ \delta_3 \\ \delta_4 \end{Bmatrix}_O = \begin{bmatrix} 1 & 0 & 0 \\ 0 & 1 & 0 \\ 0 & 0 & -3/4 \\ 0 & 0 & 3/4 \end{bmatrix} \begin{Bmatrix} q_1 \\ q_2 \\ q_3 \end{Bmatrix}_N$$

---

† Note that the force Q_3, corresponding to q_3 in the "new" coordinates of the beam, is not an actual axial force, but a virtual force which does the same amount of work on displacement q_3, as forces P_3 and P_4 do on displacements δ_3 and δ_4 in the "old" coordinates.

These equations are analogous to Equation (7.21); hence the element stiffness matrices in the δ coordinates can be transformed to the q coordinates by Equation (7.22). Using this equation, the new stiffness matrices are computed and the code numbers are attached to them as shown in Table 9.3. The system stiffness is now computed as in the example of Figure 9.13.

TABLE 9.3

SYNTHESIS OF STIFFNESS MATRIX FOR FRAME OF FIGURE 9.14

$$[k]_{\text{system}} = 2 \quad \begin{bmatrix} 27 & | & 9 & | & 9 \\ +\frac{75}{4}+\frac{75}{4} & | & -\frac{30}{4} & | & -\frac{30}{4} \\ \hline 9 & | & 4 & | \\ -\frac{30}{4} & | & +4 & | & 2 \\ \hline 9 & | & 2 & | & 4 \\ -\frac{30}{4} & | & | & +4 \end{bmatrix} = \begin{bmatrix} 64.5 & 1.5 & 1.5 \\ 1.5 & 8 & 2 \\ 1.5 & 2 & 8 \end{bmatrix}$$

Use of Code Numbers in General

For beamlike elements in space, we number in sequence six coordinates δ at each end, as shown in Figure 9.15, and derive the corresponding stiffness matrix $[\kappa]_\delta$. Each such stiffness matrix is transformed to a new stiffness matrix $[\kappa]_q$ for which the element coordinates have a one-to-one correspondence to the system coordinates q. The coordinate transformation is effected by a matrix of direction cosines† which relates the orientation of the system coordinates at each end of the member to its element coordinates, which are shown in Figure 9.15. Or

$$\left\{ \begin{array}{c} \{\delta\}_{\text{I}} \\ \hline \{\delta\}_{\text{II}} \end{array} \right\} = \left[\begin{array}{c|c} [T]_{\text{I}} & [0] \\ \hline [0] & [T]_{\text{II}} \end{array} \right] \left\{ \begin{array}{c} \{q\}_{\text{I}} \\ \hline \{q\}_{\text{II}} \end{array} \right\} \tag{9.34}$$

---

† See reference 26 pp. 82–84 and reference 28 pp. 172–174.

in which $\{\delta\}_I$, $\{\delta\}_{II}$ are, respectively, the displacements at ends I and II in the "old" coordinates δ, and $\{q\}_I$, $\{q\}_{II}$ are, respectively, the displacements at ends I and II in the new coordinates q. $[T]_I$ and $[T]_{II}$ are, respectively, the matrices of direction cosines for the q coordinates at ends I and II of the member.

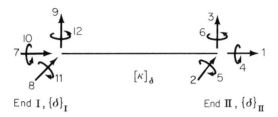

Figure 9.15.

The rotation coordinates at each end (4, 5, 6 and 10, 11, 12) are transformed by the same 3×3 matrix of direction cosines $[L]$ as the corresponding linear displacement coordinates (1, 2, 3 and 7, 8, 9), because small rotations (which are consistent with small deflection theory) may be treated as vectors (see Ref. 73, pp. 253–254). That is,

$$[T]_I = \begin{bmatrix} [L] & [0] \\ [0] & [L] \end{bmatrix}_I \quad \text{and} \quad [T]_{II} = \begin{bmatrix} [L] & [0] \\ [0] & [L] \end{bmatrix}_{II}$$

Matrices [0] here and in Equation (9.34) are null matrices. Each column of $[L]$ represents the three projections of one system coordinate $q_i = 1$ on the corresponding element coordinates δ. For an evaluation of matrix $[L]$ see Reference 28 page 173, or Reference 74 pp. 288–296.

When the system coordinates q at each end of the member have the same orientation with respect to an x, y, z frame of reference, then $[T]_I = [T]_{II}$, or

$$\begin{bmatrix} [T]_I & [0] \\ [0] & [T]_{II} \end{bmatrix} = \begin{bmatrix} [L] & & & \\ & [L] & & \\ & & [L] & \\ & & & [L] \end{bmatrix} \begin{array}{l} \leftarrow \text{Submatrices not shown} \\ \text{are null matrices} \end{array}$$

Equation 9.34 represents an orthogonal transformation as discussed in Section 7.9. Using this transformation we can write

$$[\kappa]_q = \begin{bmatrix} [T]_I & [0] \\ [0] & [T]_{II} \end{bmatrix}^T [\kappa]_\delta \begin{bmatrix} [T]_I & [0] \\ [0] & [T]_{II} \end{bmatrix} \qquad (9.35)$$

$[\kappa]_q$ of the element can now be assigned to the system stiffness matrix using the procedure discussed earlier in this section by writing a code which consists of 12 boxes with numbers.

The code system can also be used with structures in which the elements consist of triangular or rectangular plates as well as other types of elements. The stiffness matrix of each element is transformed through the use of direction cosines in a manner similar to Equation (9.35) (see Section 12.6). The number of boxes in the code of each element is, of course, equal to the number of element coordinates.

Suggested Exercises: Do problems 17, 18, 19 and 20.

9.9 COMPUTER PROGRAM FOR THE CODE SYSTEM

Table 9.4 shows a portion of the computer program (a subroutine) which employs the system code to account for the contribution of each member to the synthesis of the system stiffness matrix.

TABLE 9.4

PORTION OF COMPUTER PROGRAM TO SYNTHESIZE SYSTEM
STIFFNESS MATRIX BY THE CODE SYSTEM APPROACH

Statement Number	*Statement*
1	DO 7 $K = 1, 4$
2	$I = $ NOSC (K)
3	DO 7 $N = 1, 4$
4	$IF\,(I*$NOSC $(N))\,5, 7, 5$
5	$J = $ NOSC (N)
6	SSTF $(I, J) = $ SSTF $(I, J) + $ ESTF (K, N)
7	CONTINUE

Symbols
The following symbols are used in the program of Table 9.4:

$K = $ row number of an element stiffness matrix (or position of box in element code).

$N = $ column number of an element stiffness matrix (or position of box in element code).

ESTF $(K, N) = $ Element STiFfness in row K column N, $\kappa_{K, N}$

NOSC $(K) = $ Number Of System Coordinate corresponding to element coordinate K, or number inside the box with address or position K.

$I = $ Row number of System Stiffness Matrix

$J = $ Column number of System Stiffness Matrix

SSTF $(I, J) = $ System STiFfness in row I column J, $k_{I,J}$.

Referring, for example, to element $\boxed{2}\ \boxed{0}\ \boxed{1}\ \boxed{0}$ of Table 9.2, then

NOSC (1) = 2	ESTF (1, 1) = 4
NOSC (2) = 0	ESTF (2, 1) = 2
NOSC (3) = 1	ESTF (3, 1) = −6
NOSC (4) = 0	ESTF (4, 1) = 6

etc.

Description of Program

Consider that all SSTF (I, J) are initially set equal to zero and that the computer reads the code numbers NOSC (K) and the stiffness matrix ESTF (K, N) for one element, and then it processes this information as it follows the program of Table 9.4. Let us consider element $\boxed{2}\ \boxed{0}\ \boxed{1}\ \boxed{0}$ of Table 9.2 and follow the computer as it processes the code numbers and stiffness matrix.

Statement 1 The computer sets $K = 1$.

Statement 2 The computer assigns code number NOSC (1) to I. Hence $I = 2$.

Statement 3 The computer sets $N = 1$.

Statement 4 is interpreted as follows: The current value of $I*$ NOSC(N) is evaluated (the asterisk designates multiplication). Control is transferred to Statement numbers 5, 7, or 5 according to whether the value of this product is less than, equal to, or greater than zero. A zero value for the product means that at least one of the code numbers is zero and therefore the corresponding row and column of ESTF (K, N) does not contribute to SSTF (I, J) and control is transferred to Statement 7. This causes the program to go back to the beginning of the inner do loop (Statement 3), increment N by 1, and continue with the program execution. If the value of $I * $NOSC (N) is not zero, then the computer goes to Statement 5.

Statement 5 The computer assigns J the value of NOSC (N). In our present example NOSC $(N) = 2$, hence $J = 2$.

Statement 6 The stiffness coefficient ESTF (K, N) in position (K, N) of the element coordinates is added to the current value of SSTF (I, J) to which the elements processed earlier contributed. In our present example

$$\overset{I\ J}{\text{SSTF (2, 2)}} = \overset{I\ J}{\text{SSTF (2, 2)}} + \overset{K\ N}{\text{ESTF (1, 1)}}$$

in which ESTF $(1, 1) = 4$ (see Table 9.2).

Statement 7 (CONTINUE) The computer continues with the inner do loop by returning to Statement 3 and setting $N = 2$. In our present example NOSC $(2) = 0$; hence Statement 4 will cause control to go to Statement 7 from which it returns to Statement 3. Now $N = 3$ and NOSC $(3) = 1$; hence the computer will set $J = 1$ (I is still 1 and so is K because they are in the outer loop, and the inner loop must first be satisfied for all values of N, from 1 to 4, before K and I are incremented). From Statement 6 we compute

$$\overset{I\ J}{\text{SSTF }(1, 2)} = \overset{I\ J}{\text{SSTF }(1, 2)} + \overset{K\ N}{\text{ESTF }(1, 3)}$$

Returning again to Statement 3, the computer sets $N = 4$, but NOSC $(4) = 0$; hence we go from Statement 4 to 7. The inner loop has now been satisfied for all values of N so we return to the outer loop and begin with Statement 1 by setting $K = 2$.

So far we assigned the contributions for the first row of ESTF, or [κ], to SSTF, or [k]. Now the second row will be assigned and so on.

We suggest that the reader follow the execution of the program beginning with element ② ⓪ ① ⓪ of Table 9.2 and then proceeding with the other elements. Recall that SSTF is initially a null matrix.

When an element of the system has M coordinates (boxes), then in Table 9.4 the upper limit of the do loop in Statements 1 and 3 is changed from 4 to M, all the rest remains the same.

Table 9.5 represents a more efficient version of the program in Table 9.4. This program (Table 9.5) will cause the computer to skip any row of ESTF with a zero code number in one operation after the execution of statement 2. Verify this by following the execution of the program with elements of Table 9.2.

TABLE 9.5

A MORE EFFICIENT VERSION OF THE PROGRAM IN TABLE 9.4

1	DO 8 $K = 1, 4$
2	IF (NOSC (K)) 3, 8, 3
3	$I = $ NOSC (K)
4	DO 8 $N = 1, 4$
5	IF (NOSC (N)) 6, 8, 6
6	$J = $ NOSC (N)
7	SSTF $(I, J) = $ SSTF $(I, J) + $ ESTF (K, N)
8	CONTINUE

Suggested Exercises: Do problems 21 and 22.

9.10. WHICH METHOD: STIFFNESS OR FLEXIBILITY

In selecting a method of analysis there are two basic considerations: (1) problem formulation; (2) problem solution.

The key feature in formulating problems by the flexibility and stiffness methods is generating matrices $[b]$ and $[\beta]$, respectively [Equations (7.1, 7.2)]. It is simpler in general to generate $[\beta]$ because, for indeterminate structures, the submatrix $[b]^0$ of $[b]$ corresponds to a choice of redundants and the choice of a "good" set of redundants is generally not an easy task (see Section 8.3).

Relative to the solution of the problem, the ease and speed of the solution depends on the number of unknowns. If we consider, as we did, the displacements $u_i(i = 1, 2, \ldots, n)$ at the intersection of elements to be the unknowns in the stiffness method, then to compute these displacements for any set of forces F_i acting at the coordinates which identify displacements u_i, we must invert a matrix of order n.† On the other hand, the flexibility method requires the inversion of a matrix of order equal to the degree of redundancy of the structure. If we consider the structures of Figure 9.16, then in terms of problem solution, the flexibility method will be preferred for the structure of Figure 9.16(a), whereas the stiffness method will be preferred for the structure of Figure 9.16(b). This is so because the truss of Figure 9.16(a) is redundant to the second degree and therefore the

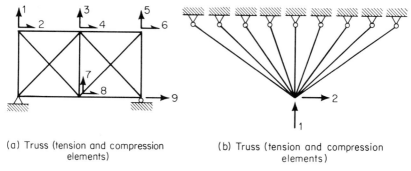

(a) Truss (tension and compression elements)

(b) Truss (tension and compression elements)

Figure 9.16.

flexibility method will require the inversion of a 2×2 matrix. On the other hand, considering arbitrary forces at the nine coordinates shown, then the stiffness method will require the inversion of a 9×9 matrix in order to compute the corresponding displacements.

---

† In Chapter 10 we shall show how the order of the matrix which must be inverted can be reduced.

In Figure 9.16(b) the degree of redundancy is seven; hence a 7×7 matrix must be inverted in the flexibility method, whereas only a 2×2 matrix must be inverted by the stiffness method for arbitrary forces at coordinates 1 and 2.

Much of the recent literature deals with the stiffness method, which indicates that there is in practice a general tendency to prefer this method. There are cases when the flexibility method is more suitable, as can be seen from the foregoing considerations, as well as others which have to do with a dynamic analysis in which the lower modes of vibration are of interest[39].

Suggested Exercises: Do problems 23 and 24.

PROBLEMS

Problem 1: Use the method of Section 9.2 to solve Problem 3, Chapter 6. Consider the beam and the spring as two separate elements in your formulation of the problem.

Problem 2: Use the method of Section 9.2 to compute the internal forces at the ends of each element in the structure of Problem 9, Chapter 6.

Problem 3: Repeat Problem 2 for the structure of Problem 11, Chapter 6.

Problem 4: Use the method of Section 9.2 to compute the internal forces in the structure shown.

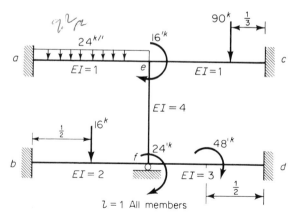

$l = 1$ All members

Problem 5: Compute the internal forces for the structure of Figure 6.20(b), Section 6.9. Use the method of Section 9.2.

Problem 6: Prove that the fixed coordinate forces $\{F\}^0$ discussed in Section 9.2 can be computed from the corresponding element (fixed coordinate) forces $\{P\}^0$ from the relation

$$\{F\}^0 = [\beta]^T \{P\}^0$$

and show that this equation expresses the conditions of equilibrium at the system coordinates in the fixed coordinate state.

Problem 7: Construct the reduced stiffness matrix $[k]^*$ for coordinates 1 and 2 of the structure in Problem 8, Chapter 6. The forces at coordinates 3 and 4 are zero and $k_b = 3.5$.

Problem 8: Define four element coordinates (a rotation and displacement at each end) for each of the three members of the structure in Problem 8, Chapter 6, and one coordinate for the spring. Construct the $[\beta]$ matrix which will relate these element coordinates to the four system coordinates shown in Problem 8, Chapter 6. Use $[\beta]$ to transform the element fixed coordinate state forces $\{P\}^0$ to system forces $\{F\}^0$ considering the forces shown in Figure (b) of Problem 8, Chapter 6.

Problem 9: Show how to analyze an indeterminate structure which is subjected to forces $\{F\}^f$ at the coordinates, forces Q_i not at the coordinates, and to an increase in temperature which will cause its elements to undergo a thermal expansion $\{\Delta\}$ when not connected to the system. (Write the equations and describe how you will generate each term.)

Problem 10: In Figure 9.6 let $l = 12' - 0''$,

$$EA = 30 \times 10^6 \times 20 \frac{\text{lb}}{\text{in.}^2} \text{in.}^2$$

$$EI = 30 \times 10^6 \times 10^3 \frac{\text{lb}}{\text{in.}^2} \text{in.}^4$$

and $\Delta_3 = \Delta_6 = \frac{1}{4}$ in.
  $\Delta_j = 0$ for $j = 1, 2, 4, 5$
Compute the internal forces $\{P\}^f$.

Problem 11: Expand the stiffness matrix of the stepped beam in Problem 5, Chapter 3 to include rigid body motions identified by coordinates 5 and 6 at the left and right ends of the beam, respectively (arrows pointing upward).

Problem 12: Expand the stiffness matrix for the structure of Figure 3.8, Chapter 3 to include the following coordinates in place of the constraints at the fixed end:

$$u_4 \rightarrow \quad u_5 \uparrow \quad u_6 \quad \curvearrowleft$$

Problem 13: Let

$$F_1 = 10$$
$$F_2 = 30$$
$$F_3 = 48$$
$$F_4 = 12$$

in Figure 9.9. Compute the displacements u_i and the internal moments at the ends of each member. (Exploit symmetry.)

Problem 14: Show the force groups on the structure of Figure 9.12 which correspond to generalized forces $Q_i = (i = 1, 2, 3, 4)$ when the forces F_i are $F_1 = 10$, $F_2 = 30$, $F_3 = 48$, $F_4 = 12$.

Problem 15: Exploit symmetry to compute u_i and the internal moments at the ends of each member for the structure of Figure 9.12 for

$$F_1 = 10$$
$$F_2 = 30$$
$$F_3 = 48$$
$$F_4 = 12$$

Problem 16: Exploit the symmetry of the structure shown to compute $u_i(i = 1, 2, 3, 4)$ and the internal moments at the ends of each member.

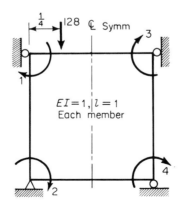

Problem 17: Construct the stiffness matrix for the frame shown using the code system. All members are inextensible, and $EI = l = 1$ for each.

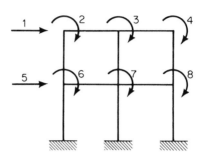

Problem 18. Use Equation (9.35) to transform matrix $[\kappa]_\delta$ for the element in Figure (a) to matrix $[\kappa]_q$ for the same element with coordinates oriented as shown in Figure (b). All coordinates are in the plane of the paper.

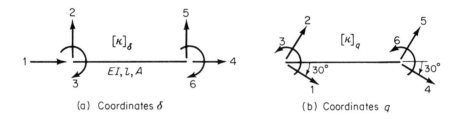

(a) Coordinates δ (b) Coordinates q

Problem 19: Construct the stiffness matrix for the frame shown using the code system. All members are inextensible and $EI = 1$ for each.

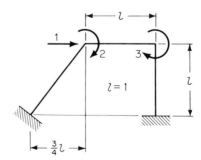

Problem 20: Use the results of Problem 19 to compute the displacements at the system coordinates and the moments at the ends of each member caused by the forces shown.

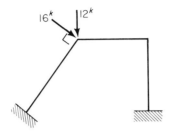

Problem 21: Follow the execution of the program in Table 9.4 for the frame of Figure 9.14. (See Table 9.3.)

Problem 22: Show that the following program will account for the contribution of the forces P_i^0 in the fixed coordinate state of elements to the corresponding forces F_i^0 of the system, or will essentially accomplish what is accomplished by equation

$$\{F\}^0 = [\beta]^T \{P\}^0$$

of Section 9.2, Steps 5 or 8.

Program

Statement Number	Statement
1	DO 5 $K = 1, 4$
2	IF (NOSC (K)) 3, 5, 3
3	$I = $ NOSC (K)
4	$F(I) = F(I) + FEF(K)$
5	CONTINUE

Symbols

$F(I) = F_I^0$, that is, force at system coordinate I in the fixed coordinate state

$FEF(K) = P_K^0$, that is, force at element coordinate K in the fixed coordinate state

NOSC $(K) = $ Number Of System Coordinate corresponding to element coordinate K.

Problem 23: Consider the fixed supports at a and b in the structure of Problem 4 Chapter 9 to settle downward with $u_a = \frac{1}{960}$ $u_b = \frac{1}{1440}$. Compute the rotations at joints e and f due to u_a and u_b only. *Hint*: start with an expanded stiffness matrix which includes coordinates in the direction where settlement of support takes place, that is where boundary motion takes place.

Problem 24: Compute the internal forces due to the settlement of supports a and b in problem 23.

CHAPTER 10

ANALYSIS BY SUBSTRUCTURES
AND BY RECURSION

10.1. INTRODUCTION

When the methods of Chapters 8 and 9 are applied to the analysis of large structures which are highly redundant or which consist of many elements, then the resulting matrices which must be inverted in the solution process may get very large. This may cause computational difficulties, or may prove impossible when the order of the matrices exceeds the capacity of the available computer. It is possible, however, to avoid the inversion of large matrices by applying the stiffness or flexibility methods and treating substructures as elements of the large structure which is analyzed. A substructure may be any portion of the large structure.

Another way to avoid the inversion of large matrices in the analysis of large structures is to select the system coordinates in such a way that the resulting matrix which must be inverted will be a band matrix. [See Equation (8.21).] Using the band matrix, the analysis is conducted by a recursion procedure which requires the inversion of low-order matrices.†

Two more ways to deal with large structures are the relaxation and iteration procedures. In the relaxation procedure, the displacements $\{u\}$ in the equation

$$(\{F\}^f - \{F\}^0) = [k]\{u\}$$

are computed by a procedure similar to the one discussed in Section 5.7[46].

---

† Not all structures lend themselves to this procedure. (See Section 10.6.)

The final internal forces $\{P\}^f$ are then computed from the equation

$$\{P\}^f = \{P\}^0 + [\kappa][\beta]\{u\}$$

The moment distribution method developed by Hardy Cross[47] is a relaxation procedure.

In the iteration procedure again the last two equations apply except that the displacements $\{u\}$ are computed by the iteration procedure discussed in Section 5.6. The Kani method[48] is an iteration procedure which is applied to frames to yield directly the final moments at the ends of each member. This method uses a form of the last two equations simultaneously.

In this chapter, we discuss the analysis of large structures by substructures and by recursion. The analysis of frames by the Kani iteration method is treated in Chapter 11.

10.2. ANALYSIS BY SUBSTRUCTURES

The analysis by substructures consists of a repeated application of the procedures developed in Chapters 8 and 9. We shall therefore not introduce new notation in connection with the analysis by substructure but shall use the notation of Chapters 8 and 9. The analysis by substructures will be developed using the stiffness method[42, 49] in Section 10.3 and using the flexibility method[50] in Section 10.4. In each case the development will be related to the appropriate sections in Chapters 8 and 9.

10.3. ANALYSIS BY SUBSTRUCTURES USING THE STIFFNESS METHOD

Consider the structure of Figure 10.1(a) loaded as shown in Figure 10.2(a). Let us analyze this structure with the following objectives:

1. To find the displacements at any point on the structure
2. To find all internal forces

If we define a system coordinate at each joint of the structure, the analysis requires the inversion of a 6×6 matrix. To avoid this inversion and instead obtain a solution by inverting matrices of order no larger than two, we conduct an analysis by substructures. This amounts to applying the procedure in Section 9.2 to the total structure and to the substructures, as will become evident from the following development.

Total Structure

Using the steps of Section 9.2 for the structure of Figure 10.1(a), we proceed as follows:

1. We define two system coordinates, Figure 10.1(b), so that we can write

$$\{F\} = [k]\{u\} \tag{10.1}$$

The choice of only two system coordinates will cause the solution for $\{u\}$ to involve the inversion of a 2×2 matrix.

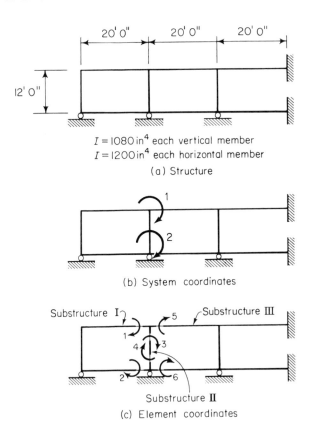

$I = 1080 \text{ in}^4$ each vertical member
$I = 1200 \text{ in}^4$ each horizontal member

(a) Structure

(b) System coordinates

(c) Element coordinates

Figure 10.1.

2. Select elements and element coordinates so that system coordinates occur only at their ends. The elements in Figure 10.1(c) consist of three substructures designated by I, II, and III. Using this designation, we write

$$\left\{ \begin{array}{c} \{P\}_\text{I} \\ \{P\}_\text{II} \\ \{P\}_\text{III} \end{array} \right\} = \left[\begin{array}{ccc} [\kappa]_\text{I} & & \\ & [\kappa]_\text{II} & \\ & & [\kappa]_\text{III} \end{array} \right] \left\{ \begin{array}{c} \{\delta\}_\text{I} \\ \{\delta\}_\text{II} \\ \{\delta\}_\text{III} \end{array} \right\} \qquad (10.2)$$

or in general and compact form [see Equation (9.1)]

$$\{P\} = [\kappa]\{\delta\} \qquad (10.3)$$

The choice of substructures was made in such a way that, again, no greater than a 2 × 2 matrix must be inverted in dealing with any

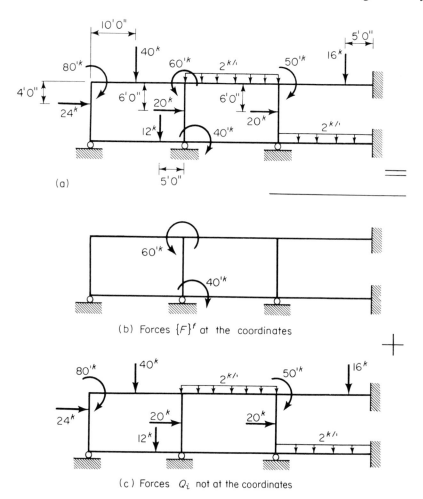

(a)

(b) Forces $\{F\}^f$ at the coordinates

(c) Forces Q_i not at the coordinates

Figure 10.2. Superposition of forces.

substructure. This will become more apparent later when we deal with the substructures separately.

3. Using Figures 10.1(b, c) we write

$$\{\delta\} = [\beta]\{u\} \tag{10.4}$$

in which

$$[\beta] = \begin{bmatrix} 1 & 0 \\ 0 & 1 \\ \hline 1 & 0 \\ 0 & 1 \\ \hline 1 & 0 \\ 0 & 1 \end{bmatrix}$$

in the present example.

4. $[k]$ of Step 1 is synthesized from $[\kappa]$ and $[\beta]$ of Steps 2 and 3, respectively†

$$[k] = [\beta]^T[\kappa][\beta] \tag{10.5}$$

Step 4 requires that we know $[\kappa]$ which contains the stiffness matrices of the substructures (the elements). We shall generate these matrices separately later. For the time being let us assume that they have been generated and proceed with Step 5 for the total structure.

5. Apply to the structure of Figure 10.2(a) a superposition of forces followed by a superposition of displacements as shown in Figures 10.2 and 10.3, respectively. Compare these figures with Figures 9.2 and 9.3, respectively. The fixed coordinate forces $\{F\}^0$ in Figure 10.3(b) are computed from the corresponding forces $\{P\}_s^0$ ($s =$ I, II, III) in that figure

$$\{F\}^0 = [\beta]^T\{P\}^0 \tag{10.6}$$

Forces $\{P\}_s^0$ ($s =$ I, II, III) will be computed later when we deal separately with each substructure. For the present we assume that they have been computed and proceed to Step 6.

6. From Figures 10.2(b) and 10.3(c) we compute the displacements u_i at the system coordinates

$$\{u\} = [k]^{-1}(\{F\}^f - \{F\}^0) \tag{10.7}$$

7. Substituting Equation (10.7) into Equation (10.4) gives [see Equation (9.1a)]

$$\{\delta\} = [\beta][k]^{-1}(\{F\}^f - \{F\}^0) \tag{10.8}$$

and using this expression in Equation (10.3) [see Equation (9.1b)]

$$\{P\} = [\kappa][\beta][k]^{-1}(\{F\}^f - \{F\}^0) \tag{10.9}$$

---

† The code system method of Section 9.8 may be used instead.

8. The final forces $\{P\}^f$ at the element coordinates in Figure 10.1(c) are obtained by superposition from Figures 10.2(b), 10.3(b, c). [See Equation (9.1c).]

$$\{P\}^f = \{P\}^0 + [\kappa][\beta][k]^{-1}(\{F\}^f - \{F\}^0) \qquad (10.10)$$

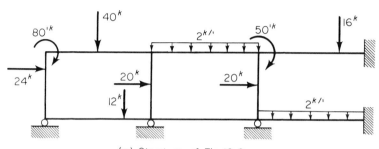

(a) Structure of Fig 10.2 c

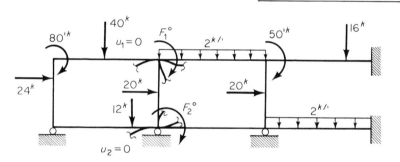

(b) Fixed coordinate state $(u_1 = u_2 = 0)$

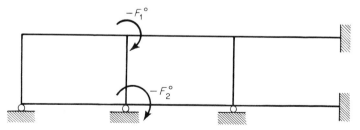

(c) Displacement under the action of forces $-F_i^0$

Figure 10.3. Superposition of displacements.

The results obtained by Equations (10.7) and (10.10) will yield the displacements at the system coordinates of Figure 10.1(b) and the internal forces at the element coordinates of Figure 10.1(c). But how about displacements and internal forces at other points on the structure of Figure 10.2(a)? To answer this question we now apply the procedure of Section 9.2 to each substructure.

Substructure I

We now treat Substructure I as a completely separate structure and compute all its displacements and internal forces in Figures 10.1(b), 10.3(b, c). It is convenient therefore to define additional system coordinates at all

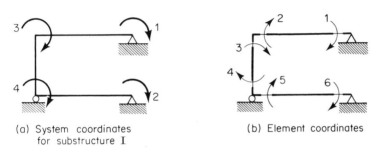

(a) System coordinates   (b) Element coordinates
    for substructure I

Figure 10.4.

joints as shown in Figure 10.4(a). The element coordinates are shown in Figure 10.4(b). The 4×4 stiffness matrix $[k]_\mathrm{I}$ for the coordinates of Figure 10.4(a) is synthesized from the $[\kappa]$ matrices of the elements in Figure 10.4(b)

$$[k]_\mathrm{I} = [\beta]^T[\kappa][\beta] \qquad (10.11)$$

To compute $[\kappa]_\mathrm{I}$ which is required in Step 4, Equation (10.5), we partition the foregoing matrix and write

$$[\kappa]_\mathrm{I} = [k]_{11} - [k]_{12}[k]_{22}^{-1}[k]_{21} \qquad (10.12)$$

in which the submatrices are identified from the following equation:

$$\left\{\dfrac{\{F\}_1}{\{F\}_2}\right\}_\mathrm{I} = \left[\begin{array}{c|c} [k]_{11} & [k]_{12} \\ \hline [k]_{21} & [k]_{22} \end{array}\right]_\mathrm{I} \left\{\dfrac{\{u\}_1}{\{u\}_2}\right\}_\mathrm{I} \qquad (10.13)$$

In Equation (10.13) $\{u\}_1$ and $\{F\}_1$ are displacements and forces at the coordinates where the substructure connects to the system [coordinates 1 and 2 in Figure 10.4(a)], whereas $\{u\}_2$ and $\{F\}_2$ are displacements and forces at the additional coordinates defined for the substructure [coordinates 3, 4 in Figure 10.4(a)].

To analyze substructure I, loaded as shown in Figure 10.3(b), we write

$$\{u\}_1 = \{0\}$$

and therefore from Equation (10.13)

$$\{F\}_2 = [k]_{22}\{u\}_2$$

Also, writing the equation $\{\delta\} = [\beta]\{u\}$, which applies to Figure 10.4, in the partitioned form

$$\{\delta\} = \left[[\beta]_1 \mid [\beta]_2\right] \left\{\begin{matrix} \{u\}_1 \\ \overline{\{u\}_2} \end{matrix}\right\}$$

then, for $\{u\}_1 = \{0\}$

$$\{\delta\} = [\beta]_2\{u\}_2$$

Using Equation (9.1c), we compute for the coordinates in Figure 10.4(b)

$$\{P\}^f = \{P\}^0 + [\kappa][\beta]_2[k]_{22}^{-1}(\{F\}^f - \{F\}^0)_2 \qquad (10.14)$$

in which

$$[k]_{22}^{-1}(\{F\}^f - \{F\}^0)_2 = \{u\}_2 \qquad (10.14a)$$

Using the appropriate components of vector $\{P\}^f$ in Equation (10.14), we obtain $\{P\}^0_I$ of Step 5, Equation (10.6). In the present example the vector

$$\left\{\begin{matrix} P_1 \\ P_6 \end{matrix}\right\}^f$$

of Equation (10.14) is identically equal to

$$\left\{\begin{matrix} P_1 \\ P_2 \end{matrix}\right\}^0_I$$

(that is $\{P\}^0_I$) which is required in Equation (10.6) of Step 5.

Following the preceding steps [Equations (10.12) and (10.14)] for each of the substructures of Figure 10.1(c), we obtain

$$[\kappa]_s \quad \text{and} \quad \{P\}^0_s \qquad \text{for } s = \text{I, II, III}$$

Using these values, Equation (10.7)–(10.10) inclusive can be evaluated.

Internal Forces and Displacements in Substructure I. As we pointed out earlier, to get internal forces P_i ($i = 1, 2 \ldots, 6$) at the coordinates in Figure 10.4(b) for the structure loaded as shown in Figure 10.2(a), we must superpose the corresponding forces from Figures 10.2(b), 10.3(b, c). For Figure 10.3(b), these forces are computed by Equation (10.14). In Figures 10.2(b), 10.3(c), we have

$$\{u\}_1 = \{u\} \quad \text{and} \quad \{F\}_2 = \{0\} \qquad (10.15)$$

in which $\{u\}$ is given by Equation (10.7) and $\{u\}_1$ and $\{F\}_2$ are identified in Equation (10.13). Substituting these relations into Equation (10.13) we write for Substructure I (using only the second matrix equation)

$$\{0\} = [k]_{21}\{u\} + [k]_{22}\{u\}_2 \tag{10.16}$$

Solving for $\{u\}_2$ from Equation (10.16) gives

$$\{u\}_2 = -[k]_{22}^{-1}[k]_{21}\{u\} \tag{10.17}$$

Combining the first of Equations (10.15) and (10.17), we have

$$\begin{Bmatrix} \{u\}_1 \\ \hline \{u\}_2 \end{Bmatrix} = \begin{bmatrix} [I] \\ \hline -[k]_{22}^{-1}[k]_{21} \end{bmatrix}\{u\} \tag{10.18}$$

Using $[\beta]$ of Equation (10.11), we write for the element coordinates in Figure 10.4(b)

$$\{\delta\} = [\beta]\begin{Bmatrix} \{u\}_1 \\ \hline \{u\}_2 \end{Bmatrix} \tag{10.19}$$

and

$$\{P\} = [\kappa]\{\delta\}$$

Substituting from Equations (10.18) and (10.19) into the last equation, we have

$$\{P\} = [\kappa][\beta]\begin{bmatrix} [I] \\ \hline -[k]_{22}^{-1}[k]_{21} \end{bmatrix}\{u\} \tag{10.20}$$

Adding Equations (10.14) and (10.20) gives the internal forces at the coordinates of Figure 10.4(b) for the complete structure loaded as shown in Figure 10.2(a).

The displacements at any point are also computed by a superposition of the displacements in Figures 10.2(b), 10.3(b, c). For example, the displacement vector $\{u\}_2$ at coordinates 3 and 4 in Figure 10.4(a) for the structure as loaded in Figure 10.2(a) is obtained by

$$[k]_{22}^{-1}(\{F\}^I - \{F\}^0)_2 - [k]_{22}^{-1}[k]_{21}\{u\}$$

The left and right term can be identified from Equations (10.14a) and (10.17), respectively.

The procedure followed here applies to all substructures so that our objectives are fulfilled.

Results for the Structure of Figure 10.2(a)

The following intermediate and final results were obtained for the structure of Figure 10.2(a) analyzed by substructures (I and l are in in.[4] and inches respectively).

For substructure I

$$[k]_\mathrm{I} = 5E \begin{bmatrix} 4 & 0 & | & 2 & 0 \\ 0 & 4 & | & 0 & 2 \\ \hline 2 & 0 & | & 10 & 3 \\ 0 & 2 & | & 3 & 10 \end{bmatrix}$$

$$[\kappa]_\mathrm{I} = 5E \left(\begin{bmatrix} 4 & 0 \\ 0 & 4 \end{bmatrix} - \begin{bmatrix} 2 & 0 \\ 0 & 2 \end{bmatrix} \begin{bmatrix} 10 & 3 \\ 3 & 10 \end{bmatrix}^{-1} \begin{bmatrix} 2 & 0 \\ 0 & 2 \end{bmatrix} \right)$$

$$= \tfrac{15}{91} E \begin{bmatrix} 108 & 4 \\ 4 & 108 \end{bmatrix}$$

For substructure II

$$[k]_\mathrm{II} = [\kappa]_\mathrm{II} = 5E \begin{bmatrix} 6 & 3 \\ 3 & 6 \end{bmatrix}$$

For substructure III

$$[\kappa]_\mathrm{III} = \frac{20E}{187} \begin{bmatrix} 173 & 3 \\ 3 & 173 \end{bmatrix}$$

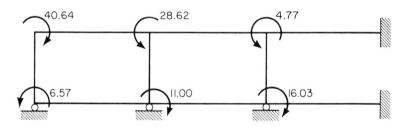

(a) Displacements u_i (arrows show direction of displacements)

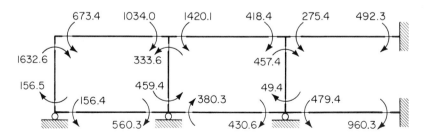

(b) Internal forces P_i in units of in-kip (arrows show direction of forces)

Figure 10.5. Displacements u_i and internal forces P_i for the structure of Fig. 10.2(a).

Using these submatrices in Equation (10.5) (or using the code system method of Section 9.8)

$$[k] = 5E\begin{bmatrix} 13.26 & 3.19 \\ 3.19 & 13.26 \end{bmatrix}$$

For convenience let us set $E = 1^{\kappa}/\text{in.}^2$. Then

$$[k]^{-1} = \frac{1}{828.2}\begin{bmatrix} 13.26 & -3.19 \\ -3.19 & 13.26 \end{bmatrix}$$

Applying Equation (10.7)

$$\{u\} = [k]^{-1}(\{F\}^f - \{F\}^0)$$

$$= \frac{1}{828.2}\begin{bmatrix} 13.26 & -3.19 \\ -3.19 & 13.26 \end{bmatrix}\left(\begin{Bmatrix} -720 \\ 480 \end{Bmatrix} - \begin{Bmatrix} 1002.3 \\ 208.16 \end{Bmatrix}\right) = \begin{Bmatrix} -28.62 \\ 11.00 \end{Bmatrix}$$

The complete solution for all joint rotations and all internal forces is given in Figures 10.5(a) and 10.5(b), respectively.

Suggested Exercise: Do problem 1.

10.4. ANALYSIS BY SUBSTRUCTURES USING THE FLEXIBILITY METHOD

Consider the structure of Figure 10.6. Let us analyze this structure to fulfill the following objectives:

1. Generate the 4 × 4 flexibility matrix $[a]^*$ which will transform forces F_i^* to corresponding displacements u_i^* at the coordinates of Figure 10.6(a).
2. Compute the internal forces $\{P\}$ caused by the externally applied loads F_i^*.

If we proceed with the analysis according to the steps of Section 8.2, then a 4 × 4 matrix must be inverted because the degree of indeterminacy of the structure is four. To avoid this inversion and instead obtain a solution by inverting matrices of order no larger than two, we conduct an analysis by substructures. This will amount to an application of the procedure in Section 8.2 to the total structure and to the substructures.

Total Structure

Using the steps of Section 8.2, we select two redundants as shown in Figure 10.6(b). The structure of Figure 10.6(b) is not determinate. The choice of two redundants will, however, cause the solution to involve the inversion of a 2 × 2 matrix.

The elements and element coordinates are shown in Figure 10.6(c). Here the elements are two substructures I and II. Element coordinates 1 to 4 inclusive go with substructure I which is a cantilever constrained at the junction with substructure II. (Recall that a structure must be supported in at least a statically determinate fashion in order for its flexibility matrix to exist.) Coordinates 5 to 10 inclusive go with substructure II. Element

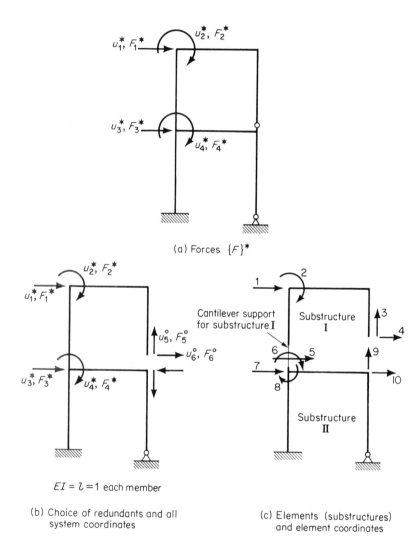

(a) Forces $\{F\}^*$

$EI = l = 1$ each member

(b) Choice of redundants and all system coordinates

(c) Elements (substructures) and element coordinates

Figure 10.6.

coordinates are defined at the following points:

1. At all points where external forces are applied (coordinates 1 and 2 in substructure I)
2. At the statically determinate connection of substructures (coordinates 5 and 6 in substructure II)
3. At redundants where substructures were separated (coordinates 3, 4 for substructure I and coordinates 9, 10 for substructure II)

From Figures 10.6(b, c) we can write

$$
\begin{Bmatrix} P_1 \\ P_2 \\ P_3 \\ P_4 \\ P_5 \\ P_6 \\ P_7 \\ P_8 \\ P_9 \\ P_{10} \end{Bmatrix} =
\left[\begin{array}{cccc|cc}
1 & 0 & 0 & 0 & 0 & 0 \\
0 & 1 & 0 & 0 & 0 & 0 \\
0 & 0 & 0 & 0 & 1 & 0 \\
0 & 0 & 0 & 0 & 0 & 1 \\
1 & 0 & 0 & 0 & 0 & 1 \\
1 & 1 & 0 & 0 & -1 & 0 \\
0 & 0 & 1 & 0 & 0 & 0 \\
0 & 0 & 0 & 1 & 0 & 0 \\
0 & 0 & 0 & 0 & -1 & 0 \\
0 & 0 & 0 & 0 & 0 & -1
\end{array}\right]
\begin{Bmatrix} F_1^* \\ F_2^* \\ F_3^* \\ F_4^* \\ \hline F_5^0 \\ F_6^0 \end{Bmatrix}
$$

In compact form we write

$$
\{P\} = \left[\,[b]^* \mid [b]^0\,\right] \begin{Bmatrix} \{F\}^* \\ \hline \{F\}^0 \end{Bmatrix} \tag{10.21}
$$

or

$$
\{P\} = [b]\{F\}
$$

To get the 6×6 $[a]$ matrix for the coordinates in Figure 10.6(b), we write

$$
[a] = [b]^T[\alpha][b] \tag{10.22}
$$

In the present example,

$$
[\alpha] = \begin{bmatrix} [\alpha]_\text{I} & \\ & [\alpha]_\text{II} \end{bmatrix}
$$

$[\alpha]_\text{I}$ and $[\alpha]_\text{II}$ are the flexibility matrices for substructures I and II, respectively. For the coordinates as shown in Figure 10.6(b), $[\alpha]_\text{I}$ is of order 4 and $[\alpha]_\text{II}$ of order 6.

Substructure I

To get $[\alpha]_I$ we apply the procedure of Section 8.1 to Figure 10.7(a) treated as a separate structure

$$[\alpha]_I = [a]_I = [b]_I^T[\alpha][b]_I \qquad (10.23)$$

in which

$$\{P\} = [b]_I\{F\}_I \qquad (10.24)$$

$\{P\}$ refers to the internal forces in Figure 10.7(b)

$$[\alpha]_I = \tfrac{1}{6}\begin{bmatrix} 2 & 3 & -3 & -1 \\ 3 & 6 & -6 & -3 \\ -3 & -6 & 8 & 6 \\ -1 & -3 & 6 & 10 \end{bmatrix} \qquad (10.25)$$

Substructure II

To get $[\alpha]_{II}$ we apply the procedure of Section 8.2 to Figure 10.8(a) because substructure II is indeterminate to the second order. This will involve the inversion of a matrix of order two only as we required.

From Figures 10.8(b, c), we have

$$\begin{Bmatrix} P_1 \\ P_2 \\ P_3 \\ P_4 \\ P_5 \\ P_6 \end{Bmatrix} = \begin{bmatrix} 1 & 0 & 1 & 0 & 0 & 1 & \vdots & 0 & 1 \\ 0 & 1 & 0 & 1 & -1 & 0 & \vdots & -1 & -1 \\ 0 & 0 & 0 & 0 & -1 & 0 & \vdots & -1 & 0 \\ 0 & 0 & 0 & 0 & 0 & 0 & \vdots & 0 & -1 \\ 0 & 0 & 0 & 0 & 0 & 0 & \vdots & 0 & -1 \\ 0 & 0 & 0 & 0 & 0 & 0 & \vdots & 0 & 0 \end{bmatrix} \begin{Bmatrix} F_5^* \\ F_6^* \\ F_7^* \\ F_8^* \\ F_9^* \\ F_{10}^* \\ \hline F_{11}^0 \\ F_{12}^0 \end{Bmatrix}$$

$$\underbrace{\qquad\qquad [b]_{II}^* \qquad\qquad}\quad \underbrace{\quad [b]_{II}^0 \quad}$$

$\{F\}_{II}^*$

$\{F\}_{II}^0$

that is,

$$\{P\} = \left[[b]_{II}^* \vdots [b]_{II}^0 \right]\begin{Bmatrix} \{F\}_{II}^* \\ \hline \{F\}_{II}^0 \end{Bmatrix} \qquad (10.26)$$

or

$$\{P\} = [b]_{II}\{F\}_{II}$$

and

$$[a]_{II} = [b]_{II}^T[\alpha][b]_{II}$$

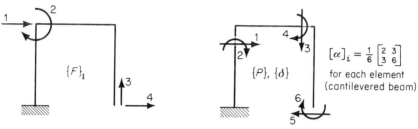

(a) Substructure I and system coordinates

(b) Element coordinates

Figure 10.7.

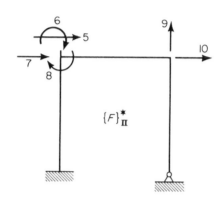

(a) Substructure II

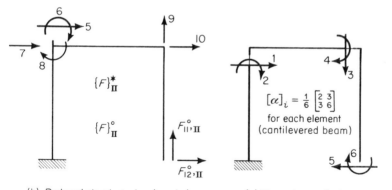

(b) Reduced structure showing choice of redundants and all system coordinates

(c) Element coordinates

Figure 10.8.

From Equations (8.11) and (8.13)

$$\{F\}_{\text{II}}^{0} = -[a]_{22}^{-1}[a]_{21}\{F\}_{\text{II}}^{*} \tag{10.27}$$

and

$$[\alpha]_{\text{II}} = [a]_{\text{II}}^{*} = [a]_{11} - [a]_{12}[a]_{22}^{-1}[a]_{21} \tag{10.28}$$

in which the $[a]_{11}$, $[a]_{12}$, $[a]_{21}$, and $[a]_{22}$ are submatrices of $[a]_{\text{II}}$. In the present example,

$$[a]_{\text{II}} = \frac{1}{6}
\begin{bmatrix}
2 & 3 & 2 & 3 & -3 & 2 & -3 & -1 \\
3 & 6 & 3 & 6 & -6 & 3 & -6 & -3 \\
2 & 3 & 2 & 3 & -3 & 2 & -3 & -1 \\
3 & 6 & 3 & 6 & -6 & 3 & -6 & -3 \\
-3 & -6 & -3 & -6 & 8 & -3 & 8 & 6 \\
2 & 3 & 2 & 3 & -3 & 2 & -3 & -1 \\
-3 & -6 & -3 & -6 & 8 & -3 & 8 & 6 \\
-1 & -3 & -1 & -3 & 6 & -1 & 6 & 10
\end{bmatrix} \tag{10.29}$$

with $[a]_{\overline{11}}$, $[a]_{12}$, $[a]_{\overline{21}}$, $[a]_{22}$ indicated.

$$[a]_{22}^{-1} = \tfrac{3}{11}
\begin{bmatrix}
5 & -3 \\
-3 & 4
\end{bmatrix}$$

$$[\alpha]_{\text{II}} = \frac{1}{11 \times 12}
\begin{bmatrix}
13 & 9 & 13 & 9 & 0 & 13 \\
9 & 24 & 9 & 24 & 0 & 9 \\
13 & 9 & 13 & 9 & 0 & 13 \\
9 & 24 & 9 & 24 & 0 & 9 \\
0 & 0 & 0 & 0 & 0 & 0 \\
13 & 9 & 13 & 9 & 0 & 13
\end{bmatrix} \tag{10.30}$$

The Solution

Using $[\alpha]_{\text{I}}$ and $[\alpha]_{\text{II}}$ from Equations (10.25) and (10.30) in Equation (10.22), we obtain for the coordinates in Figure 10.6(b)

$$[a] =
\begin{bmatrix}
99 & 99 & 22 & 33 & -99 & -22 \\
99 & 156 & 9 & 24 & -156 & -66 \\
22 & 9 & 13 & 9 & -9 & 0 \\
33 & 24 & 9 & 24 & -24 & 0 \\
-99 & -156 & -9 & -24 & 200 & 132 \\
-22 & -66 & 0 & 0 & 132 & 220
\end{bmatrix} \tag{10.31}$$

with $[a]_{\overline{11}}$, $[a]_{12}$, $[a]_{\overline{21}}$, $[a]_{22}$ indicated.

$$[a]_{22}^{-1} = \frac{3}{151} \begin{bmatrix} 55 & -33 \\ -33 & 50 \end{bmatrix} \tag{10.32}$$

Using Equation (8.13) gives

$$[a]^* = \frac{1}{151 \times 4 \times 12} \begin{bmatrix} 1969 & & & \text{Symm.} \\ 534 & 1320 & & \\ 857 & 18 & 677 & \\ 876 & 48 & 396 & 1056 \end{bmatrix} \tag{10.33}$$

This fulfills objective 1.

Using Equation (8.11) we compute now $\{F\}^0$ in Figure 10.6(b). From $\{F\}^0$ and $\{F\}^*$, vector $\{P\}$ of Figure 10.6(c) is computed by Equation (10.26). Identifying the components of $\{P\}$ in Figure 10.6(c) with $\{F\}_I$ and $\{F\}_{II}$ of Figures 10.7(a) and 10.8(a), we have

$$\{F\}_I = \begin{Bmatrix} F_1 \\ F_2 \\ F_3 \\ F_4 \end{Bmatrix}_I = \begin{Bmatrix} P_1 \\ P_2 \\ P_3 \\ P_4 \end{Bmatrix} \tag{10.34}$$

see Fig. 10.7(a) →   ← see Fig. 10.6(c)

$$\{F\}_{II}^* = \begin{Bmatrix} F_5 \\ F_6 \\ F_7 \\ F_8 \\ F_9 \\ F_{10} \end{Bmatrix}_{II} = \begin{Bmatrix} P_5 \\ P_6 \\ P_7 \\ P_8 \\ P_9 \\ P_{10} \end{Bmatrix} \tag{10.35}$$

see Fig. 10.8(a) →   ← see Fig. 10.6(c)

Substituting from Equation (10.34) into Equation (10.24) gives the internal forces at the coordinates of Figure 10.7(b). Substituting from Equation (10.35) into Equation (10.27) gives $\{F\}_{II}^0$, and using $\{F\}_{II}^*$ and $\{F\}_{II}^0$ in Equation (10.26) gives the internal forces at the coordinates in Figure 10.8(c). This fulfills our second objective.

Checking the Results of Equation (10.33). The result given by Equation (10.33) was checked by generating the corresponding stiffness matrix. Additional coordinates 5 and 6 were defined as shown in Figure 10.9. Using the code system method of Section 9.8, the following 6×6 stiffness matrix was generated.

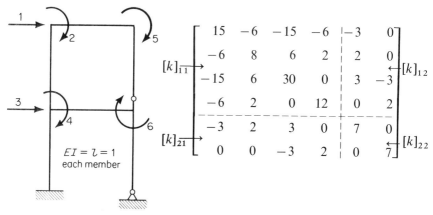

Figure 10.9.

The reduced 4×4 stiffness matrix $[k]^*$ for coordinates $1, 2, 3, 4$ was obtained from the equation

$$[k]^* = [k]_{11} - [k]_{12}[k]_{22}^{-1}[k]_{21}$$

$$= \tfrac{1}{7}\begin{bmatrix} 96 & -36 & -96 & -42 \\ -36 & 52 & 36 & 14 \\ -96 & 36 & 192 & 6 \\ -42 & 14 & 6 & 80 \end{bmatrix} \qquad (10.36)$$

Multiplying $[a]^*$ and $[k]^*$ of Equations (10.33) and (10.36) yields the identity matrix.

Concluding Remarks on the Analysis by Substructures

The analysis by substructures can be applied repeatedly by treating each substructure as a separate system which is analyzed by substructures. It is also possible to mix the methods of stiffness and flexibility, because it may prove simpler to analyze some substructures by the stiffness and others by the flexibility method based on the considerations of Section 9.10.

Suggested Exercise: Do problem 2.

10.5. ANALYSIS BY TRIDIAGONALIZATION WITH STIFFNESS METHOD[42, 46, 51]
Numbering Coordinates

Consider the continuous beam of Figure 10.10. For the coordinates as shown the resulting stiffness matrix is a band matrix of the following form.

$$[k] = \begin{bmatrix} k_{11} & k_{12} & & & & & & \\ k_{21} & k_{22} & k_{23} & & & & & \\ & k_{32} & k_{33} & k_{34} & & & & \\ & & k_{43} & k_{44} & k_{45} & & & \\ & & & & \ddots & & & \\ & & & & & k_{j,j-1} & k_{jj} & k_{j,j+1} \\ & & & & & & \ddots & \\ & & & & & & & k_{n,n-1} & k_{nn} \end{bmatrix} \tag{10.37}$$

Each coordinate j (except for coordinates 1 and n which are coupled to only a single coordinate) is coupled to two coordinates; the coordinate

Figure 10.10.

$j - 1$ that precedes it and the coordinate $j + 1$ that follows it. If the numbering of coordinates in Figure 10.10(a) was not in sequence, then the preceding band matrix would not result. For example, if we interchange the coordinate numbers 2 and n in Figure 10.10, then the first column of $[k]$ will have nonzero elements in rows 1 and n.

Similar considerations apply to larger systems. In Figure 10.11, we number the coordinates of each floor in sequence. The resulting stiffness matrix is a band matrix of the following form:

$$[k] = \begin{bmatrix} [k]_{11} & [k]_{12} & & & & & \\ [k]_{21} & [k]_{22} & [k]_{23} & & & & \\ & [k]_{32} & [k]_{33} & [k]_{34} & & & \\ & & & \cdot & & & \\ & & & [k]_{j,j-1} & [k]_{jj} & [k]_{j,j+1} & \\ & & & & \cdot & & \\ & & & & & \cdot & \\ & & & & [k]_{n,n-1} & [k]_{nn} \end{bmatrix} \quad (10.38)$$

The results in Equations (10.37) and (10.38) are similar, except that in Equation (10.38) each "element" $[k]_{jj}$ corresponds to the stiffness matrix of level j, and matrices $[k]_{j-1,j}$ and $[k]_{j+1,j}$ are the coupling matrices from which we can compute the forces at levels $j - 1$ and $j + 1$ required to produce displacements at level j. Again, if we change the numbering of coordinates, the band matrix of Equation (10.38) will not be generated. The band matrix of Equation (10.38) is referred to as a *tridiagonal band matrix* because three diagonals are occupied with submatrices.

The analysis of the structures in Figures 10.10 and 10.11 by the stiffness method (Section 9.2) will require that we invert the corresponding stiffness matrices in Equations (10.37) and (10.38). Since, however, these matrices are tridiagonal band matrices, we can avoid this inversion and compute the system displacements $\{u\}$ from corresponding forces $\{F\} = \{F\}^f - \{F\}^0$ at the coordinates by a recursion procedure. Then substituting $\{u\}$ for

$$[k]^{-1}(\{F\}^f - \{F\}^0) \quad \text{(see Step 6, Section 9.2)}$$

into Equation (9.1c) we compute the internal forces. Let us develop the recursion procedure.

Recursion Procedure

Using Equation (10.38) we write for the structure of Figure 10.11

$$
\begin{Bmatrix}
\{F\}_1 \\
\{F\}_2 \\
\{F\}_3 \\
\vdots \\
\{F\}_j \\
\vdots \\
\{F\}_n
\end{Bmatrix}
=
\begin{bmatrix}
[k]_{11} & [k]_{12} \\
[k]_{21} & [k]_{22} & [k]_{23} \\
& [k]_{32} & [k]_{33} & [k]_{34} \\
& & & \ddots \\
& & & [k]_{j,j-1} & [k]_{jj} & [k]_{j,j+1} \\
& & & & & \ddots \\
& & & & & [k]_{n,n-1} & [k]_{nn}
\end{bmatrix}
\begin{Bmatrix}
\{u\}_1 \\
\{u\}_2 \\
\{u\}_3 \\
\vdots \\
\{u\}_j \\
\vdots \\
\{u\}_n
\end{Bmatrix}
\qquad (10.39)
$$

In this equation $\{F\}_j$ and $\{u\}_j$ refer, respectively, to the forces and displacements at the coordinates of level j. Forces $\{F\}_j$ may arise from actual

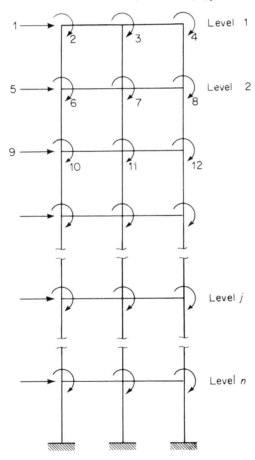

Figure 10.11.

forces $\{F\}_j^f$ and fixed coordinate state forces $\{F\}_j^0$, that is,

$$\{F\}_j = \{F\}_j^f - \{F\}_j^0 \tag{10.40}$$

Equation (10.39) can be written as n separate matrix equations. The first and second of these equations have the form

$$\{F\}_1 = [k]_{11}\{u\}_1 + [k]_{12}\{u\}_2 \tag{10.41}$$

and

$$\{F\}_2 = [k]_{21}\{u\}_1 + [k]_{22}\{u\}_2 + [k]_{23}\{u\}_3 \tag{10.42}$$

From Equation (10.41), we solve for $\{u\}_1$

$$\{u\}_1 = [k]_{11}^{-1}\{F\}_1 - [k]_{11}^{-1}[k]_{12}\{u\}_2 \tag{10.43}$$

Substituting from (10.43) into (10.42) and rearranging yields

$$\{F\}_2^* = [k]_{22}^*\{u\}_2 + [k]_{23}\{u\}_3 \tag{10.44a}$$

in which

$$\{F\}_2^* = \{F\}_2 - [k]_{21}[k]_{11}^{-1}\{F\}_1 \tag{10.44b}$$

$$[k]_{22}^* = [k]_{22} - [k]_{21}[k]_{11}^{-1}[k]_{12} \tag{10.44c}$$

From Equation (10.44a)

$$\{u\}_2 = [k]_{22}^{*-1}\{F\}_2^* - [k]_{22}^{*-1}[k]_{23}\{u\}_3 \tag{10.44d}$$

Equation (10.44a) has the form of Equation (10.41) with all subscripts in Equation (10.44a) advanced by one when compared to corresponding subscripts in Equation (10.41).

We now write the third of matrix equations (10.39)

$$\{F\}_3 = [k]_{32}\{u\}_2 + [k]_{33}\{u\}_3 + [k]_{34}\{u\}_4 \tag{10.45}$$

Equations (10.44a) and (10.45) form a second pair of equations similar to the first pair of Equations (10.41) and (10.42). All subscripts in the second pair are advanced by one when compared to the first pair. We operate on the second pair of equations as we did on the first by substituting Equation (10.44d) into Equation (10.45) and rearranging. This yields

$$\{F\}_3^* = [k]_{33}^*\{u\}_3 + [k]_{34}\{u\}_4 \tag{10.46a}$$

in which

$$\{F\}_3^* = \{F\}_3 - [k]_{32}[k]_{22}^{*-1}\{F\}_2^* \tag{10.46b}$$

$$[k]_{33}^* = [k]_{33} - [k]_{32}[k]_{22}^{*-1}[k]_{23} \tag{10.46c}$$

From Equation (10.46a)

$$\{u\}_3 = [k]_{33}^{*-1}\{F\}_3^* - [k]_{33}^{*-1}[k]_{34}\{u\}_4 \tag{10.46d}$$

We now write the fourth of matrix equations (10.39)

$$\{F\}_4 = [k]_{43}\{u\}_3 + [k]_{44}\{u\}_4 + [k]_{45}\{u\}_5 \tag{10.47}$$

Equations (10.46a) and (10.47) form a third pair similar to the second pair [Equations (10.44a, 10.45)]. All the subscripts in the third pair are advanced by one when compared to the second pair. A similar relation exists between Equations (10.44b, c, d) and (10.45b, c, d). We operate on the third pair of equations as we did on the second by substituting Equation (10.46d) into (10.47) and obtain

$$\{F\}_4^* = [k]_{44}^*\{u\}_4 + [k]_{45}\{u\}_5 \tag{10.48a}$$

in which

$$\{F\}_4^* = \{F\}_4 - [k]_{43}[k]_{33}^{*-1}\{F\}_3^* \tag{10.48b}$$

$$[k]_{44}^* = [k]_{44} - [k]_{43}[k]_{33}^{*-1}[k]_{34} \tag{10.48c}$$

From Equation (10.48a)

$$\{u\}_4 = [k]_{44}^{*-1}\{F\}_4^* - [k]_{44}^{*-1}[k]_{45}\{u\}_5 \tag{10.48d}$$

Equations (10.48a, b, c, d) are similar to Equations (10.46) with all subscripts advanced by one.

Proceeding in this manner, the general equations in the recursion process have the following form [compare with Equations (10.46) and (10.48)]:

$$\{F\}_j^* = [k]_{jj}^*\{u\}_j + [k]_{j,\,j+1}\{u\}_{j+1} \tag{10.49a}$$

in which

$$\{F\}_j^* = \{F\}_j - [k]_{j,\,j-1}[k]_{j-1,\,j-1}^{*-1}\{F\}_{j-1}^* \tag{10.49b}$$

$$[k]_{jj}^* = [k]_{jj} - [k]_{j,\,j-1}[k]_{j-1,\,j-1}^{*-1}[k]_{j-1,\,j} \tag{10.49c}$$

From Equation (10.49a)

$$\{u\}_j = [k]_{jj}^{*-1}\{F\}_j^* - [k]_{jj}^{*-1}[k]_{j,\,j+1}\{u\}_{j+1} \tag{10.49d}$$

Equation (10.49a) is paired with the $j + 1$ of matrix equations (10.39)

$$\{F\}_{j+1} = [k]_{j+1,\,j}\{u\}_j + [k]_{j+1,\,j+1}\{u\}_{j+1} + [k]_{j+1,\,j+2}\{u\}_{j+2} \tag{10.50}$$

and the process is continued until finally we pair Equation (10.49a) for $j = n - 1$ with the last of matrix equations (10.39)

$$\{F\}_n = [k]_{n,\,n-1}\{u\}_{n-1} + [k]_{n,\,n}\{u\}_n \tag{10.51}$$

This last pair yields

$$\{F\}_n^* = [k]_{nn}^*\{u\}_n \tag{10.52a}$$

in which

$$\{F\}_n^* = \{F\}_n - [k]_{n,n-1}[k]_{n-1,n-1}^{*-1}\{F\}_{n-1}^* \qquad (10.52b)$$

$$[k]_{nn}^* = [k]_{nn} - [k]_{n,n-1}[k]_{n-1,n-1}^{*-1}[k]_{n-1,n} \qquad (10.52c)$$

From Equation (10.52a), we solve for $\{u\}_n$

$$\{u\}_n = [k]_{nn}^{*-1}\{F\}_n^* \qquad (10.52d)$$

Using Equation (10.49d) with $j = n - 1$, we can solve for $\{u\}_{n-1}$, and by further back substitutions we solve for all $\{u\}_j$.

More on Numbering Coordinates

The recursion process requires the inversion of matrices whose largest order is equal to the order of the largest matrix $[k]_{jj}$ [see Equations (10.49)]. In the structure of Figure 10.11 this matrix is of order four which is equal to the number of coordinates per level. To keep the size of this matrix small we suggest that the structure be examined before numbering the coordinates. For example in the structure of Figure 10.12, it is advantageous to number the coordinates from one column line to another. In general, to keep matrix $[k]_{jj}$ small, it is advantageous to proceed with the coordinate numbering across the narrow dimension of the structure as was done in Figures 10.11 and 10.12.

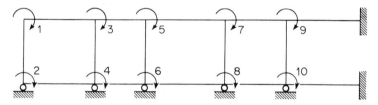

Figure 10.12.

Advantages and Disadvantages of the Recursion Solution

Analysis of the frame in Figure 10.11 by the recursion procedure is advantageous when the frame is relatively tall and narrow and only a single or very few loading conditions are considered. We point out that the computation time will be linearly related to the number of levels in the frame of Figure 10.11 when the recursion procedure is used[46], whereas the inversion time for a matrix is related to the cube of the order of the matrix.

The recursion approach has these disadvantages: it must be repeated for each loading condition and it is not too efficient when matrices $[k]_{jj}$ of Equation (10.39) are of a high order; that is, for structures that are wide as well as tall. For such structures the iteration method of Chapter 11 is more efficient.

Suggested Exercises: Do problems 3 and 4.

10.6. COMBINING ANALYSIS BY SUBSTRUCTURES WITH TRIDIAGONALIZATION

When a structure has the form of a closed ring (see Figure 10.13), then it is not possible to number the coordinates in a way which will yield a tridiagonal band matrix in which the matrices $[k]_{jj}$ are of low order. In such a case it may be advantageous to combine analysis by substructures and analysis by tridiagonalization. Figure 10.14 shows the choice of system coordinates for the total structure and the substructures so as to exploit the features of the tridiagonalization.

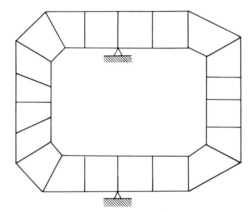

Figure 10.13. Closed ring frame.

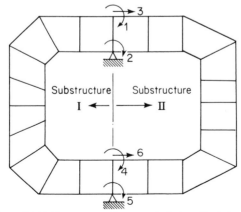

Figure 10.14. System coordinates and choice of substructures.

In the fixed coordinate state [as in Figure 10.3(b), for example], the substructures are analyzed by tridiagonalization as discussed in the last section. To complete the analysis by substructures we must compute the stiffnesses of the substructures considered as elements. This is accomplished by the following recursion procedure:

Computing Stiffness $[\kappa]_s$ of Substructure s by Tridiagonalization

Consider substructure I for the structure of Figure 10.14 as shown in Figure 10.15. To compute the stiffness matrix for the coordinates at end regions 1 and n only, where this substructure is connected to form the system, we proceed as follows:

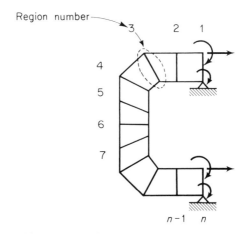

Region number

Figure 10.15. Substructure I of Fig. 10.14.

We define coordinates at the joints of each region† (there are two joints per region in Figure 10.15) proceeding from region 1 to n in sequence. To compute the desired stiffness matrix $[\kappa]_1$ we set $\{F\}_j = \{0\}$ for all regions j except for $j = 1$ and $j = n$ and write

$$
\begin{Bmatrix} \{F\}_1 \\ \{0\} \\ \{0\} \\ \vdots \\ \{0\} \\ \{F\}_n \end{Bmatrix}
=
\begin{bmatrix}
[k]_{11} [k]_{12} & & & & \\
[k]_{21} [k]_{22} [k]_{23} & & & & \\
& [k]_{32} [k]_{33} [k]_{34} & & & \\
& & \ddots & & \\
& & & [k]_{n-1,n-2} [k]_{n-1,n-1} [k]_{n-1,n} \\
& & & [k]_{n,n-1} \quad [k]_{nn}
\end{bmatrix}
\begin{Bmatrix} \{u\}_1 \\ \{u\}_2 \\ \{u\}_3 \\ \vdots \\ \{u\}_{n-1} \\ \{u\}_n \end{Bmatrix}
$$

(10.53)

---
† A *region* in Figure 10.15 is equivalent in concept to a *level* in Figure 10.11.

We compute the desired stiffness matrix in two steps:

Step 1. To get the columns of $[\kappa]_l$ which correspond to the coordinates at region n we set $\{u\}_1 = \{0\}$ and compute $\{F\}_1$ and $\{F\}_n$ in terms of $\{u\}_n$.

Step 2. To get the columns of $[\kappa]_l$ which correspond to the coordinates at region 1 we set $\{u\}_n = \{0\}$ and compute $\{F\}_1$ and $\{F\}_n$ in terms of $\{u\}_1$.

Step 1: We set $\{u\}_1 = \{0\}$ in Equation (10.53) and write the first three matrix equations

$$\{F\}_1 = [k]_{12}\{u\}_2 \tag{10.54}$$

$$\{0\} = [k]_{22}\{u\}_2 + [k]_{23}\{u\}_3 \tag{10.55}$$

$$\{0\} = [k]_{32}\{u\}_2 + [k]_{33}\{u\}_3 + [k]_{34}\{u\}_4 \tag{10.56}$$

From Equation (10.55),

$$\{u\}_2 = -[k]_{22}^{-1}[k]_{23}\{u\}_3 \tag{10.57}$$

Substituting Equation (10.57) into (10.56) and solving for $\{u\}_3$, we have

$$\{u\}_3 = -[k]_{33}^{*-1}[k]_{34}\{u\}_4 \tag{10.58a}$$

in which

$$[k]_{33}^* = [k]_{33} - [k]_{32}[k]_{22}^{-1}[k]_{23} \tag{10.58b}$$

Using Equation (10.58a) in the fourth of Equations (10.53) and solving for $\{u\}_4$, we obtain

$$\{u\}_4 = -[k]_{44}^{*-1}[k]_{45}\{u\}_5 \tag{10.59a}$$

in which

$$[k]_{44}^* = [k]_{44} - [k]_{43}[k]_{33}^{*-1}[k]_{34} \tag{10.59b}$$

Proceeding this way, we obtain for the displacement vector $\{u\}_j$ at region j

$$\{u\}_j = -[k]_{jj}^{*-1}[k]_{j,j+1}\{u\}_{j+1} \tag{10.60a}$$

in which

$$[k]_{jj}^* = [k]_{jj} - [k]_{j,j-1}[k]_{j-1,j-1}^{*-1}[k]_{j-1,j} \tag{10.60b}$$

The last of matrix Equations (10.53) has the form

$$\{F\}_n = [k]_{n,n-1}\{u\}_{n-1} + [k]_{n,n}\{u\}_n \tag{10.61}$$

Using Equation (10.60a) all $\{u\}_j$ ($j = n - 1, n - 2, \ldots, 2$) can be expressed in terms of $\{u\}_n$ by back substitution, so that $\{F\}_1$

and $\{F\}_n$ of Equations (10.54) and (10.61) can also be expressed in terms of $\{u\}_n$ when $\{u\}_1 = \{0\}$.

Step 2: We set $\{u\}_n = \{0\}$ and write the last three of matrix equations (10.53) beginning with the last

$$\{F\}_n = [k]_{n,n-1}\{u\}_{n-1} \tag{10.62}$$

$$\{0\} = [k]_{n-1,n-2}\{u\}_{n-2} + [k]_{n-1,n-1}\{u\}_{n-1} \tag{10.63}$$

$$\{0\} = [k]_{n-2,n-3}\{u\}_{n-3} + [k]_{n-2,n-2}\{u\}_{n-2} + [k]_{n-2,n-1}\{u\}_{n-1} \tag{10.64}$$

From Equation (10.63),

$$\{u\}_{n-1} = -[k]_{n-1,n-1}^{-1}[k]_{n-1,n-2}\{u\}_{n-2} \tag{10.65}$$

Substituting Equation (10.65) into Equation (10.64), we solve for $\{u\}_{n-2}$ in terms of $\{u\}_{n-3}$

$$\{u\}_{n-2} = -[k]_{n-2,n-2}^{*-1}[k]_{n-2,n-3}\{u\}_{n-3} \tag{10.66a}$$

in which

$$[k]_{n-2,n-2}^{*} = [k]_{n-2,n-2} - [k]_{n-2,n-1}[k]_{n-1,n-1}^{-1}[k]_{n-1,n-2} \tag{10.66b}$$

Substituting Equation (10.66a) into the fourth (counting from the bottom) of matrix equations (10.53), we solve for $\{u\}_{n-3}$ in terms of $\{u\}_{n-4}$. Proceeding this way, we obtain for the displacement vector $\{u\}_j$ at region j

$$\{u\}_j = -[k]_{jj}^{*-1}[k]_{j,j-1}\{u\}_{j-1} \tag{10.67a}$$

in which

$$[k]_{jj}^{*} = [k]_{jj} - [k]_{j,j+1}[k]_{j+1,j+1}^{*-1}[k]_{j+1,j} \tag{10.67b}$$

The last (counting from the bottom) of matrix equations (10.53) has the form

$$\{F\}_1 = [k]_{11}\{u\}_1 + [k]_{12}\{u\}_2 \tag{10.68}$$

Using Equation (10.67a) all $\{u\}_j$ $(j = 2, 3, \ldots, n-1)$ can be expressed in terms of $\{u\}_1$ by back substitution, so that $\{F\}_n$ and $\{F\}_1$ of Equations (10.62) and (10.68) can also be expressed in terms of $\{u\}_1$ when $\{u\}_n = \{0\}$.

Using the results of our two steps in the equation

$$\begin{Bmatrix} \{F\}_1 \\ \{F\}_n \end{Bmatrix} = [\kappa]_1 \begin{Bmatrix} \{u\}_1 \\ \{u\}_n \end{Bmatrix} \tag{10.69}$$

(which relates forces and displacement at regions 1 and n of Figure 10.15 with all $\{F\}_j = \{0\}$ for $j \neq 1, n$), we obtain the desired matrix $[\kappa]_1$.

The Complete Solution

When the analysis by substructures is completed, the internal forces due to displacements $\{u\}_1$ and $\{u\}_n$ (system coordinates of Figure 10.14) are superposed on the internal forces in the fixed coordinate state. Once $\{u\}_1$ and $\{u\}_n$ are known, the corresponding displacements $\{u\}_j$ of the substructures can be computed by adding for each region j the results from Equations (10.60a) and (10.67a) and those obtained from the fixed coordinate state part of the analysis. With displacements $\{u\}_j$ established, the internal forces can be computed at any point in the structure.

Suggested Exercises: Do problems 5 and 6.

10.7. ANALYSIS BY TRIDIAGONALIZATION WITH FLEXIBILITY METHOD

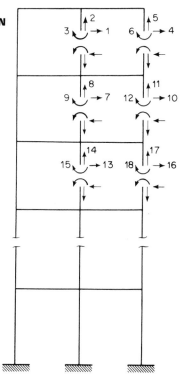

We can also use the tridiagonalization approach to compute internal forces in redundant structures by the flexibility method. In Section 10.5 a proper numbering of coordinates led to a tridiagonal stiffness matrix; similarly, a proper choice of redundants may lead to a tridiagonal matrix $[a]_{22}$ which corresponds to the redundants, Equation (8.8). Such a choice of redundants was demonstrated in Figure 8.4(b) and led to the tridiagonal band matrix $[a]_{22}$ of Equation (8.21). This matrix corresponds to the matrix of Equation (10.37) in Section 10.5.

For the frame of Figure 10.11 a choice of redundants as shown in Figure 10.16 will lead to a tridiagonal matrix $[a]_{22}$ in which each submatrix $[a]^s_{jj}$ is of order six.† We can write then an equation similar to Equation (10.39) by using the

Figure 10.16. Choice of redundants for tridiagonalization.

---

† The superscript s in $[a]^s_{jj}$ is used to distinguish these as submatrices of $[a]_{22}$ in Equation (8.10).

second of Equations (8.10):

$$
\begin{Bmatrix} q \end{Bmatrix} \qquad\qquad [a]_{22} \qquad\qquad \{F\}^0
$$

$$
\begin{Bmatrix} \{q\}_1 \\ \{q\}_2 \\ \{q\}_3 \\ \vdots \\ \{q\}_j \\ \vdots \\ \{q\}_n \end{Bmatrix} =
\begin{bmatrix}
[a]^s_{11}[a]^s_{12} & & & \\
[a]^s_{21}[a]^s_{22}[a]^s_{23} & & & \\
 & [a]^s_{32}[a]^s_{33}[a]^s_{34} & & \\
 & & \ddots & \\
 & & [a]^s_{j,j-1}[a]^s_{jj}[a]^s_{j,j+1} & \\
 & & & \ddots \\
 & & & [a]^s_{n,n-1}[a]^s_{nn}
\end{bmatrix}
\begin{Bmatrix} \{F\}^0_1 \\ \{F\}^0_2 \\ \{F\}^0_3 \\ \vdots \\ \{F\}^0_j \\ \vdots \\ \{F\}^0_n \end{Bmatrix}
\tag{10.70}
$$

or in compact form

$$\{q\} = [a]_{22}\{F\}^0$$

in which

$$\{q\} = -[a]_{21}\{F\}^* \tag{10.71}$$

and each submatrix $\{q\}_j$ refers to the redundants at one story of the frame in Figure 10.16. The same recursion analysis applied to Equation (10.39) can be applied to Equation (10.70), so that the redundants $\{F\}^0_j$ can be solved in terms of the $\{q\}_j$ which are related to the $\{F\}^*$ through Equation (10.71). Substituting $\{F\}^0$ into Equation (8.4) the internal forces are obtained, and from Equation (8.10) the displacements $\{u\}^*$ are computed. Again, the procedure has the disadvantage of needing to be repeated for each loading condition, and for wide structures, the submatrices $[a]^s_{jj}$ in Equation (10.70) that must be inverted in the recursion analysis will get large.

PROBLEMS

Problem 1: Use the method of substructures of Section 10.3 to compute the displacements at coordinates 1, 2, and 3 for the structure shown.

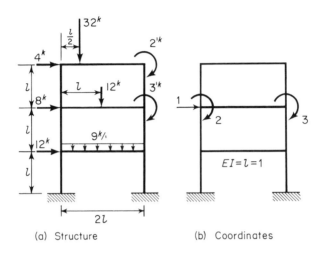

(a) Structure (b) Coordinates

Problem 2: Use the method of substructures and the results of Section 10.4 to compute the 6×6 flexibility matrix for the following structure.

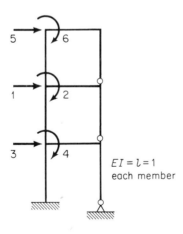

$EI = l = 1$
each member

Problem 3: Compute the rotations of the six joints in the structure of Figure 10.2(a), using the recursion procedure of Section 10.5.

Problem 4: Compute the displacements of the floors and the joint rotations in the frame of Problem 1. Use the recursion procedure of Section 10.5.

Problem 5: Compute the 2×2 stiffness matrix for the continuous beam shown, using the recursion procedure of Section 10.6. Check your result by an alternate procedure which will involve the inversion of a 3×3 matrix [see Equation (9.13)].

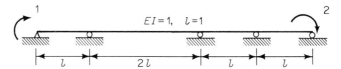

Problem 6: Compute the 4×4 stiffness matrix for the structure shown, using the recursion procedure of Section 10.6.

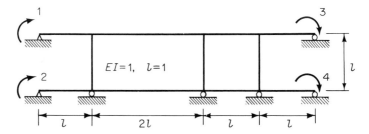

CHAPTER 11

ANALYSIS BY ITERATION

11.1. INTRODUCTION

In Section 5.6 we discussed the solution of linear equations by the Gauss–Seidel iteration method. It was pointed out that a system of equations which is most suitable for solution by iteration is a diagonal system, such as is obtained in structural analysis by the stiffness method. In this chapter, we develop the Gauss–Seidel iteration method for the analysis of rectangular building frames. This method was developed by Kani[48] and is discussed elsewhere[52, 53, 54, 70]. The extension of this method to the analysis of complex multistory frames is discussed by Thadani[55]. Another reference[56] deals with the convergence of the method.

In developing the iteration method we shall first derive the general equations for the analysis of rectangular frames with nonprismatic members. Then we shall apply the iteration to the analysis of rigidly connected beams and to frames. The last two sections of the chapter demonstrate how the iteration method can be combined with the stiffness method to analyze rectangular frames constructed of nonprismatic members with analytically complex shapes.

The notation adopted in this chapter for developing the iteration method is slightly different from that used elsewhere in this book. It is, however, consistent with the notation in the references and relates the concepts used in the iteration method to the familiar concepts of the moment distribution method developed by Hardy Cross[47].

11.2. ITERATION METHOD FOR FRAMES WITH NONPRISMATIC MEMBERS†

The final end moments for a member of a rigid frame in which only bending energy is considered can be obtained by superposition as shown

---

† The development in this section is taken from Rubinstein[54].

in Figure 11.1. In Figure 11.1(a) the loads acting on the member are applied with ends i and k constrained. In Figure 11.1(b) the final rotation θ_i is produced by applying end moments and corresponding end shears (not shown in the figure). In Figures 11.1(c) and (d), respectively, the final rotation

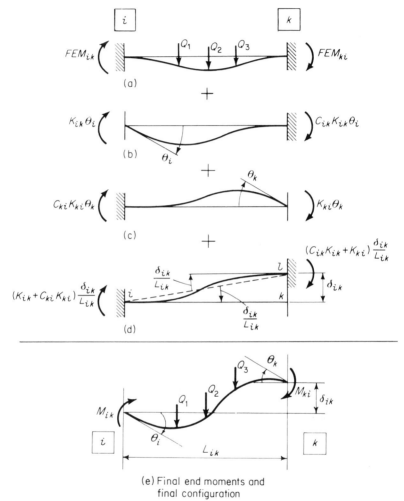

(e) Final end moments and
final configuration

Figure 11.1. The final moments and final configuration of a frame member obtained by superposition.

of end k, θ_k, and the displacement of end k with respect to end i, δ_{ik}, are produced. Note that Figure 11.1(d) is a linear combination of Figures 11.1(b) and (c) in which $\theta_i = \theta_k = \delta_{ik}/L_{ik}$. The member ik is first moved as a rigid body from position ik to il and then a rotation δ_{ik}/L_{ik} is applied in the clockwise direction to each end.

The final end moments M_{ik} and M_{ki} are obtained by superposition of the end moments in Figures 11.1(a, b, c, d). Hence, at end i (clockwise moments are taken as positive),

$$M_{ik} = FEM_{ik} + K_{ik}\theta_i + C_{ki}K_{ki}\theta_k + (K_{ik} + C_{ki}K_{ki})\frac{\delta_{ik}}{L_{ik}} \qquad (11.1)$$

in which

M_{ik} = the final end moment at end i of member ik.

FEM_{ik} = the fixed end moment at end i of member ik.

K_{ik} = stiffness at i for member ik, or the moment required to rotate end i of member ik through a unit rotation with end k fixed, $K_{ik} = 4EI_{ik}/L_{ik}$ for prismatic members, where E, I_{ik}, and L_{ik} are, respectively, the modulus of elasticity, moment of inertia of cross section, and length of member.

C_{ki} = carry-over factor from k to i, or $C_{ki}K_{ki}$ is the moment required at i to permit a unit rotation at k with end i fixed.

θ_i, θ_k = rotation of end i and k, respectively.

δ_{ik} = displacement of end i with respect to end k.

In order to make notation compatible with the references[48, 54] let

$$\overline{M}_{ik} = FEM_{ik} \qquad \text{(a)}$$

$$M'_{ik} = C_{ik}K_{ik}\theta_i \qquad \text{(b)}$$

$$M'_{ki} = C_{ki}K_{ki}\theta_k \qquad \text{(c)} \qquad (11.2)$$

$$M''_{ik} = 3C_{ki}K_{ki}\frac{\delta_{ik}}{L_{ik}} = 3C_{ik}K_{ik}\frac{\delta_{ik}}{L_{ik}} \qquad \text{(d)}$$

Relation (11.2d) implies that†

$$C_{ik}K_{ik} = C_{ki}K_{ki} \qquad (11.3)$$

Using relations (11.2) and (11.3), Equation (11.1) becomes

$$M_{ik} = \overline{M}_{ik} + \frac{1}{C_{ik}}M'_{ik} + M'_{ki} + B_{ik}M''_{ik} \qquad (11.4)$$

where

$$B_{ik} = \frac{1}{3}\frac{1 + C_{ik}}{C_{ik}} \qquad (11.5)$$

---

† This can be verified by setting $\theta_i = \theta_k = 1$ in Figures 11.1 (b and c) and applying Betti's law (see Section 6.8).

Similarly, for end k of member ik in Figure 11.1

$$M_{ki} = \overline{M}_{ki} + \frac{1}{C_{ki}} M'_{ki} + M'_{ik} + B_{ki}M''_{ik} \tag{11.6}$$

In order to obtain the final end moments M_{ik} and M_{ki} from Equations (11.4) and (11.6), the values of M'_{ik}, M'_{ki}, and M''_{ik} must be determined. C_{ik}, C_{ki}, $\overline{M}_{ik}$, and $\overline{M}_{ki}$ can be computed earlier for each member of the frame.

Computations for M'_{ik}

For equilibrium at any joint i (see Figure 11.2)

$$\sum_k M_{ik} = 0 \tag{11.7}$$

For instance for joint $i = 6$ in Figure 11.2, $k = 2, 5, 10, 7$ and Equation (11.7) becomes

$$\sum_k M_{6,k} = M_{6,2} + M_{6,5} + M_{6,10} + M_{6,7} = 0$$

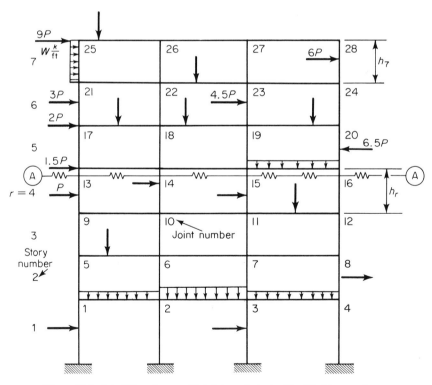

Figure 11.2. A building frame with joints and stories identified by numbers.

Substituting for M_{ik} from Equation (11.4) into Equation (11.7) and re-arranging

$$\sum_k \frac{1}{C_{ik}} M'_{ik} = -(\overline{M}_i + \sum_k M'_{ki} + \sum_k B_{ik}M''_{ik}) \qquad (11.8)$$

where

$$\overline{M}_i = \sum_k \overline{M}_{ik} \qquad (11.8a)$$

Dividing each side of Equation (11.2b) by C_{ik}

$$\frac{1}{C_{ik}} M'_{ik} = K_{ik}\theta_i \qquad (11.9)$$

Summing each side of Equation (11.9) on k and recalling that θ_i has the same value for all members rigidly connected at joint i

$$\sum_k \frac{1}{C_{ik}} M'_{ik} = \theta_i \sum_k K_{ik} \qquad (11.10)$$

Dividing Equation (11.9) by Equation (11.10) (corresponding sides of each equation) and solving for $(1/C_{ik})M'_{ik}$

$$\frac{1}{C_{ik}} M'_{ik} = \frac{K_{ik}}{\sum_k K_{ik}} \sum_k \frac{1}{C_{ik}} M'_{ik} \qquad (11.11)$$

Substituting for

$$\sum_k \frac{1}{C_{ik}} M'_{ik}$$

from Equation (11.8) into Equation (11.11) and multiplying each side by C_{ik} results in the following expression for M'_{ik}:

$$M'_{ik} = \mu_{ik}(\overline{M}_i + \sum_k M'_{ki} + \sum_k B_{ik}M''_{ik}) \qquad (11.12)$$

where

$$\mu_{ik} = -\frac{C_{ik}K_{ik}}{\sum_k K_{ik}} \qquad (11.12a)$$

Equation (11.12) is the equation used in the iteration process to solve for the M'_{ik} values. The values for M'_{ki} are computed from the same equation when the iteration is performed at joint k with i taking on the values of the joint numbers linked to joint k by members with one end at k.

Computations for M_{ik}''

For equilibrium of the portion of the building frame above Section A–A at the top of any story r (such as, for instance, $r = 4$ in Figure 11.2)

$$\sum P + \sum_r H_{ik} = 0 \tag{11.13}$$

where $\sum P$ is the sum of all the external horizontal loads acting on the building frame above the top of the rth story (above Section A–A for $r = 4$ in Figure 11.2), and $\sum_r H_{ik}$ is the sum of the column shears at the top of the rth story (at Section A–A for $r = 4$ in Figure 11.2). Note that $\sum_r$ in $\sum_r H_{ik}$ designates summing for all columns of the rth story, so that r in this case is not a summation index in the usual sense. This designation will be retained throughout the following development. Hence, in $\sum_r H_{ik}$ subscript i takes on the values of the joint numbers at the top of the rth story, whereas k takes on the value of the joint number corresponding to each column at the bottom of the rth story. For instance, for $r = 4$ in Figure 11.2, Equation (11.13) takes the form

$$(1.5P + 2P + 3P + 9P + 6P + 4.5P - 6.5P + wh_7)$$

$$+ (H_{13,9} + H_{14,10} + H_{15,11} + H_{16,12}) = 0$$

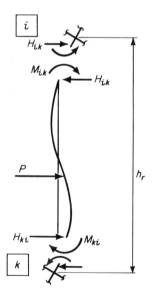

Figure 11.3. Column ik in the rth story.

From Figure 11.3 the shear H_{ik} at the top of any column ik can be written as

$$H_{ik} = R_{ik} + \frac{M_{ik} + M_{ki}}{h_r} \tag{11.14}$$

where R_{ik} is the shear at the top end i of column ik when its ends are simply supported; (that is, $M_{ik} = M_{ki} = 0$), and h_r is the rth story height. All columns within a given story are assumed to be of equal height in the development here (for frames with columns of unequal heights see Thadani[55]).

Substituting H_{ik} from Equation (11.14) into Equation (11.13) and multiplying by h_r

$$h_r \sum P + h_r \sum_r R_{ik} + \sum_r (M_{ik} + M_{ki}) = 0 \tag{11.15}$$

In Equation (11.15), i and k designate, respectively, the joint numbers at the top and the bottom of the column. Using Equations (11.4), (11.5), and (11.6), Equation (11.15) becomes

$$h_r \sum P + h_r \sum_r R_{ik} + \sum_r (\overline{M}_{ik} + \overline{M}_{ki}) + 3 \sum_r B_{ik} M'_{ik}$$
$$+ 3 \sum_r B_{ki} M'_{ki} + \sum_r (B_{ik} + B_{ki}) M''_{ik} = 0 \tag{11.16}$$

Let FES_{ik} designate the fixed end shear at the top i of column ik, then

$$FES_{ik} = R_{ik} + \frac{\overline{M}_{ik} + \overline{M}_{ki}}{h_r} \tag{11.17}$$

Multiplying Equation (11.17) by h_r and summing for all columns in story r

$$h_r \sum_r FES_{ik} = h_r \sum_r R_{ik} + \sum_r (\overline{M}_{ik} + \overline{M}_{ki})$$

Substituting from this identity in Equation (11.16) and rearranging yields

$$\sum_r (B_{ik} + B_{ki}) M''_{ik} = -3 \left[\frac{h_r}{3} (\sum P + \sum_r FES_{ik}) + \sum_r B_{ik} M'_{ik} + \sum_r B_{ki} M'_{ki} \right] \tag{11.18}$$

Now from Equation (11.2d) we can write for each column in the rth story

$$M''_{ik} = 3 C_{ik} K_{ik} \frac{\delta_{ik}}{h_r} \tag{11.19}$$

Multiplying Equation (11.19) by $(B_{ik} + B_{ki})$ and summing for all columns of story r, and recalling that δ_{ik} has the same value for all columns within the rth story†, then

$$\sum_r (B_{ik} + B_{ki}) M''_{ik} = 3 \frac{\delta_{ik}}{h_r} \sum_r (B_{ik} + B_{ki}) C_{ik} K_{ik} \tag{11.20}$$

Dividing Equation (11.19) by Equation (11.20) (corresponding sides of each equation), M''_{ik} can be expressed as

$$M''_{ik} = \frac{C_{ik} K_{ik}}{\sum_r (B_{ik} + B_{ki}) C_{ik} K_{ik}} \sum_r (B_{ik} + B_{ki}) M''_{ik} \tag{11.21}$$

Substituting for $\sum_r (B_{ik} + B_{ki}) M''_{ik}$ from Equation (11.18) into Equation (11.21)

$$M''_{ik} = v_{ik} [\overline{M}_r + \sum_r B_{ik} M'_{ik} + \sum_r B_{ki} M'_{ki}] \tag{11.22}$$

---

† This follows from the assumptions that the frame members do not change in length and all columns within a story are of equal height.

where

$$v_{ik} = -\frac{3C_{ik}K_{ik}}{\sum_r (B_{ik} + B_{ki})C_{ik}K_{ik}} \qquad (11.22a)$$

and

$$\overline{M}_r = \frac{h_r}{3}\left(\sum P + \sum_r FES_{ik}\right) \qquad (11.22b)$$

The Iteration

Using Equations (11.12) and (11.22) an iteration procedure is used to compute the quantities M'_{ik} and M''_{ik}. Equation (11.12) is applied at each joint of the frame and Equation (11.22) at each story. The iteration may proceed in an arbitrary order, but it is desirable to start at joints with the largest fixed end joint moment $\overline{M}_i$ or at a story with the largest story moment $\overline{M}_r$. For the convenience of writing a computer program, however, it is easier to proceed with the iteration in sequential order through all the joints and the stories in the frame. As the iteration continues, new values of M'_{ik} and M''_{ik} calculated by applying Equations (11.12) and (11.22) replace the preceding values. Initially the values of M'_{ik} and M''_{ik} are set equal to zero (or values other than zero may be guessed). The iteration is continued until the difference between iterated values in two successive cycles is small and is within the limits of the numerical accuracy desired. Using the computed values of M'_{ik} and M''_{ik}, the final moments at the ends of each member are obtained from Equations (11.4) or (11.6). The joint rotations and floor displacements can be computed from Equations (11.2). The iteration procedure will become clearer with the following examples.

Summary of Equations

For ease of reference, we summarize here the equations and expressions used in the iteration method.

$$M_{ik} = \overline{M}_{ik} + \frac{1}{C_{ik}}M'_{ik} + M'_{ki} + B_{ik}M''_{ik} \qquad (11.4)$$

$$M_{ki} = \overline{M}_{ki} + \frac{1}{C_{ki}}M'_{ki} + M'_{ik} + B_{ki}M''_{ik} \qquad (11.6)$$

$$M'_{ik} = \mu_{ik}\left[\overline{M}_i + \sum_k M'_{ki} + \sum_k B_{ik}M''_{ik}\right] \qquad (11.12)$$

$$\mu_{ik} = -\frac{C_{ik}K_{ik}}{\sum_k K_{ik}} \qquad (11.12a)$$

$$\overline{M}_i = \sum_{i} \overline{M}_{ik} \tag{11.8a}$$

$$B_{ik} = \frac{1}{3}\frac{1 + C_{ik}}{C_{ik}} \tag{11.5}$$

$$M''_{ik} = v_{ik}[\overline{M}_r + \sum_{r} B_{ik}M'_{ik} + \sum_{r} B_{ki}M'_{ki}] \tag{11.22}$$

$$v_{ik} = -\frac{3C_{ik}K_{ik}}{\sum_{r}(B_{ik} + B_{ki})C_{ik}K_{ik}} \tag{11.22a}$$

$$\overline{M}_r = \frac{h_r}{3}(\sum P + \sum_{r} FES_{ik}) \tag{11.22b}$$

$$FES_{ik} = R_{ik} + \frac{\overline{M}_{ik} + \overline{M}_{ki}}{h_r} \tag{11.17}$$

Suggested Exercises: Do problems 1, 2 and 3.

11.3. THE ITERATION METHOD APPLIED TO RIGIDLY CONNECTED BEAMS

Consider the rigidly connected beams of Figure 11.4 which are resting on nonyielding supports and loaded as shown. The displacements δ_{ik} are zero and therefore, from Equation (11.2d), $M''_{ik} = 0$ for each member, so that Equations (11.4) and (11.6) become

$$M_{ik} = \overline{M}_{ik} + \frac{1}{C_{ik}}M'_{ik} + M'_{ki} \tag{11.23}$$

and

$$M_{ki} = \overline{M}_{ki} + \frac{1}{C_{ki}}M'_{ki} + M'_{ik} \tag{11.24}$$

The final end moments M_{ik} for each beam can now be computed once the values M'_{ik} and M'_{ki} are known. These values can be computed from Equation (11.12) in which $M''_{ik} = 0$ for the present case, or

$$M'_{ik} = \mu_{ik}[\overline{M}_i + \sum_{k} M'_{ki}] \tag{11.25}$$

μ_{ik} and $\overline{M}_i$ are given by Equations (11.12a) and (11.8a) respectively. Equation (11.25) is the equation used in the iteration procedure to solve for the M'_{ik} values. The iteration may start at any joint and proceed in an arbitrary order from joint to joint. Assume the iteration to start at any joint i. In the absence of values M'_{ki}, they may be assumed zero as a first approximation and Equation (11.25) becomes

$$M'_{ik} = \mu_{ik}\overline{M}_i$$

As the iteration proceeds from joint to joint, subsequent values of M'_{ik} replace their values from the preceding cycle of iteration. The iteration may be continued until the difference between M'_{ik} values in successive cycles is within the limit of the desired accuracy. The final end moments are obtained by substituting the values of M'_{ik} and M'_{ki} in Equations (11.23).

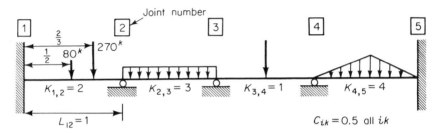

Figure 11.4.

Example†

We shall now analyze the structure of Figure 11.4 by iteration. The values, μ_{ik}, $\overline{M}_{ik}$, and $\overline{M}_i$ are shown in Figure 11.5. K_{ik} values are noted in Figure 11.4. The fixed end moments $\overline{M}_{ik}$ are computed from the applied loads on each member in the same way as forces $\{P\}^0$ were computed in Chapter 9. For instance $\overline{M}_{2,1} = 80(\frac{1}{2})(\frac{1}{2})^2 + 270(\frac{1}{3})(\frac{2}{3})^2 = 50$.

For simplicity we consider all beams in Figure 11.4 to be prismatic, then $C_{ik} = 0.5$ for all beams, and $K_{ik} = K_{ki}$ for each beam. The values of $\overline{M}_i$ and μ_{ik} at joint 3, for example, are computed as follows:

$$\overline{M}_3 = \sum_k \overline{M}_{3k} = \overline{M}_{3,2} + \overline{M}_{3,4} = 100 - 40 = 60$$

$$\mu_{3,2} = -\frac{0.5 \times 3}{3 + 1} = -0.375$$

$$\mu_{3,4} = -\frac{0.5 \times 1}{3 + 1} = -0.125$$

The values of M'_{ik} resulting from one cycle of iteration are recorded in Figure 11.5. The iteration proceeds from joint 2 to joint 4 in consecutive order. No iteration is required at joints 1 and 5 since $\theta_1 = \theta_5 = 0$ and

† Taken from Rubinstein[53].

consequently, $M'_{1,2} = M'_{5,4} = 0$. Other boundary conditions (at joints 1 and 5) can easily be accommodated in the analysis by modifying the relevant constant.[†]

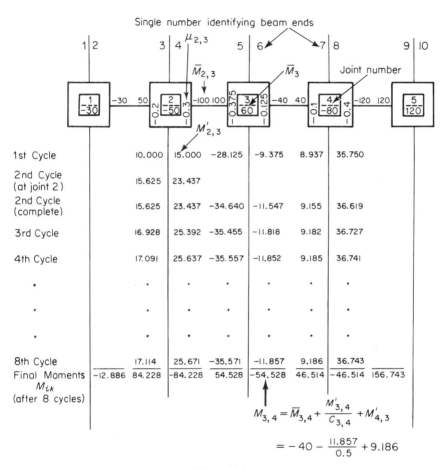

Figure 11.5.

To demonstrate the iteration, we start a second iteration cycle at joint 2, $(i = 2, k = 1, 3)$.

From the results of the first cycle of iteration

$$\sum_k M'_{k,2} = M'_{1,2} + M'_{3,2} = 0 - 28.125 = -28.125$$

[†] For a prismatic beam with end k pinned, K_{ik} (modified) $= \frac{3}{4}K_{ik}$; for a cantilever end $K_{ik} = 0$, etc.

Using Equation (11.25) with $i = 2$

$$M'_{2,k} = \mu_{2,k}(\overline{M}_2 + \sum_k M'_{k,2})$$

then,

$M'_{2,1} = -0.2(-50 - 28.125) = 15.625,$ replacing 10.000

$M'_{2,3} = -0.3(-50 - 28.125) = 23.437,$ replacing 15.000

We continue the iteration at joint 3, $(i = 3, k = 2, 4)$. Using the last recorded values of $M'_{k,3}$,

$$\sum_k M'_{k,3} = M'_{2,3} + M'_{4,3} = 23.437 + 8.937 = 32.374$$

then from Equation (11.25),

$M'_{3,2} = -0.375(60 + 32.374) = -34.640,$ replacing -28.125

$M'_{3,4} = -0.125(60 + 32.374) = -11.547,$ replacing -9.375

The results of the first, second, third, fourth, and eighth cycles, as well as the final end moments as obtained from Equation (11.23) are recorded in Figure 11.5. For example, the final end moment $M_{3,4}$ after eight cycles of iteration is computed as follows:

$$M_{3,4} = \overline{M}_{3,4} + \frac{1}{C_{3,4}} M'_{3,4} + M'_{4,3} = -40 - \frac{1}{0.5} 11.857 + 9.186 = -54.528$$

Suggested Exercises: Do problems 4, 5, 6, 7, 8 and 9.

11.4. A COMPUTER PROGRAM FOR THE ANALYSIS OF RIGIDLY CONNECTED BEAMS[53]

A computer program for the analysis of rigidly connected beams by the iteration method is given in Table 11.1. For clarity and conciseness the program does not include computations for the values of C_{ik}, K_{ik}, and $\overline{M}_{ik}$. In order to increase the size of the problem that can be handled by the computer, a number was assigned to each end of a beam as shown in Figure 11.6. This made it possible to identify the quantities μ_{ik}, $\overline{M}_{ik}$, C_{ik}, K_{ik}, M_{ik}, and M'_{ik} by a single subscript instead of two. For convenience in writing the program, a number was also assigned to the left of the first joint and to the right of the last joint. Since two numbers are recorded at each joint, then if I designates the joint number and J identifies the beam end to the right of joint I, we have $J = 2I$. (See Figure 11.6.)

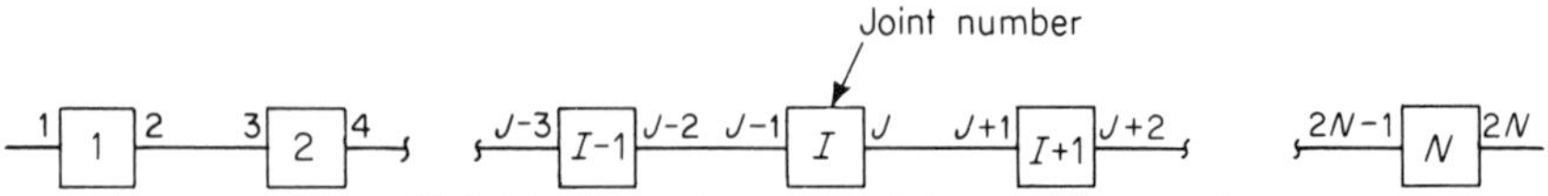

Figure 11.6. Number assignment to joints and beam ends.

TABLE 11.1
COMPUTER PROGRAM FOR THE ANALYSIS
OF RIGIDLY CONNECTED BEAMS

Statement Number	Fortran Statement
1	DIMENSION COF (99), STIFF (99), FEM (99), VAR (99), DISTF (99), FIMOM (99)
2	READ 20, N, L
3	$K = 2*N$
4	DO $6 J = 1$, K
5	READ 21, COF (J), STIFF (J), FEM (J)
6	VAR $(J) = 0.0$
7	$KK = K - 2$
8	DO 10 $J = 4$, KK, 2
9	DISTF$(J - 1) = -$ COF$(J - 1)*$STIFF$(J - 1)/($STIFF$(J - 1) +$ STIFF$(J))$
10	DISTF$(J) = -$ COF$(J)*$STIFF$(J)/($STIFF$(J - 1) +$ STIFF$(J))$
11	DO 14 $JJ = 1$, L
12	DO 14 $J = 4$, KK, 2
13	VAR$(J - 1) =$ DISTF$(J - 1)*($FEM$(J - 1) +$ FEM$(J) +$ VAR$(J - 2) +$ VAR$(J + 1))$
14	VAR$(J) =$ DISTF$(J)*($FEM$(J - 1) +$ FEM$(J) +$ VAR$(J - 2) +$ VAR$(J + 1))$
15	DO 17 $J = 2$, KK, 2
16	FIMOM$(J) =$ FEM$(J) +$ VAR$(J)/$COF$(J) +$ VAR$(J + 1)$
17	FIMOM$(J + 1) =$ FEM$(J + 1) +$ VAR$(J + 1)/$COF$(J + 1) +$ VAR(J)
18	DO 19 $J = 3$, K
19	PRINT 21, FIMOM$(J - 1)$
20	FORMAT$(I4, I4)$
21	FORMAT$(F11.3, F11.3, F11.3)$
22	STOP
23	END

Symbols: The symbols used in the program are as follows:†

COF $(J) = C_{I,I+1}$, Carryover Factor at J (from I to $I + 1$)
STIFF $(J) = K_{I,I+1}$, STIFFness at J
FEM $(J) = \overline{M}_{I,I+1}$, Fixed End Moment at J
DISTF $(J) = \mu_{I,I+1}$, DISTribution Factor at J
FIMOM $(J) = M_{I,I+1}$, FInal end MOMent at J
VAR $(J) = M'_{I,I+1}$, moment at J due to rotation of joint I
N = number of joints
L = number of iteration cycles desired.

---

† Using the Fortran programming language, 1 to 5 alphabetic or numerical characters may be used to designate varying quantities. The first letter of the name must be $I, J, K, L, M,$ or N for integer quantities[9].

Description of Program

Let us follow the computer as it executes the program of Table 11.1 for the example of Figure 11.4.

Statement 1. The computer makes room for all subscripted quantities appearing in the program. Thus the computer will prepare room for 99 COF (J) values, 99 STIFF (J) values, etc., in order to accommodate an analysis for up to 50 joints or 49 rigidly connected beams.

Statement 2. The computer reads two numbers from a data card and assigns the first of these numbers to N, and the second to L. The 20, following the word READ, refers to the statement number indicating the FORMAT (form) of the two numbers on this data card.

Statement 20 states that the FORMAT of N and L is $I4$, in which I indicates that these numbers are integers (N is the number of joints and L is the number of iteration cycles), and the 4 indicates four spaces to a number. Digits, a sign, and blank spaces between numbers, count as spaces. For $N = 5$ and $L = 3$, the numbers on the first data card will appear in the form:

$$bbb5bbb3$$

in which b is used here to designate a blank space.

Statement 3. The computer assigns the value of 2 times N to K. In Statement 2, N was already assigned the value 5 in our example; consequently the computer sets $K = 10$.

Statement 4. The computer sets $J = 1$. Statements 4, 5, and 6 form a DO loop. For example after this DO loop has been satisfied for $J = 1, 2, \ldots, 6$ the computer sets $J = 7$, reads from the next data card three numbers, and assigns them to COF (7), STIFF (7), and FEM (7), respectively. The format of these numbers is described by Statement 21 because the number 21 follows the word READ in Statement 5.

Statement 21 records format $F11.3$ for each of the three numbers. In $F11.3$, F indicates a fixed decimal number, 11 is the number of spaces (decimal point counts as one space), and the 3 following the decimal indicates the number of digits after the decimal. In our example the numbers on the punched data card which correspond to COF (7), STIFF (7), and FEM (7), respectively, will appear in the form

$$bbbbbb0.500bbbbbb1.000bbbbb40.000$$

Proceeding now to *Statement 6* the computer will assign the value of 0.0 to VAR (7). Next the computer will increment J by 1 (set $J = 8$) and return to Statement 5. Finally after Statements 5 and 6 are satisfied for $J = K$, the computer will proceed to Statement 7.

Statement 7. The computer assigns the value $K - 2$, $(10 - 2 = 8$ in our case), to KK.

Statements 8 to 10 inclusive form another DO loop in which the DISTF (J) are computed for all beam ends numbered 3 to KK (8 in our case). The 2 following KK in Statement 8 indicates that J is to be incremented by 2 each time the DO loop is satisfied. Thus J is assigned the value 4 first, then the value 6, 8, and finally the value KK.

Statement 9 or 10 is the Fortran language representation of Equation (11.12a).

Statements 11, 12, 13, 14 represent two DO loops. The inner DO loop (Statements 12 to 14) represents one complete cycle of iteration for all rotating joints using Equation (11.25). Statement 11 causes a repetition of this complete iteration L times.

Statements 15, 16, 17 form a DO loop evaluating the final end moments from Equation (11.23).

Statements 18, 19. All final moments are typed out in the format described by Statement 21.

Statement 22 stops the program.

Statement 23 is a control statement which must appear as the last statement of a source program.

11.5. THE ITERATION METHOD APPLIED TO FRAMES WITH PRISMATIC MEMBERS

When all the members of a rectangular frame are prismatic, then for each member,

$$C_{ik} = C_{ki} = 0.5$$

$$K_{ik} = K_{ki} = 4\frac{EI_{ik}}{L_{ik}}$$

$$B_{ik} = 1 \text{ [see Equation (11.5)]}$$

Using these values in the equations of the iteration method summarized at the end of Section 11.2, we obtain

$$M_{ik} = \overline{M}_{ik} + 2M'_{ik} + M'_{ki} + M''_{ik} \tag{11.26}$$

$$M_{ki} = \overline{M}_{ki} + 2M'_{ki} + M'_{ik} + M''_{ik} \tag{11.27}$$

$$M'_{ik} = \mu_{ik}[\overline{M}_i + \sum_k (M'_{ki} + M''_{ik})] \tag{11.28}$$

$$\mu_{ik} = -\frac{1}{2}\frac{K_{ik}}{\sum\limits_{k} K_{ik}} \tag{11.28a}$$

$$M''_{ik} = v_{ik}[\overline{M}_r + \sum_r (M'_{ik} + M'_{ki})] \tag{11.29}$$

$$v_{ik} = -\frac{3}{2}\frac{K_{ik}}{\sum\limits_{r} K_{ik}} \tag{11.29a}$$

The expressions for $\overline{M}_i$, $\overline{M}_r$, and FES_{ik} as given by Equations (11.8a), (11.22b), and (11.17), respectively, are unchanged.

Using Equations (11.28) and (11.29) the iteration procedure described in Section 11.2 is applied to compute all values M'_{ik} and M''_{ik}. The final end moments are computed from Equation (11.26).

Example†

Consider the frame of Figure 11.7‡. The values for μ_{ik}, v_{ik}, $\overline{M}_i$, and $\overline{M}_r$ are recorded in Figure 11.8. A sample computation of these values at joint 5 and story 1 follows.

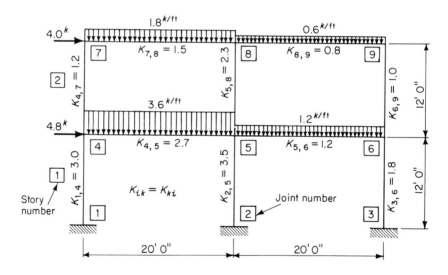

Figure 11.7. Two story building frame.

---

† This example is taken from Rubinstein[52].
‡ This frame is solved by other methods[13].

At joint 5 (i = 5):

$$\overline{M}_{i=5} = \overline{M}_{5,6} + \overline{M}_{5,4} = -40 + 120 = 80'^k$$

$$\sum_k K_{ik} = K_{5,4} + K_{5,8} + K_{5,6} + K_{5,2} = 9.7$$

$$\mu_{ik} = -\frac{1}{2} \frac{K_{ik}}{\sum_k K_{ik}} = -\frac{1}{2} \frac{K_{5,k}}{9.7}$$

For $k = 4$,

$$\mu_{5,4} = -\frac{1}{2} \frac{K_{5,4}}{9.7} = -\frac{1}{2} \frac{2.7}{9.7} = -0.139$$

At story 1 (r = 1):

$$\sum_r FES_{ik} = 0$$

$$\sum P = 4.0 + 4.8 = 8.8^k$$

$$\overline{M}_r = \frac{h_r}{3} \sum P = \frac{12}{3} \times 8.8 = 35.2'^k$$

$$\sum_r K_{ik} = K_{1,4} + K_{2,5} + K_{3,6} = 8.3$$

$$v_{ik} = -\frac{3}{2} \frac{K_{ik}}{\sum_{r=1} K_{ik}} = -\frac{3}{2} \frac{K_{ik}}{8.3}$$

For $k = 5$,

$$v_{2,5} = -\frac{3}{2} \frac{K_{2,5}}{8.3} = -\frac{3}{2} \frac{3.5}{8.3} = -0.633$$

Iteration:

The values of M'_{ik} and M''_{ik} resulting from one cycle of iteration are recorded in Figure 11.8. The iteration proceeds from joint 4 to joint 9 in consecutive order, then to stories 1 and 2. The column bases at the first story are fixed $\theta_i = 0$ ($i = 1, 2, 3$) and therefore $M'_{ik} = 0$ ($i = 1, 2, 3$). Let us start a second cycle of iteration at joint $i = 4$

$$\overline{M}_4 = -120$$

$$\sum_k (M'_{ki} + M''_{ik}) = 11.00 - 14.38 - 2.88 - 19.00 = -25.26$$

Using Equation (11.28)

$$M'_{4,7} = \mu_{4,7}[-120 - 25.26] = (-0.087)(-145.26) = 12.64, \text{ replacing } 10.44$$

Similarly,

$$M'_{4,5} = (-0.1955)(-145.26) = 28.40, \quad \text{replacing } 23.46$$

$$M'_{4,1} = (-0.2175)(-145.26) = 31.59, \quad \text{replacing } 26.10$$

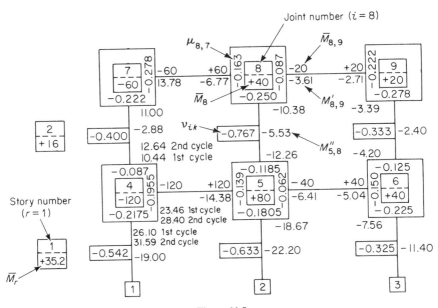

Figure 11.8.

If the iteration were to proceed at this point to the second story, we have

$$\overline{M}_{r=2} = 16$$

$$\sum_{r=2} (M'_{ik} + M'_{ki}) = 11.00 + 12.64 - 10.38 - 12.26 - 3.39 - 4.20 = -6.59$$

Using Equation (11.29)

$$M''_{4,7} = v_{4,7}[16 - 6.59] = (-0.40)(9.41) = -3.76, \quad \text{replacing } -2.88$$

Similarly,

$$M''_{5,8} = (-0.767)(9.41) = -7.22, \quad \text{replacing } -5.53$$

$$M''_{6,9} = (-0.333)(9.41) = -3.13, \quad \text{replacing } -2.40$$

The final end moments are computed from Equation (11.26) after the desired accuracy has been achieved in the iteration. For example, the final end moment $M_{5,8}$ after one cycle of iteration is

$$M_{5,8} = \overline{M}_{5,8} + 2M'_{5,8} + M'_{8,5} + M''_{5,8}$$

$$= 0 + 2(-12.26) + (-10.38) + (-5.53) = -40.43'^k$$

The rotations of the frame joints and the floor displacements can be computed from relations (11.2). The shear and axial force at the ends of each member can be computed from equilibrium.

The final end moments computed after three, four, five, six, seven, and eight cycles of iteration are recorded in Table 11.2. These results agree very closely with those obtained by other methods[13].

TABLE 11.2

FINAL END MOMENTS M_{ik} FOR THE BUILDING FRAME OF FIGURE 11.7

Final End Moment M_{ik} at	3 Cycles	4 Cycles	5 Cycles	6 Cycles	7 Cycles	8 Cycles	Results obtained by Parcel and Moorman[13]
7, 8	−30.90	−30.41	−30.16	−30.05	−30.01	−29.99	−30.00
8, 7	66.64	67.39	67.70	67.83	67.88	67.91	67.91
8, 9	−27.50	−26.97	−26.78	−26.71	−26.67	−26.66	−26.66
9, 8	13.45	13.96	14.14	14.21	14.24	14.25	14.26
7, 4	30.63	30.19	30.06	30.01	29.99	29.98	30.00
4, 7	29.95	29.76	29.70	29.68	29.67	29.67	29.67
8, 5	−41.28	−41.24	−41.26	−41.27	−41.27	−41.27	−41.27
5, 8	−39.39	−39.18	−39.11	−39.08	−39.07	−39.07	−39.08
9, 6	−14.38	−14.28	−14.27	−14.26	−14.26	−14.26	−14.26
6, 9	−13.53	−13.24	−13.13	−13.08	−13.06	−13.06	−13.06
4, 5	−68.67	−66.44	−65.46	−65.21	−65.06	−65.01	−64.94
5, 4	134.76	137.08	138.01	138.39	138.54	138.60	138.63
5, 6	−48.28	−47.07	−46.58	−46.38	−46.30	−46.26	−46.24
6, 5	33.17	34.51	35.06	35.28	35.37	35.41	35.44
1, 4	2.43	1.82	1.57	1.47	1.43	1.41	1.38
4, 1	35.03	35.21	35.27	35.29	35.30	35.30	35.27
2, 5	−44.68	−45.26	−45.49	−45.58	−45.62	−45.64	−45.62
5, 2	−54.12	−53.66	−53.46	−53.38	−53.35	−53.34	−53.31
3, 6	−20.78	−20.88	−20.92	−20.93	−20.93	−20.94	−20.94
6, 3	−23.47	−22.84	−22.57	−22.46	−22.41	−22.39	−22.38

Suggested Exercises: Do problems 10, 11 and 12.

11.6. USE OF STIFFNESS METHOD TO COMPUTE K_{ik}, C_{ik}, $\overline{M}_{ik}$, AND FES_{ik} FOR NONPRISMATIC MEMBERS[54]

The iteration method developed in Section 11.2 requires that we compute K_{ik}, C_{ik}, $\overline{M}_{ik}$, and FES_{ik} for each member. For a prismatic member $C_{ik} = \frac{1}{2}$

and $K_{ik} = 4EI/L$, $\bar{M}_{ik}$, and FES_{ik} can be computed by the method of Chapter 6.

When a member is nonprismatic and has a shape which cannot be expressed analytically, or is too complex for analysis, it can be approximated by a number of prismatic segments or by a combination of prismatic and tapered segments as shown in Figure 11.9. Using the values of K_{ik}, C_{ik}, $\bar{M}_{ik}$, and FES_{ik} for the prismatic and tapered segments, the corresponding values for the nonprismatic member can be computed by applying the stiffness method of Chapter 9 as we shall do in the following pages.

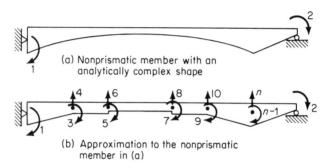

Figure 11.9. Complex nonprismatic member approximated by prismatic and tapered segments.

Computing K_{ik} and C_{ik} for a Nonprismatic Member. Let us compute K_{ik} and C_{ik} for the member of Figure 11.9(a) which is approximated by prismatic and tapered segments as shown in Figure 11.9(b). Using the procedure of Section 4.14, we define one system coordinate at each end and two coordinates at each intersection of the member segments as shown in Figure 11.9(b). The total number of coordinates, n, is equal then to twice the number of segments. Using the stiffness matrices of the segments considered

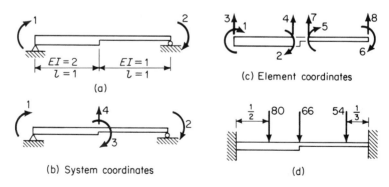

Figure 11.10.

as elements we synthesize an $n \times n$ stiffness matrix $[k]$. Using the procedure of Sections 9.3 and 4.14, we compute a reduced 2×2 stiffness matrix $[k]^*$ for coordinates 1 and 2 at the ends of the nonprismatic member.

$$[k]^* = [k]_{11} - [k]_{12}[k]_{22}^{-1}[k]_{21} \qquad (11.30)$$

The matrices on the right-hand side of Equation (11.30) are submatrices of $[k]$, in which $[k]_{11}$ is of order two and corresponds to the coordinates at the ends of the nonprismatic member and $[k]_{22}$ is of order $n - 2$ and corresponds to coordinates $3, 4, \ldots, n$ at the intersections of the segments. The values K_{ik} and C_{ik} are obtained from the elements of $[k]^*$.

$$K_{12} = k_{11}^*$$

$$K_{21} = k_{22}^*$$

$$C_{12} = k_{12}^*/k_{11}^* \qquad (11.31)$$

$$C_{21} = k_{21}^*/k_{22}^*$$

As an example let us consider Figure 11.10(a) which may represent a nonprismatic member approximated by two prismatic segments. The system and element coordinates are shown in Figures 11.10(b, c), respectively. Using the methods of Chapter 9 we synthesize the following stiffness matrix for the system coordinates (see Section 4.14):

$$[k] = \begin{bmatrix} 8 & 0 & 4 & 12 \\ 0 & 4 & 2 & -6 \\ 4 & 2 & 12 & 6 \\ 12 & -6 & 6 & 36 \end{bmatrix}$$

Using Equation (11.30), we obtain

$$[k]^* = \begin{bmatrix} 8 & 0 \\ 0 & 4 \end{bmatrix} - \begin{bmatrix} 4 & 12 \\ 2 & -6 \end{bmatrix} \begin{bmatrix} 12 & 6 \\ 6 & 36 \end{bmatrix}^{-1} \begin{bmatrix} 4 & 2 \\ 12 & -6 \end{bmatrix} = \frac{1}{11}\begin{bmatrix} 40 & 16 \\ 16 & 24 \end{bmatrix}$$

and therefore, from Equations (11.31),

$$K_{12} = \tfrac{40}{11}, \qquad K_{21} = \tfrac{24}{11}$$

$$C_{12} = \tfrac{2}{5}, \qquad C_{21} = \tfrac{2}{3}$$

Computing $\overline{M}_{ik}$ *and* FES_{ik} *for a Nonprismatic Member.* To compute $\overline{M}_{ik}$ and FES_{ik} for a member, such as that of Figure 11.9(b), when it is subjected to loads, we set to zero the rotations at coordinates 1 and 2 and apply Equation (9.1c) of section 9.2.

$$\{P\}^f = \{P\}^0 + [\kappa][\beta][k]_{22}^{-1}(\{F\}^f - \{F\}^0) \qquad (11.32)$$

In this equation $[k]_{22}$ is the stiffness matrix corresponding to the coordinates at $3, 4, \ldots, n$ in Figure 11.9(b). To evaluate $\overline{M}_{ik}$ and FES_{ik} only four values of $\{P\}^f$ which correspond to the internal forces at the fixed ends must be evaluated.

Let us apply Equation (11.32) to the member of Figure 11.10 loaded as shown in Figure 11.10(d). Since $[k]_{22}$ is defined for system coordinates 3 and 4 with coordinates 1 and 2 fixed, then, relating coordinates 3 and 4 to the element coordinates of Figure 11.10(c), we have

$$[\beta] = \begin{bmatrix} 0 & 0 \\ 1 & 0 \\ 0 & 0 \\ 0 & 1 \\ \hline 1 & 0 \\ 0 & 0 \\ 0 & 1 \\ 0 & 0 \end{bmatrix}$$

For $[\kappa]$ we have

$$\begin{bmatrix} [\kappa]_1 & \\ & [\kappa]_2 \end{bmatrix}$$

in which $[\kappa]_2 = \begin{bmatrix} 4 & 2 & -6 & 6 \\ 2 & 4 & -6 & 6 \\ -6 & -6 & 12 & -12 \\ 6 & 6 & -12 & 12 \end{bmatrix}$ and $[\kappa]_1 = 2[\kappa]_2$

$$[k]_{22}^{-1} = \begin{bmatrix} 12 & 6 \\ 6 & 36 \end{bmatrix}^{-1} = \tfrac{1}{66} \begin{bmatrix} 6 & -1 \\ -1 & 2 \end{bmatrix}$$

$$\{F\}^f = \left\{ \begin{array}{c} 0 \\ -66 \end{array} \right\} \quad \text{and} \quad \{F\}^0 = \left\{ \begin{array}{c} 6 \\ 54 \end{array} \right\}$$

In the example of Figure 11.10(d)

$$P_1^f = \overline{M}_{12} \quad \text{and} \quad P_6^f = \overline{M}_{21}$$

and FES_{12} and FES_{21} correspond to P_3^f and P_8^f, respectively. Let us compute $\overline{M}_{12}$ and $\overline{M}_{21}$. This requires that we evaluate the elements in the first and sixth row in Equation (11.32). Multiplying row 1 and 6 of $[\kappa]$ by $[\beta]$ gives

$$\begin{bmatrix} 4 & 12 \\ 2 & -6 \end{bmatrix}$$

Substituting this result and

$$\begin{Bmatrix} P_1^0 \\ P_6^0 \end{Bmatrix} = \begin{Bmatrix} -10 \\ 8 \end{Bmatrix}$$

in Equation (11.32) gives

$$\begin{Bmatrix} P_1^f \\ P_6^f \end{Bmatrix} = \begin{Bmatrix} -10 \\ 8 \end{Bmatrix} + \tfrac{1}{66} \begin{bmatrix} 4 & 12 \\ 2 & -6 \end{bmatrix} \begin{bmatrix} 6 & -1 \\ -1 & 2 \end{bmatrix} \left(\begin{Bmatrix} 0 \\ -66 \end{Bmatrix} - \begin{Bmatrix} 6 \\ 54 \end{Bmatrix} \right)$$

$$= \begin{Bmatrix} -10 \\ 8 \end{Bmatrix} - \tfrac{1}{11} \begin{Bmatrix} 412 \\ -262 \end{Bmatrix} = \tfrac{1}{11} \begin{Bmatrix} -522 \\ 350 \end{Bmatrix}$$

In the example of this section the stiffness method was applied, for simplicity and clarity, to a member approximated by two prismatic segments of equal length and with moments of inertia I and $2I$, respectively (see Figure 11.10). The application of the method to compute K_{ik}, C_{ik}, $\overline{M}_{ik}$, and FES_{ik} for members which are approximated by a series of tapered and prismatic segments of varying lengths follows the same steps.

Suggested Exercises: Do problems 13 and 14

11.7. THE ITERATION METHOD APPLIED TO FRAMES WITH NONPRISMATIC MEMBERS

Using the results of the last section, the iteration method of Section 11.2 will be used to analyze the building frame of Figure 11.11.† The coefficients μ_{ik}, ν_{ik}, B_{ik}, and the joint and story moments $\overline{M}_i$ and $\overline{M}_r$ are shown in Figure 11.12. A sample computation of these quantities at joint 5 and story 2 follows.

At Joint 5:
From Equation (11.8a)

$$\overline{M}_{i=5} = \sum_k \overline{M}_{5,k} = \overline{M}_{5,2} + \overline{M}_{5,4} + \overline{M}_{5,8} + \overline{M}_{5,6}$$

$$= -14 - 30 - 20 - 80 = -144$$

† This example is taken from Rubinstein[54].

To compute the $\mu_{5,k}$ values from Equation (11.12a), we write

$$\sum_k K_{5,k} = K_{5,2} + K_{5,4} + K_{5,8} + K_{5,6} = \frac{144}{33} + \frac{120}{33} + \frac{120}{33} + \frac{120}{33} = \frac{504}{33}$$

For $k = 2$,

$$\mu_{5,2} = -\frac{C_{5,2}K_{5,2}}{\sum\limits_k K_{5,k}} = -\frac{2/3(144/33)}{504/33} = -0.1905$$

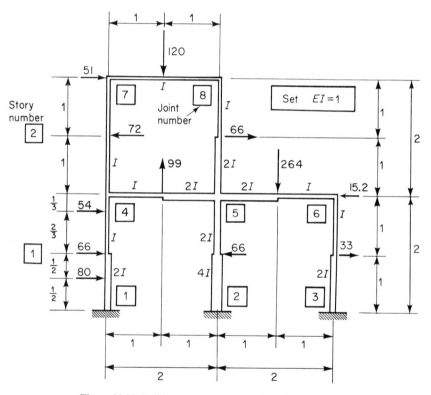

Figure 11.11. Building frame with nonprismatic members.

Similarly for $k = 4, 6, 8$

$$\mu_{5,4} = \mu_{5,6} = \mu_{5,8} = -\frac{2/5(120/33)}{504/33} = -0.0953$$

From Equation (11.5),

$$B_{5,2} = \frac{1}{3}\frac{1+(2/3)}{2/3} = \frac{5}{6}; \qquad B_{5,4} = B_{5,6} = B_{5,8} = \frac{1}{3}\frac{1+(2/5)}{2/5} = \frac{7}{6}$$

The B_{ik} for the beams are not required in the present example because $\delta_{ik} = 0$, and hence $M''_{ik} = 0$ for all beams.

At Story 2:
For column 7, 4 [Using Equation (11.17)],

$$FES_{7,4} = R_{7,4} + \frac{\overline{M}_{7,4} + \overline{M}_{4,7}}{h_2} = -\frac{72}{2} + \frac{-18 + 18}{2} = -36$$

$$C_{4,7} = C_{7,4} = \frac{1}{2}; \quad B_{4,7} = B_{7,4} = \frac{1}{3}\frac{1 + \frac{1}{2}}{\frac{1}{2}} = 1.0; \quad K_{4,7} = K_{7,4} = 2.0$$

For column 8, 5

$$FES_{8,5} = R_{8,5} + \frac{\overline{M}_{8,5} + \overline{M}_{5,8}}{h_2} = \frac{66}{2} + \frac{14 - 20}{2} = 30$$

$$C_{8,5} = \tfrac{2}{3}, \quad B_{8,5} = \tfrac{5}{6}, \quad K_{8,5} = \tfrac{72}{33}, \quad C_{5,8} = \tfrac{2}{5}, \quad B_{5,8} = \tfrac{7}{6},$$

$$K_{5,8} = \tfrac{120}{33}$$

To compute $v_{4,7}$ and $v_{5,8}$ we evaluate

$$\sum_r (B_{ik} + B_{ki})C_{ik}K_{ik} = (B_{7,4} + B_{4,7})C_{7,4}K_{7,4}$$

$$+ (B_{8,5} + B_{5,8})C_{8,5}K_{8,5} = 4.91$$

and then from Equation (11.22a)

$$v_{4,7} = -\frac{3(1/2)2}{4.91} = -0.611, \quad v_{5,8} = -\frac{3(2/5)120/33}{4.91} = -0.889$$

$\overline{M}_{r=2}$ is computed from Equation (11.22b)

$$\overline{M}_{r=2} = \tfrac{2}{3}(\textstyle\sum P + FES_{7,4} + FES_{8,5}) = \tfrac{2}{3}(51 - 36 + 30) = 30$$

Iteration:
The values of M'_{ik} and M''_{ik} as obtained from Equations (11.12) and (11.22) after one cycle of iteration are shown in Figure 11.12. These results were obtained by proceeding with the iteration in consecutive order from joints 4 to 8 and then to stories 1 and 2. Because the bases of the first-story columns are fixed, no rotation takes place at joints 1, 2, 3; hence

$$M'_{1,4} = M'_{2,5} = M'_{3,6} = 0.$$

To demonstrate the iteration procedure, we assume that the first cycle of iteration has just been completed and a second cycle is started at joint 5.

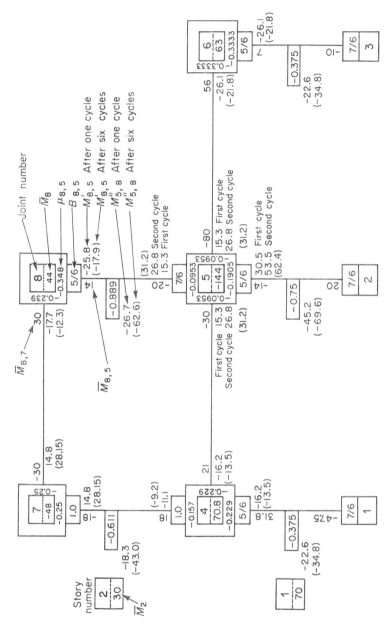

Figure 11.12. Results of M'_{ik} and M''_{ik} after one cycle and after six cycles of iteration.

(The results of M'_{ik} and M''_{ik} after six cycles of iteration are enclosed in parentheses.)

To apply Equation (11.12), the following quantities are computed from Figure 11.12:

$$\sum_k M'_{k,5} = (M'_{2,5} + M'_{4,5} + M'_{8,5} + M'_{6,5})$$

$$= (0 - 16.2 - 25.8 - 26.1) = -68.1$$

$$\sum_k B_{ik}M''_{ik} = B_{5,8}M''_{5,8} + B_{5,2}M''_{5,2} = \tfrac{7}{6}(-26.7) + \tfrac{5}{6}(-45.2) = -68.8$$

Using these values and $\overline{M}_{i=5} = -144$ from Figure 11.12 in Equation (11.12), then $M'_{5,2} = -0.1905(-144 - 68.1 - 68.8) = 53.5$, replacing 30.5 from the first cycle. Similarly,

$$M'_{5,4} = M'_{5,6} = M'_{5,8} = -0.0953(-280.9) = 26.8, \text{ replacing } 15.3.$$

To show how the iteration proceeds at any story using Equation (11.22), we continue the second cycle at the second story. To apply Equation (11.22), the following quantities are computed from Figure 11.12:

$$\sum_r B_{ik}M'_{ik} = B_{7,4}M'_{7,4} + B_{8,5}M'_{8,5} = 1.0(14.8) + \tfrac{5}{6}(-25.8) = -6.7$$

$$\sum_r B_{ki}M'_{ki} = B_{4,7}M'_{4,7} + B_{5,8}M'_{5,8} = 1.0(-11.1) + \tfrac{7}{6}(26.8) = 20.2$$

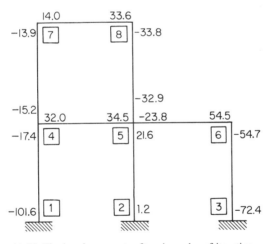

Figure 11.13. Final end moments after six cycles of iteration.

Using these values and $\overline{M}_{r=2} = 30$ (see Figure 11.12) in Equation (11.22), then $M'_{4,7} = -0.611(30 - 6.7 + 20.2) = -26.6$, replacing -18.3 from the first cycle. $M'_{5,8} = -0.889(43.5) = -38.6$, replacing -26.7.

Using a slide rule, one complete iteration cycle took approximately 6 minutes, which indicates that the method is efficient even for hand computations. The results of the sixth cycle are shown in Figure 11.12. The final end moments after six cycles are recorded in Figure 11.13 and are obtained by applying Equation (11.4) or (11.6). For instance, for moment $M_{5,8}$

$$M_{5,8} = \overline{M}_{5,8} + \frac{1}{C_{5,8}} M'_{5,8} + M'_{8,5} + B_{5,8} M''_{5,8}$$

$$= -20 + \frac{1}{2/5}(31.2) + (-17.9) + \frac{7}{6}(-62.6) = -32.9$$

11.8. EFFICIENCY OF THE ITERATION METHOD

The iteration method of this chapter is efficient in the analysis of frames with a large number of column lines (wide frame) and for cases in which a single (or few) loading condition is involved. The tridiagonal method of Chapter 10 is more efficient in the analysis of frames with a large number of floors and a small number of column lines (tall narrow frame) when a large number of loading conditions is involved. For a comparative study of the tridiagonal matrix method and the relaxation procedure mentioned in Section 10.1 see Clough[46].

Suggested Exercises: Do problems 15 and 16.

PROBLEMS

Problem 1: Use Betti's law to show that relation (11.3) holds true.

Problem 2: Relate K_{ik}, C_{ik}, $\overline{M}_{ik}$, FES_{ik}, and M_{ik} to their corresponding terms used in the stiffness method of Chapter 9. What is the equivalent of relation (11.3), using the notation of Chapter 9?

Problem 3: Simplify the equations summarized at the end of Section 11.2 to analyze frames in which the only loads applied are horizontal loads at the floor levels.

Problem 4: Use the iteration method to compute the moments at the ends of each member in the structure of Figure 9.1(d). Compare your results with the results given in Section 9.2.

Problem 5: Use the iteration method to compute the moments at the ends of each member in the structure of Problem 4 (Chapter 9).

Problem 6: Use the results of the iteration in Problems 4 and 5 to compute the joint rotations in the corresponding structures. Compare your results with the results obtained by the stiffness method (Section 9.2, step 6).

Problem 7: Use the iteration method to compute the joint rotations and the internal moments at the ends of each member for the structure of Problem 16 (Chapter 9).

Problem 8: Use the iteration method to compute the moments and rotations at the ends of each member in the structure of Figure 10.2(a).

Problem 9: In Figure 11.4 replace the fixed end condition at joint 1 by a roller and re-analyze the structure by the iteration method.

Problem 10: Introduce hinges at joints 1, 2 and 3 in the structure of Figure 11.7. The moment M_{ik} at the top of each column in the first story can then be written as

$$M_{ik} = \frac{1}{C_{ik}} M'_{ik} + M''_{ik}$$

in which

$$M'_{ik} = C_{ik} K^R_{ik} \theta_i, \qquad K^R_{ik} = \tfrac{3}{4} K_{ik}$$

and

$$M''_{ik} = \tfrac{3}{2} C_{ik} K_{ik} \frac{\delta_{ik}}{L_{ik}}$$

(a) Show that the iteration procedure may be applied as in the case of the first story columns with fixed bases, except the following quantities must be redefined at the first story: (no external load is applied to the columns of the first story)

$$\overline{M}_1 = \tfrac{1}{2} h_1 \Sigma P = \tfrac{1}{2} 12 \times 8.8 = 52.8'^k$$

At the top of each column

$$\mu_{ik} = -\tfrac{1}{2} \frac{K^R_{ik}}{\displaystyle\sum_k K_{ik}}$$

in which $\displaystyle\sum_k K_{ik}$ includes K^R_{ik} for the first story columns.

$$\nu_{ik} = -2 \frac{K_{ik}}{\displaystyle\sum_r K_{ik}}$$

(b) Using the results in part (a), compute the moments at the ends of each member after two cycles of iteration. Apply the equations of equilibrium [Equations (11.7) and (11.13)] and explain why they are not satisfied.

Problem 11: Compute the floor displacements and the joint rotations after 4 cycles of iteration in Problem 10. Compute also the final moments at the ends of each member and apply again Equations (11.7) and (11.13). Consider the values of K_{ij} recorded in Figure 11.7 to represent the ratios I_{ij}/L_{ij} of the members, in units of in.[3]. Take $E = 30 \times 10^6$ psi.

Problem 12: Compute the moments at the ends of each member in the structure shown. Use the iteration method. All members are prismatic and their K_{ik} values are recorded in the figure next to each member. The bay numbers stand here for the story numbers. Note that here $\overline{M}_{r=1} = 133.3^{'k}$, $\overline{M}_{r=3} = \overline{M}_{r=2} = -66.7^{'k}$, and $\overline{M}_i = 0$ for all i. $M''_{ik} \neq 0$ for any member.

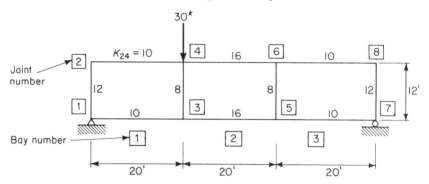

Problem 13: How would you compute the values of $\overline{M}_{ik}$ for a member when it is subjected to a continuously distributed load with a very irregular intensity which cannot be expressed analytically?

Problem 14: Use the method of Section 11.6 to compute $\overline{M}_{ik}$, FES_{ik} for each member of Figure 11.11. Compare your results with those given in Figure 11.12.

Problem 15: Use the results of the sixth cycle in Figure 11.12 to go through a seventh cycle of iteration. Compute the final end moments and compare with the results given in Figure 11.13.

Problem 16: Do problem 4 Chapter 10 using the iteration method.

CHAPTER 12

ANALYSIS OF PLATES AND SHELLS—INTRODUCTION

12.1. INTRODUCTION

So far the stiffness and flexibility methods and related techniques for dealing with large structures were applied primarily to structures whose elements were beams. This was done for simplicity and convenience, because the application of these methods to the analysis of plates and shells is more involved. In principle, however, the procedure is the same. Using the characteristics of the elements (stiffness or flexibility matrices), we synthesize the characteristics of the system (stiffness or flexibility matrices) and then compute the internal forces and displacements. The basic difference between the analysis of plates or shells and the analysis of beam-type structures lies in the choice and characterization of elements.

In the analysis of beam-type structures, we always considered the stress distribution at any cross section of the beam to be linear in accordance with beam-bending theory. In selecting elements this assumption was maintained irrespective of the dimensions of the element as long as it could still be considered a beam.

In the analysis of plates or shells the choice and characterization of elements require more consideration[58, 59, 65, 66]. Let us refer to the plate of Figure 12.1, which is under the action of forces F_i, F_j. To compute the internal stresses and the displacements of the plate by the stiffness method, for instance, requires that we synthesize a stiffness matrix for the system from the corresponding stiffness matrices of the constituent elements. We may choose as elements rectangular plates, triangular plates (as shown in Figure 12.1), or other shapes in various sizes. To generate the stiffness matrix of an element requires that we also choose a displacement configuration, (with associated stress and strain distributions), corresponding to a unit displacement at each coordinate (defined at the element corners as shown in Figure 12.1), so that we can apply Equation (6.22) or (6.30).† The question is then what to choose for the stress or strain distribution in an element.

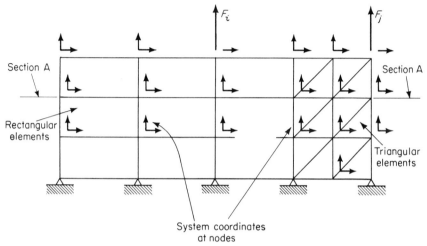

Figure 12.1. Plate structure showing two possible choices of elements.

We know, of course, that the stress distribution across a section of the plate in Figure 12.1 (section A for instance) is not necessarily linear. Therefore, if we select a small number of large elements and assume a linear stress or displacement distribution on the faces of each element, the analysis will lead to inaccurate results. On the other hand, if we select a large number of small elements, then assuming a linear stress or displacement distribution for each element may be satisfactory. This, however, will require that we invert a larger matrix because system coordinates are defined at the element nodes, and the smaller the elements we choose, the larger the number of system coordinates. In some cases in which the load is known in advance, it is possible to approximate the displacement configuration of sections of the structure then select a small number of relatively large elements and define appropriate nonlinear displacement configurations for the elements. Using these configurations, the corresponding stiffness matrices of the elements are generated by Equation (6.22) or (6.30), and an analysis is conducted which may yield acceptable results in a relatively small computation time. Such a procedure was tried[57] for a plate loaded by a concentrated load in its plane (plane stress problem), and the choice of a small

---

† To generate the flexibility matrix we apply Equation (6.25) or (6.32).

number of rectangular plate elements with nonlinear displacement configurations led to reasonably acceptable results in the region of peak stresses.

Studies are still in progress on idealizing structures by selecting appropriate models as elements[58, 59] and characterizing elements by selecting appropriate displacement functions or stress distribution[60, 61].

The choice of stress distribution or displacement configuration for the elements may lead to compatibility not being satisfied at the element boundaries except at the nodal points where it is satisfied explicitly. In such a case the structure is approximated by a model in which cuts have been introduced and therefore is more flexible than the real structure. When equilibrium is violated and compatibility satisfied it is equivalent to imposing constraints on the structure. Then the model is stiffer than the actual structure. (For a treatment of these matters in matrix structural analysis see References 59, 62).

The considerations in the preceding discussion relative to plates apply also to shell structures. The choice of elements and the choice of stress distribution or displacement functions represent the key tasks. Once these choices are made, the analysis proceeds as in the case of beamlike structures. Figure 12.2(a) shows a conical shell in which the elements are small flat triangles[63] and Figure 12.2(b) shows a shell of revolution with truncated cone elements[64].

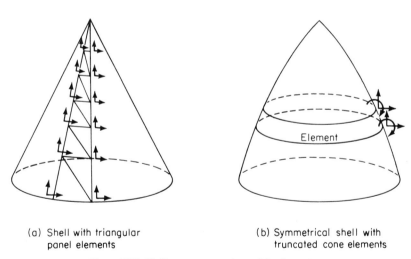

(a) Shell with triangular
panel elements

(b) Symmetrical shell with
truncated cone elements

Figure 12.2. Shell structures and possible elements.

The treatment in this chapter is an introduction to the analysis of plate and shell structures limited to plate elements with in-plane forces. The basic concepts, however, apply to elements with out-of-plane as well as in-plane forces.†

In Section 12.2, we analyze a box beam by the flexibility method. In Sections 12.3 and 12.4, we respectively generate the stiffness and flexibility matrices of a triangular plate element. Finally in Section 12.5 we apply the stiffness method to analysis of a plate.

12.2. ANALYSIS OF A BOX BEAM BY THE FLEXIBILITY METHOD[21,65,69]

In the analysis of slender monocoque structures, it is common to idealize the structure by representing it as a box beam, which is an assembly of flange elements with axial load-carrying capacity and plates (or panels) with shear capacity, as shown in Figure 12.3. In this idealization process, the axial load-carrying capacity of the plates is lumped with the flange elements by adding to the flanges an appropriate portion of the cross-sectional area of the plates. The idealization process requires much experience and skill on the part of the analyst. (For a discussion of structural idealizations see Reference 58).

For our purposes here let us consider a cantilevered box beam with dimensions as shown in Figure 12.3, and let our objectives be as follows:

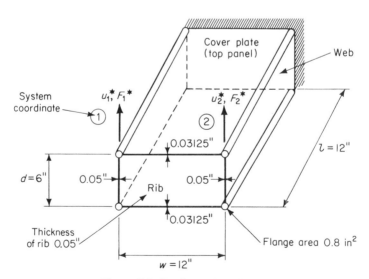

Figure 12.3. Cantilevered box beam.

---

† Studies on idealized models for elements in three dimensional elastic media are in progress[72].

1. Generate the flexibility matrix $[a]^*$ for system coordinates 1, 2 shown in Figure 12.3.
2. Generate a matrix $[b]$ which will transform forces F_1^*, F_2^* at the system coordinates to internal forces P_i.

To proceed with an analysis which will fulfill our objectives we use the development in Section 8.2. We select as elements the four flanges and the five panels. Now we must introduce assumptions relative to the stress distribution of the elements so that we may generate their flexibility matrices. We make the following assumptions:

1. The flanges carry axial forces only.
2. The panels carry shear only.

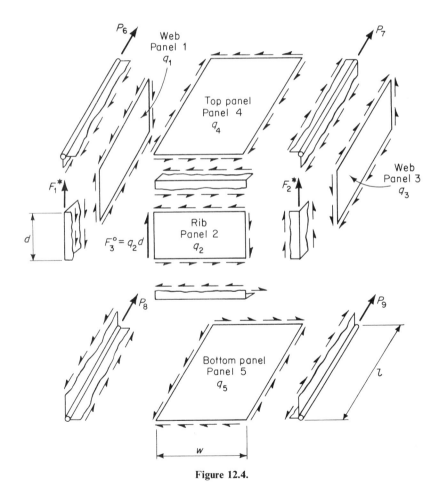

Figure 12.4.

3. The shear distribution in the panels is uniform, or the axial force varies linearly along each flange.

The box beam is shown disassembled into the nine elements in Figure 12.4. The panels are numbered from 1 to 5 and the shear flow in the panels is indicated by $q_i (i = 1, 2, \ldots, 5)$ with i corresponding to the panel number. The force at the end of each flange element i is indicated by $P_i (i = 6, 7, 8, 9)$. The structure of Figure 12.3 is redundant to the first degree. We select as a redundant, F_3^0, the shearing force $q_2 d$ acting on the rib in the vertical direction.

Computing Matrix [*b*]

The internal forces which we wish to compute consist of the shear flows in the five panels and the axial forces in the four flanges. To keep the units consistent let us define the vector of internal forces $\{P\}$ as follows (d and l designate the depth and length of the box beam respectively. See Figures 12.3 and 12.4).

$$\begin{Bmatrix} P_1 \\ P_2 \\ P_3 \\ P_4 \\ P_5 \\ P_6 \\ P_7 \\ P_8 \\ P_9 \end{Bmatrix} = \begin{Bmatrix} q_1 d \\ q_2 d \\ q_3 d \\ q_4 l \\ q_5 l \\ P_6 \\ P_7 \\ P_8 \\ P_9 \end{Bmatrix} \tag{12.1}$$

To compute the first column of [*b*] in the equation

$$\{P\} = [b]\{F\}$$

we apply in Figure 12.4 $F_1^* = 1$ with $F_2^* = F_3^0 = 0$ and compute the corresponding internal forces $\{P\}$ from equilibrium. Similarly, to generate the second and third columns of [*b*] we set $F_2^* = 1$, $F_1^* = F_3^0 = 0$, and $F_3^0 = 1$, $F_1^* = F_2^* = 0$, respectively, and compute the corresponding internal forces $\{P\}$. Proceeding this way, we obtain

$$
\begin{Bmatrix} P_1 \\ P_2 \\ P_3 \\ P_4 \\ P_5 \\ P_6 \\ P_7 \\ P_8 \\ P_9 \end{Bmatrix} =
\begin{bmatrix}
1 & 0 & -1 \\
0 & 0 & 1 \\
0 & -1 & -1 \\
0 & 0 & l/d \\
0 & 0 & l/d \\
-l/d & 0 & 2l/d \\
0 & -l/d & -2l/d \\
l/d & 0 & -2l/d \\
0 & l/d & 2l/d
\end{bmatrix}
\begin{Bmatrix} F_1^* \\ F_2^* \\ F_3^0 \end{Bmatrix}
\qquad (12.2)
$$

$$
\underset{[b]^*}{\uparrow} \qquad \underset{[b]^0}{\uparrow}
$$

Using matrix $[b]$ from Equation (12.2) in Equation (8.6) (repeated below) we can generate the 3×3 flexibility matrix $[a]$, corresponding to the co-ordinates which identify the forces F_1^*, F_2^*, and F_3^0.

$$
[a] = [b]^T[\alpha][b] \qquad (12.3)
$$

But in order to do so we must first determine the flexibility matrices of the elements, $[\alpha]_s$, in $[\alpha]$.

Computing the Flexibility Matrices of the Elements

Shear Panels. For shear panel 1 shown in Figure 12.5, we write the strain energy, U, in terms of the shear force, P_1, using Equation (6.6) (note that P_1 here corresponds to V in this equation).

$$
U = \frac{1}{2}\int_0^l \frac{P_1^2}{GA}\,dx = \frac{1}{2}\frac{P_1^2 l}{GA}
$$

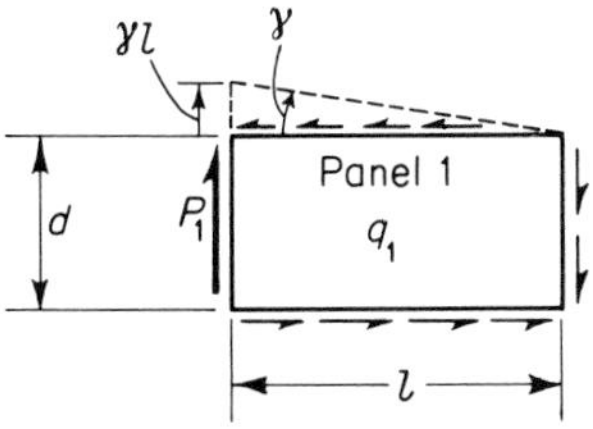

From Equation (6.25), we have

$$
\alpha_1 = \frac{\partial^2 U}{\partial P_1^2} = \frac{l}{GA} = \frac{l}{Gt_1 d} \qquad (12.4)
$$

Figure 12.5. Shear panel element.

in which t_1 is the thickness of panel 1 and d is the dimension of the panel where force P_1 is defined (see Figure 12.5). Using Equation

(12.4) we obtain for the other shear panels

$$\alpha_2 = \frac{w}{Gt_2\,d}, \qquad \alpha_3 = \frac{l}{Gt_3\,d}, \qquad \alpha_4 = \frac{w}{Gt_4 l}, \qquad \alpha_5 = \frac{w}{Gt_5 l}$$

in which w is the width of the box beam (see Figures 12.3 and 12.4) and t_i is the thickness of panel number i.

Flanges. For any flange element, such as shown in Figure 12.6, the axial force varies linearly along the length according to our assumption of uniform shear. Hence the axial force $p(x)$ at any section a distance x from the left in Figure 12.6 is given by

$$p(x) = \frac{x}{l}\,P \tag{12.5}$$

The strain energy U is given by [see Equation (6.6)]

$$U = \frac{1}{2}\int_0^l \frac{p^2(x)}{EA}\,dx$$

Substituting for $p(x)$ from Equation (12.5) and integrating

$$U = \frac{1}{6}\frac{P^2 l}{EA}$$

From Equation (6.25) we have

$$\alpha_i = \frac{\partial^2 U}{\partial P_i^2} = \frac{1}{3}\frac{l}{EA}$$

$$i = 6, 7, 8, 9 \tag{12.6}$$

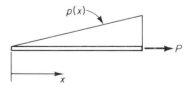

Figure 12.6. Flange element showing distribution of axial force $p(x)$.

Fulfilling the Objectives. Using the flexibility matrices of all nine elements we assemble $[\alpha]$

$$[\alpha] = \begin{bmatrix} \dfrac{l}{Gt_1 d} & & & & & & & & \\[2ex] & \dfrac{w}{Gt_2 d} & & & & & & & \\[2ex] & & \dfrac{l}{Gt_3 d} & & & & & & \\[2ex] & & & \dfrac{w}{Gt_4 l} & & & & & \\[2ex] & & & & \dfrac{w}{Gt_5 l} & & & & \\[2ex] & & & & & \dfrac{l}{3EA} & & & \\[2ex] & & & & & & \dfrac{l}{3EA} & & \\[2ex] & & & & & & & \dfrac{l}{3EA} & \\[2ex] & & & & & & & & \dfrac{l}{3EA} \end{bmatrix} \tag{12.7}$$

Substituting $[\alpha]$ and $[b]$ into Equation (12.3), we obtain (in the computations we set $G = E/2.5$),

$$[a] = \begin{matrix} [a]_{11} \rightarrow \\ \\ \\ [a]_{21} \rightarrow \end{matrix} \frac{1}{E} \left[\begin{array}{cc|c} 140 & 0 & -180 \\ 0 & 140 & 180 \\ \hline -180 & 180 & 1260 \end{array} \right] \begin{matrix} \leftarrow [a]_{12} \\ \\ \leftarrow [a]_{22} \end{matrix} \tag{12.8}$$

Using Equation (8.13) we compute $[a]^*$

$$[a]^* = \frac{1}{E}\begin{bmatrix} 140 & 0 \\ 0 & 140 \end{bmatrix} - \frac{1}{E}\begin{bmatrix} -180 \\ 180 \end{bmatrix}\frac{1}{1260}[-180 \quad 180]$$

$$= \frac{1}{E}\begin{bmatrix} 140 & 0 \\ 0 & 140 \end{bmatrix} - \frac{1}{7E}\begin{bmatrix} 180 & -180 \\ -180 & 180 \end{bmatrix}$$

$$= \frac{1}{7E}\begin{bmatrix} 800 & 180 \\ 180 & 800 \end{bmatrix}$$

This fulfills our first objective.

To fulfill the second objective, we compute F_3^0 using Equation (8.11) which yields in the present example

$$F_3^0 = - [a]_{22}^{-1}[a]_{21}\{F\}^*$$

$$= - \frac{1}{1260}[-180 \quad 180]\begin{Bmatrix} F_1^* \\ F_2^* \end{Bmatrix}$$

$$= \frac{1}{7}(F_1^* - F_2^*)$$

Using this expression for F_3^0 in Equation (12.2) we can compute the internal forces $\{P\}$ for any given values of F_1^* and F_2^*. This fulfills our second objective.

Suggested Exercises: Do problems 1, 2, 3, 4 and 5.

12.3. STIFFNESS MATRIX OF A TRIANGULAR PLATE ELEMENT[65,67]

Figure 12.7 shows a triangular plate element with its corners identified by numbers 1, 2, 3. The quantities (x_i, y_i) give the position of corner i (or

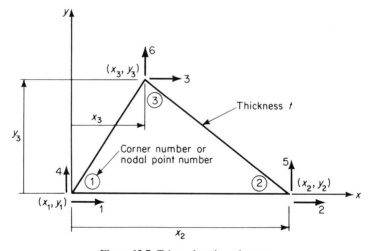

Figure 12.7. Triangular plate element.

nodal point i) with respect to the xy axes with origin at corner 1 and the x axis oriented along the base of the triangle.

$$(x_1, y_1) = (0, 0) \qquad (x_2, y_2) = (x_2, 0)$$

The area of the triangle is $\frac{1}{2}x_2y_3$ and its volume for a uniform thickness t is $\frac{1}{2}tx_2y_3$.

We define six coordinates, two at each corner, and wish to compute the corresponding 6×6 element stiffness matrix $[\kappa]$. To do so we must establish the displacement configuration which the plate assumes between the nodal points, as one coordinate at a time undergoes a unit displacement. We note that an infinite number of such displacement configurations can be selected so as to correspond to a unit displacement at any given coordinate $1, 2, \ldots, 6$. Also, the forces required to produce a unit displacement will not be concentrated forces at the coordinates but rather distributed forces along the faces of the element. In fact, if we try to generate the stiffness matrix of the triangle in a laboratory by applying concentrated forces at the corners of a model, we will chip the corners before any measurement could be made. The forces at the coordinates must therefore be considered as generalized forces; that is, these forces (which are in equilibrium with the distributed forces) will do work on the coordinate displacements, and this work will be equal to the work done by the distributed forces on the corresponding displacements of the element (which are compatible with the coordinate displacements).

For the development here we assume the displacements of the element to be linear functions of x and y at all times and write

$$\delta_x(x, y) = a_1 + a_2 x + a_3 y$$
$$\delta_y(x, y) = a_4 + a_5 x + a_6 y \tag{12.9}$$

in which

$\delta_x(x, y) = $ displacement in the x direction of any point (x, y)
$\delta_y(x, y) = $ displacement in the y direction of any point (x, y)
$a_i(i = 1, 2, \ldots, 6) = $ constants

Equation (12.9) can be written in the matrix form

$$\{\delta(x, y)\} = [A]\{a\} \tag{12.10}$$

where

$$\{\delta(x, y)\} = \begin{Bmatrix} \delta_x(x, y) \\ \delta_y(x, y) \end{Bmatrix}$$

$$[A] = \begin{bmatrix} 1 & x & y & 0 & 0 & 0 \\ 0 & 0 & 0 & 1 & x & y \end{bmatrix}$$

$$\{a\} = \begin{Bmatrix} a_1 \\ a_2 \\ \vdots \\ a_6 \end{Bmatrix}$$

To compute the 6×6 stiffness matrix for the element of Figure 12.7 we apply Equation (6.30), repeated here for convenience.

$$\kappa_{ij} = \sum_{s=1}^{4} \int_V \sigma_{sj} \varepsilon_{si} \, dV$$

This equation can also be written as†

$$\kappa_{ij} = \sum_{r=1}^{6} \int_V \sigma_{rj} \varepsilon_{ri} \, dV \tag{12.11}$$

in which $r = 1, 2, \ldots, 6$ identifies the six components of stress (axial and shear) and strain in the x, y, z coordinate system.

In our present problem, which is a plane stress problem, only two normal stress components a single shear and corresponding strains are involved; therefore, Equation (12.11) can be written as

$$\kappa_{ij} = \int_V \{\sigma\}_j^T \{\varepsilon\}_i \, dV \tag{12.12}$$

where

$$\{\sigma\}_j = \begin{cases} \sigma_x \\ \sigma_y \\ \tau \end{cases}_j \quad \begin{matrix} \text{stress in } x \text{ direction} \\ \text{stress in } y \text{ direction} \\ \text{shear stress} \end{matrix}$$

$$\{\varepsilon\}_i = \begin{cases} \varepsilon_x \\ \varepsilon_y \\ \gamma \end{cases}_i \quad \begin{matrix} \text{strain in } x \text{ direction} \\ \text{strain in } y \text{ direction} \\ \text{shear strain} \end{matrix}$$

The subscript j in $\{\sigma\}_j$ designates that this stress vector corresponds to a unit displacement at coordinate j only; that is, $\delta_j = 1$ with all $\delta_i = 0$ for $i \neq j$. Similarly $\{\varepsilon\}_i$ is the strain vector which corresponds to $\delta_i = 1$ with all $\delta_j = 0$ for $j \neq i$.

To find the vectors $\{\sigma\}_i$ and $\{\varepsilon\}_i$ for all i so we can apply Equation (12.12), we must find the following two transformation matrices $[T_{\sigma(\delta)}]$ and $[T_{\varepsilon(\delta)}]$

$$\{\varepsilon\} = [T_{\varepsilon(\delta)}]\{\delta\} \qquad \text{(a)}$$
$$\{\sigma\} = [T_{\sigma(\delta)}]\{\delta\} \qquad \text{(b)} \tag{12.13}$$

---

† In Equation (6.30) the total work done by κ_{ij} on a unit displacement is obtained by summing the four energy forms ($s = 1, 2, 3, 4$), whereas in Equation (12.11) the same total work is obtained by adding the work done by the six stress components ($r = 1, 2, \ldots, 6$) in the xyz coordinate system.

in which

$$\{\delta\} = \begin{Bmatrix} \delta_1 \\ \delta_2 \\ \vdots \\ \delta_6 \end{Bmatrix}$$

and the jth columns of $[T_{\sigma(\delta)}]$ and $[T_{\varepsilon(\delta)}]$ are equal to $\{\sigma\}_j$ and $\{\varepsilon\}_j$, respectively.

To compute these two transformation matrices for the displacement functions of Equations (12.9) or (12.10) we proceed as follows: From theory of elasticity we have[68]

$$\varepsilon_x = \frac{\partial\,\delta_x(x, y)}{\partial x}, \qquad \varepsilon_y = \frac{\partial\,\delta_y(x, y)}{\partial y}$$

$$\gamma = \gamma_{xy} = \frac{\partial\,\delta_x(x, y)}{\partial y} + \frac{\partial\,\delta_y(x, y)}{\partial x}$$

Substituting for $\delta_x(x, y)$ and $\delta_y(x, y)$ from Equation (12.9) we obtain

$$\varepsilon_x = a_2, \qquad \varepsilon_y = a_6, \qquad \gamma_{xy} = a_3 + a_5$$

or in matrix form

$$\{\varepsilon\} = [B]\{a\} \tag{12.14}$$

in which

$$[B] = \begin{bmatrix} 0 & 1 & 0 & 0 & 0 & 0 \\ 0 & 0 & 0 & 0 & 0 & 1 \\ 0 & 0 & 1 & 0 & 1 & 0 \end{bmatrix}$$

To get $\{\varepsilon\}$ in terms of $\{\delta\}$ as is desired in Equation (12.13a), we solve for $\{a\}$ in terms of $\{\delta\}$ and substitute into Equation (12.14). This is done as follows: In Figure 12.7

$$\delta_1 = \delta_x(0, 0)$$
$$\delta_2 = \delta_x(x_2, 0)$$
$$\delta_3 = \delta_x(x_3, y_3)$$
$$\delta_4 = \delta_y(0, 0)$$
$$\delta_5 = \delta_y(x_2, 0)$$
$$\delta_6 = \delta_y(x_3, y_3)$$

Evaluating these δ_i from Equation (12.10), we have

$$\{\delta\} = [C]\{a\} \tag{12.15}$$

in which

$$[C] = \begin{bmatrix} 1 & & & & & & \\ 1 & x_2 & & \text{Elements not} & & \\ & & & \text{shown are zero} & & \\ 1 & x_3 & y_3 & & & \\ & & & 1 & & \\ & & & 1 & x_2 & \\ & & & 1 & x_3 & y_3 \end{bmatrix}$$

From Equation (12.15),

$$\{a\} = [C]^{-1}\{\delta\} \tag{12.16}$$

$$[C]^{-1} = \frac{1}{x_2 y_3} \begin{bmatrix} x_2 y_3 & & & \text{Elements not} & & \\ & & & \text{shown are zero} & & \\ -y_3 & y_3 & & & & \\ x_3 - x_2 & -x_3 & x_2 & & & \\ & & & x_2 y_3 & & \\ & & & -y_3 & y_3 & \\ & & & x_3 - x_2 & -x_3 & x_2 \end{bmatrix}$$

Substituting Equation (12.16) into Equation (12.14) leads to the first desired relationship, Equation (12.13a)

$$\{\varepsilon\} = [T_{\varepsilon(\delta)}]\{\delta\}$$

in which

$$[T_{\varepsilon(\delta)}] = [B][C]^{-1} \tag{12.17}$$

Now to get $\{\sigma\}$ in terms of $\{\delta\}$, we use the stress strain relation for plane stress[68]

$$\{\varepsilon\} = [N]\{\sigma\} \qquad \text{(a)}$$
$$\{\sigma\} = [N]^{-1}\{\varepsilon\} \qquad \text{(b)} \tag{12.18}$$

where

$$[N] = \frac{1}{E}\begin{bmatrix} 1 & -v & 0 \\ -v & 1 & 0 \\ 0 & 0 & \dfrac{E}{G} \end{bmatrix} \qquad [N]^{-1} = \frac{E}{1-v^2}\begin{bmatrix} 1 & v & 0 \\ v & 1 & 0 \\ 0 & 0 & \dfrac{1-v}{2} \end{bmatrix}$$

E = modulus of elasticity
G = shear modulus
v = Poisson's ratio

$$G = \frac{E}{2(1+v)}$$

Substituting Equation (12.13a) and then Equation (12.17) into (12.18b) leads to our second desired relationship, Equation (12.13b)

$$\{\sigma\} = [T_{\sigma(\delta)}]\{\delta\}$$

in which

$$[T_{\sigma(\delta)}] = [N]^{-1}[B][C]^{-1} \tag{12.19}$$

To compute any element κ_{ij} from Equation (12.12), we substitute for $\{\sigma\}_j^T$ row j of $[T_{\sigma(\delta)}]^T$ and for $\{\varepsilon\}_i$ column i of $[T_{\varepsilon(\delta)}]$. Therefore to compute all elements κ_{ij} of $[\kappa]$ we write

$$[\kappa] = \int_V [T_{\sigma(\delta)}]^T [T_{\varepsilon(\delta)}]\, dV \tag{12.20}$$

where the integral sign designates a separate integration over volume (of the triangular element) for each term of the matrix product $[T_{\sigma(\delta)}]^T [T_{\varepsilon(\delta)}]$. Substituting for $[T_{\varepsilon(\delta)}]$ and $[T_{\sigma(\delta)}]$ from Equations (12.17) and (12.19) into Equation (12.20), and noting that matrix $[N]^{-1}$ is a symmetrical matrix, gives

$$[\kappa] = \int_V ([C]^{-1})^T [B]^T [N]^{-1}[B][C]^{-1}\, dV \tag{12.21}$$

An inspection of matrices $[B]$, $[C]$, and $[N]$ in Equations (12.14), (12.15), and (12.18), respectively, shows that these are matrices with constant elements, consequently the matrix product in Equation (12.21) is also a matrix of constant elements. Each of these constants is multiplied by the same integral

$$\int_V dV = \tfrac{1}{2}x_2 y_3 t$$

which is equal to the volume of the triangle in Figure 12.7.

The operations on the right-hand side of Equation (12.21) yield the following stiffness matrix $[\kappa]$:

$$[\kappa] = \lambda_1 \begin{bmatrix} y_3^2 + \lambda_2\lambda_3^2 & & & & & \text{Symm.} \\ -y_3^2 - \lambda_2\lambda_3 x_3 & y_3^2 + \lambda_2 x_3^2 & & & & \\ \lambda_2\lambda_3 x_2 & -\lambda_2 x_2 x_3 & \lambda_2 x_2^2 & & & \\ -(\lambda_2 + v)y_3\lambda_3 & y_3(\lambda_2 x_3 + v\lambda_3) & -\lambda_2 x_2 y_3 & \lambda_2 y_3^2 + \lambda_3^2 & & \\ y_3(\lambda_2\lambda_3 + vx_3) & -x_3 y_3(v + \lambda_2) & \lambda_2 x_2 y_3 & -\lambda_2 y_3^2 - x_3\lambda_3 & \lambda_2 y_3^2 + x_3^2 & \\ -vx_2 y_3 & vx_2 y_3 & 0 & x_2\lambda_3 & -x_2 x_3 & x_2^2 \end{bmatrix}$$

$$(12.22)$$

$$\lambda_1 = \frac{Et}{2x_2 y_3(1 - v^2)}, \qquad \lambda_2 = \frac{1 - v}{2}, \qquad \lambda_3 = x_3 - x_2$$

Suggested Exercises: Do problems 6, 7, 8, 9 and 10.

12.4. FLEXIBILITY MATRIX OF A TRIANGULAR PLATE ELEMENT[65]

To generate a flexibility matrix for the triangular plate element of Figure 12.7, we must first select coordinates in which there exists no dependency among the force measurements (see Section 3.6). To accomplish this, we support the element in at least a statically determinate fashion and define three coordinates as shown in Figure 12.8.

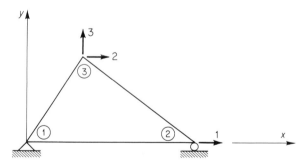

Figure 12.8. Choice of element coordinates for flexibility matrix.

To derive directly the flexibility matrix, we define a stress distribution for the element and compute the statically equivalent forces at the co-ordinates. Then we proceed with steps similar to those of Section 12.3. To enable comparison of the results in this section with those of the last section, we select a constant stress distribution which is consistent with the linear displacement function selected in the last section, Equation (12.9). The stress distribution is shown in Figure 12.9. From this figure we write

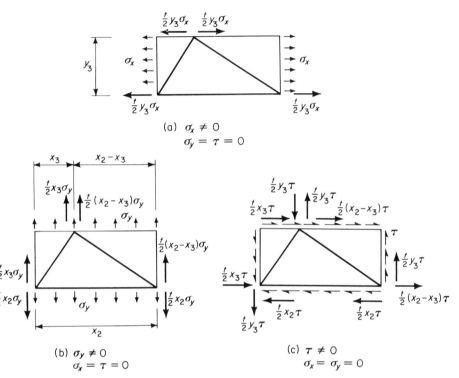

Figure 12.9. Stress distribution and equivalent forces at the coordinates (and at the supports).

for the statically equivalent forces $P_i(i = 1, 2, 3)$ at the coordinates of Figure 12.8,

$$\{P\} = [D]\{\sigma\} \tag{12.23}$$

where

$$[D] = \frac{t}{2}\begin{bmatrix} y_3 & 0 & -x_3 \\ 0 & 0 & x_2 \\ 0 & x_2 & 0 \end{bmatrix}, \quad \{P\} = \begin{Bmatrix} P_1 \\ P_2 \\ P_3 \end{Bmatrix}, \quad \{\sigma\} = \begin{Bmatrix} \sigma_x \\ \sigma_y \\ \tau \end{Bmatrix}$$

To compute the 3 × 3 flexibility matrix, we apply Equation (6.32)

$$\alpha_{ij} = \sum_{s=1}^{4} \int_V \sigma_{si} \varepsilon_{sj} \, dV$$

This equation can also be written as†

$$\alpha_{ij} = \sum_{r=1}^{6} \int_V \sigma_{ri} \varepsilon_{rj} \, dV \tag{12.24}$$

in which $r = 1, 2, \ldots, 6$ identifies the six components of stress (axial and shear) and strain in the x, y, z coordinate system. In our present problem of plane stress Equation (12.24) becomes

$$\alpha_{ij} = \int_V \{\varepsilon\}_j^T \{\sigma\}_i \, dV \tag{12.25}$$

where

$$\{\sigma\}_i = \begin{Bmatrix} \sigma_x \\ \sigma_y \\ \tau \end{Bmatrix}_i \quad \begin{matrix} \text{stress in } x \text{ direction} \\ \text{stress in } y \text{ direction} \\ \text{shear stress} \end{matrix}$$

$$\{\varepsilon\}_j = \begin{Bmatrix} \varepsilon_x \\ \varepsilon_y \\ \gamma \end{Bmatrix}_j \quad \begin{matrix} \text{strain in } x \text{ direction} \\ \text{strain in } y \text{ direction} \\ \text{shear strain} \end{matrix}$$

The subscript i in $\{\sigma\}_i$ designates that this stress vector corresponds to a unit force at coordinate i only; that is, $P_i = 1$ with all $P_j = 0$ for $j \neq i$. Similarly $\{\varepsilon\}_j$ is the strain vector which corresponds to $P_j = 1$ with all $P_i = 0$ for $i \neq j$.

To find vectors $\{\sigma\}_i$ and $\{\varepsilon\}_i$ for all i, so we can use Equation (12.25), we must find the following two transformation matrices $[T_{\sigma(P)}]$ and $[T_{\varepsilon(P)}]$

$$\begin{aligned} \{\sigma\} &= [T_{\sigma(P)}]\{P\} \quad \text{(a)} \\ \{\varepsilon\} &= [T_{\varepsilon(P)}]\{P\} \quad \text{(b)} \end{aligned} \tag{12.26}$$

The ith columns of $[T_{\sigma(P)}]$ and $[T_{\varepsilon(P)}]$ are equal to $\{\sigma\}_i$ and $\{\varepsilon\}_i$, respectively. From Equation (12.23), we obtain

$$\{\sigma\} = [D]^{-1}\{P\} \tag{12.27}$$

$$[D]^{-1} = \frac{2}{t} \begin{bmatrix} \dfrac{1}{y_3} & \dfrac{x_3}{x_2 y_3} & 0 \\[2ex] 0 & 0 & \dfrac{1}{x_2} \\[2ex] 0 & \dfrac{1}{x_2} & 0 \end{bmatrix}$$

---

† In Equation (6.32), the total work done by a unit force on displacement α_{ij} is obtained by summing the four energy forms ($s = 1, 2, 3, 4$), whereas in Equation (12.24) the same total work is obtained by adding the work done by the six stress components ($r = 1, 2, \ldots, 6$) in the xyz coordinate system.

Comparing Equations (12.26a) and (12.27), we have

$$[T_{\sigma(P)}] = [D]^{-1} \tag{12.28}$$

Substituting Equation (12.27) into Equation (12.18a), we obtain

$$\{\varepsilon\} = [N][D]^{-1}\{P\}$$

Comparing this equation with Equation (12.26b), we conclude that

$$[T_{\varepsilon(P)}] = [N][D]^{-1} \tag{12.29}$$

To compute any element α_{ij} from Equation (12.25), we substitute the jth row of $[T_{\varepsilon(P)}]^T$ for $\{\varepsilon\}_j^T$ and the ith column of $[T_{\sigma(P)}]$ for $\{\sigma\}_i$. The complete matrix $[\alpha]$ is given by

$$[\alpha] = \int_V [T_{\varepsilon(P)}]^T [T_{\sigma(P)}]\, dV \tag{12.30}$$

Substituting for $[T_{\sigma(P)}]$ and $[T_{\varepsilon(P)}]$ from Equations (12.28) and (12.29), respectively, and recalling that matrix $[N]$ is symmetrical, gives

$$[\alpha] = \int_V ([D]^{-1})^T [N][D]^{-1}\, dV \tag{12.31}$$

Matrices $[D]$ and $[N]$ have constant elements and therefore the matrix product in Equation (12.31) has constant elements. We multiply each of these constants by the same integral

$$\int_V dV = \tfrac{1}{2}x_2 y_3 t$$

which is equal to the volume of the triangle in Figure 12.7.

The operations on the right-hand side of Equation (12.31) yield the following flexibility matrix $[\alpha]$

$$[\alpha] = \frac{2x_2 y_3}{Et}
\begin{bmatrix}
\dfrac{1}{y_3^2} & & \text{Symm.} \\[2ex]
\dfrac{x_3}{x_2 y_3^2} & \left(\dfrac{x_3}{x_2 y_3}\right)^2 + \dfrac{2(1+\nu)}{x_2^2} & \\[2ex]
-\dfrac{\nu}{x_2 y_3} & -\dfrac{\nu x_3}{x_2^2 y_3} & \dfrac{1}{x_2^2}
\end{bmatrix} \tag{12.32}$$

Checking Equations (12.22) and (12.32)

To check Equation (12.32) against the results in Equation (12.22) we use the 6×6 stiffness matrix $[\kappa]$ in Equation (12.22) to obtain a 3×3 $[\kappa]$ matrix for the three coordinates of Figure 12.8. This can be achieved by eliminating columns 1, 4, 5 and rows, 1, 4, 5, and rearranging the remaining three rows and columns. The easiest way to do this is to write the code of numbers ⓪ ① ② ⓪ ⓪ ③ on top and to the left of $[\kappa]$ in Equation (12.22), and to use the procedure of Section 9.8, shown as follows:

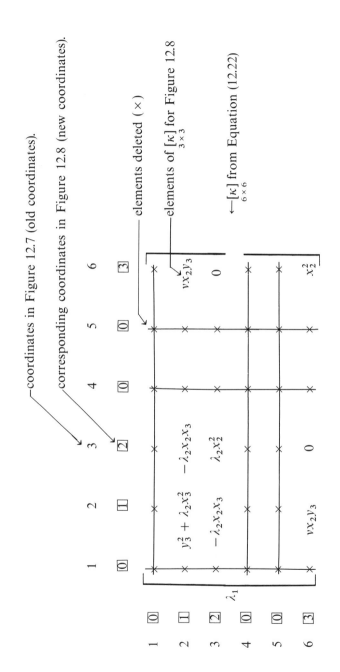

The position of each box in the code represents the coordinate in Figure 12.7 (the old coordinates); the number in the box represents the corresponding coordinate in Figure 12.8 (new coordinates). The resulting 3×3 $[\kappa]$ matrix is

$$[\kappa] = \lambda_1 \begin{bmatrix} y_3^2 + \lambda_2 x_3^2 & \text{Symm.} & \\ -\lambda_2 x_2 x_3 & \lambda_2 x_2^2 & \\ \nu x_2 y_3 & 0 & x_2^2 \end{bmatrix} \tag{12.33}$$

Multiplying this matrix by $[\alpha]$ of Equation (12.32) yields the identity matrix. This is expected because the same assumptions (linear displacement and constant stress) were introduced in deriving these matrices.

Suggested Exercises: Do problems 11, 12, 13, 14, 15 and 16.

12.5. EXAMPLE: STIFFNESS METHOD APPLIED TO A PLATE

Consider the plate of uniform thickness $t = 0.036$ in. loaded as shown in Figure 12.10. Let our objectives be to compute the displacements $u_i (i = 1, 2, 3, 4)$ at the system coordinates in Figure 12.11(a) and the internal stresses and strains. The solution proceeds as follows:

Solution procedure

We idealize the plate of Figure 12.10 by selecting two triangular elements as shown in Figure 12.11(a). The element coordinates for the two triangular plate elements are numbered in a way which is consistent with Figure 12.7, as shown in Figures 12.11(b, c).

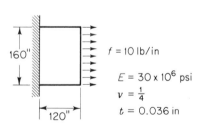

$f = 10$ lb/in

$E = 30 \times 10^6$ psi

$\nu = \frac{1}{4}$

$t = 0.036$ in

Figure 12.10. Loaded plate.

To obtain the element stiffness matrices $[\kappa]_1$ and $[\kappa]_2$ for elements 1 and 2 in Figure 12.11 we substitute the appropriate values for $\lambda_1, \lambda_2, \lambda_3, x_2, x_3,$ y_3, etc., in Equation (12.22). Using these element matrices, we write

$$\{P\} = [\kappa]\{\delta\} \tag{12.34}$$

in which

$$\{\delta\} = \left\{ \frac{\{\delta\}_1}{\{\delta\}_2} \right\}, \qquad [\kappa] = \begin{bmatrix} [\kappa]_1 & \\ & [\kappa]_2 \end{bmatrix}, \qquad \{P\} = \left\{ \frac{\{P\}_1}{\{P\}_2} \right\}$$

Subscripts 1 and 2 refer to elements 1 and 2, respectively. If more elements are present the foregoing matrices are extended as in Equation (6.54).

From Figure 12.11, we can find matrix $[\beta]$ in the equation

$$\{\delta\} = [\beta]\{u\} \tag{12.35}$$

and using $[\beta]$ we generate the system stiffness matrix $[k]$

$$[k] = [\beta]^T[\kappa][\beta] \tag{12.36}$$

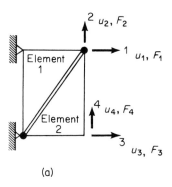

(a)

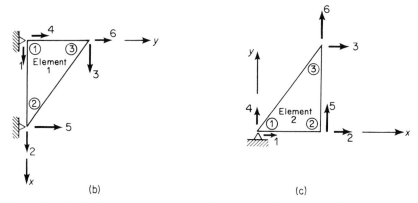

(b)   (c)

Figure 12.11. (a) Idealized model of plate in Figure 12.10 and system coordinates. (b) Element coordinates for element 1. (c) Element coordinates for element 2.

To compute displacements $u_i (i = 1, 2, 3, 4)$ we find in Figure 12.10 the generalized forces $F_i (i = 1, 2, 3, 4)$ which correspond to distributed force f. Any force F_i is equal in magnitude to the work done by distributed force f on the displacements which correspond to $u_i = 1$ with $u_j = 0$ for all $j \neq i$. In our present example,

$$F_1 = F_3 = \tfrac{1}{2} 160 f = 80 f$$
$$F_2 = F_4 = 0 \tag{12.37}$$

Using forces $\{F\}$, we have

$$\{u\} = [k]^{-1}\{F\} \tag{12.38}$$

Substituting for $\{u\}$ in Equation (12.35) gives

$$\{\delta\} = [\beta][k]^{-1}\{F\} \tag{12.39}$$

Using this equation in Equations (12.13) and recalling that Equations (12.13) refer to a single element, whereas $\{\delta\}$ in the last equation contains the vectors $\{\delta\}_i$ of all elements in the system, we compute the stresses and strains in the elements of the system. For n elements we have

$$\begin{Bmatrix} \{\sigma\}_1 \\ \{\sigma\}_2 \\ \vdots \\ \{\sigma\}_n \end{Bmatrix} = \begin{bmatrix} [T_{\sigma(\delta)}]_1 & & & \\ & [T_{\sigma(\delta)}]_2 & & \\ & & \ddots & \\ & & & [T_{\sigma(\delta)}]_n \end{bmatrix} \begin{Bmatrix} \{\delta\}_1 \\ \{\delta\}_2 \\ \vdots \\ \{\delta\}_n \end{Bmatrix} \tag{12.40a}$$

and

$$\begin{Bmatrix} \{\varepsilon\}_1 \\ \{\varepsilon\}_2 \\ \vdots \\ \{\varepsilon\}_n \end{Bmatrix} = \begin{bmatrix} [T_{\varepsilon(\delta)}]_1 & & & \\ & [T_{\varepsilon(\delta)}]_2 & & \\ & & \ddots & \\ & & & [T_{\varepsilon(\delta)}]_n \end{bmatrix} \begin{Bmatrix} \{\delta\}_1 \\ \{\delta\}_2 \\ \vdots \\ \{\delta\}_n \end{Bmatrix} \tag{12.40b}$$

Equations (12.38) and (12.40) fulfill our objectives.

Solution by the Code System of Section 9.8

An alternate procedure to arrive at the solution is offered by the code system of Section 9.8. The codes for elements 1 and 2 in Figure 12.11 are given by

	1	2	3	4	5	6 ←Element coordinates
Element 1	0	0	−2	0	0	1 ←Corresponding system coordinates

	1	2	3	4	5	6
Element 2	0	3	1	0	4	2

Proceeding as in the example of Section 9.8, we write for each element its stiffness matrix with the code written above and to the left as follows:

Element 1

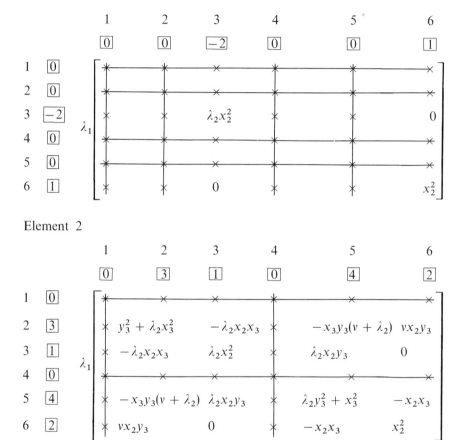

Element 2

The minus sign in box 3 of the code for element 1 indicates that element coordinate 3 and system coordinate 2 are oppositely directed and therefore all elements of row 3 and column 3 of $[\kappa]_1$ must have their signs reversed† when transferred to the system stiffness matrix $[k]$. Note that the element on the principal diagonal is not affected because its sign is changed twice. Substituting the appropriate values of λ_1, λ_2, λ_3, x_2, x_3, y_3, etc., for

---

† The computer program of Section 9.9 cannot handle negative code numbers. Therefore, in using this program, the stiffness matrix of each element must first be transformed by Equation (9.35) to yield positive code numbers. In the present example, Equation (9.35) will reverse the signs of row 3 and column 3 in the stiffness matrix, $[\kappa]_1$, of element 1. Verify.

each element, we evaluate their stiffness matrices and construct the 4×4 system stiffness matrix $[k]$ as shown below (λ_1 is the same for the two elements).

Element 2

Element 1

$$
\begin{array}{c} \boxed{-2} \\ \boxed{1} \end{array} \lambda_1 10^3 \begin{bmatrix} 9.6 & 0 \\ 0 & 25.6 \end{bmatrix}
\qquad
\begin{array}{c} \boxed{3} \\ \boxed{1} \\ \boxed{4} \\ \boxed{2} \end{array} \lambda_1 10^3 \begin{bmatrix} 31 & -5.4 & -12 & 4.8 \\ -5.4 & 5.4 & 7.2 & 0 \\ -12 & 7.2 & 24 & -14.4 \\ 4.8 & 0 & -14.4 & 14.4 \end{bmatrix}
$$

(column labels for element 2: $\boxed{3}\ \boxed{1}\ \boxed{4}\ \boxed{2}$)

(column labels for element 1: $\boxed{-2}\ \boxed{1}$)

$$
[k]_{\text{system}} = \lambda_1 10^3 \begin{array}{c} 1 \\ 2 \\ 3 \\ 4 \end{array} \begin{bmatrix} 31 & 0 & -5.4 & 7.2 \\ 0 & 24 & 4.8 & -14.4 \\ -5.4 & 4.8 & 31 & -12 \\ 7.2 & -14.4 & -12 & 24 \end{bmatrix} \qquad (12.41)
$$

(column labels: 1 2 3 4)

$$
\lambda_1 = \frac{Et}{2 \times 120 \times 160 \times (1 - v^2)}
$$

$$
= \frac{30 \times 10^6 \times 0.036}{2 \times 120 \times 160 \times 15/16}
$$

= 30 lb/in.^{3} (Units of elements within the matrix are in.^{2}; hence dimension of stiffness elements is lb/in.)

Using $[k]$ from Equation (12.41) and $\{F\}$ from Equation (12.37), we compute $\{u\}$. From $\{u\}$ we get the vectors $\{\delta\}_i$ for each element and then from Equation (12.40) we compute the stresses and strains.

Suggested Exercises: Do problems 17, 18 and 19.

12.6. STIFFNESS MATRIX OF PLATE ELEMENT AT ANY ORIENTATION

From the discussion in Section 9.8 on the use of the code system method in general, we recall that when the element and system coordinates do not have a one-to-one correspondence we transform the element stiffness matrix $[\kappa]_\delta$ in the δ coordinates to a new matrix $[\kappa]_q$ so that the code system can be applied. The transformation is accomplished by a matrix of direction cosines [see Equations (9.34) and (9.35)].

Suppose that we wish to construct the system stiffness matrix for the idealized plate with system coordinates as shown in Figure 12.12(a). To do

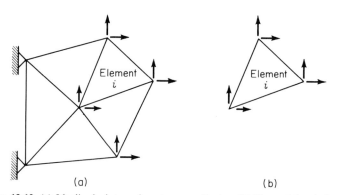

Figure 12.12. (a) Idealized plate and system coordinates. (b) Element i and element coordinates.

this by the code system approach, each triangular element must have a stiffness matrix $[\kappa]_q$ for coordinates q aligned with the system coordinates; that is, both must have the same orientation as shown for an element i in Figure 12.12(b). Now, the element stiffness matrix $[\kappa]$ of Equation (12.22) does not apply to the coordinates of element i in Figure 12.12(b). To transform the matrix of Equation (12.22) so it applies to a triangle at any orientation with its coordinates at the corners pointing in the horizontal and vertical directions [Figure 12.12(b)], we proceed as follows:

We rearrange the rows and columns of the matrix $[\kappa]$ in Equation (12.22), using the code system approach, so that it applies to the coordinates

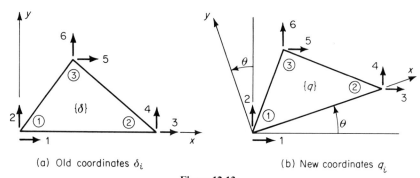

(a) Old coordinates δ_i (b) New coordinates q_i

Figure 12.13.

numbered in sequence from corner to corner as shown in Figure 12.13(a). (See Problem 20). We designate the corresponding matrix by $[\kappa]_\delta$ and refer to the coordinates δ_i as the old coordinates. The new coordinates q_i (also numbered in sequence for each corner) for the element in a rotated orientation are shown in Figure 12.13(b). We designate the corresponding element stiffness matrix by $[\kappa]_q$. The transformation from the "old" coordinates δ_i to the "new" coordinates q_i is given by

$$
\begin{Bmatrix} \delta_1 \\ \delta_2 \\ \hline \delta_3 \\ \delta_4 \\ \hline \delta_5 \\ \delta_6 \end{Bmatrix} = \begin{bmatrix} [T] & \text{Submatrices not shown} \\ & \text{are null matrices} \\ \hline & [T] & \\ \hline & & [T] \end{bmatrix} \begin{Bmatrix} q_1 \\ q_2 \\ \hline q_3 \\ q_4 \\ \hline q_5 \\ q_6 \end{Bmatrix} \qquad (12.42)
$$

in which [see Equation (7.27), Section 7.9]

$$
[T] = \begin{bmatrix} \cos\theta & \sin\theta \\ -\sin\theta & \cos\theta \end{bmatrix}
$$

and θ is the angle of rotation of the old coordinates δ_i in Figure 12.13(a) to the new orientation of the element in Figure 12.13(b). The desired stiffness matrix $[\kappa]_q$ is obtained from the equation

$$
[\kappa]_q = \begin{bmatrix} [T] & & \\ & [T] & \\ & & [T] \end{bmatrix}^T [\kappa]_\delta \begin{bmatrix} [T] & & \\ & [T] & \\ & & [T] \end{bmatrix} \qquad (12.43)
$$

Proceeding with the operations described in this section, we obtain the following results shown in Equations (12.44) and (12.45) for $[\kappa]_\delta$ and $[\kappa]_q$. The letters S and C in Equation (12.45) designate $\sin\theta$ and $\cos\theta$ respectively, and the numbers (ij) in parentheses represent the elements ij of matrix $[\kappa]_\delta$ in Equation (12.44). For example,

$$(53) \text{ stands for } \lambda_1(-\lambda_2 x_2 x_3)$$

and the term in row 5 column 4 of $[\kappa]_q$ is interpreted as

$$C^2(54) - S^2(63) + SC[(53) - (64)] = (\lambda_1\lambda_2 x_2 y_3)\cos^2\theta - (\lambda_1 \nu x_2 y_3)\sin^2\theta$$

$$+ (-\lambda_1\lambda_2 x_2 x_3 + \lambda_1 x_2 x_3)\sin\theta\cos\theta$$

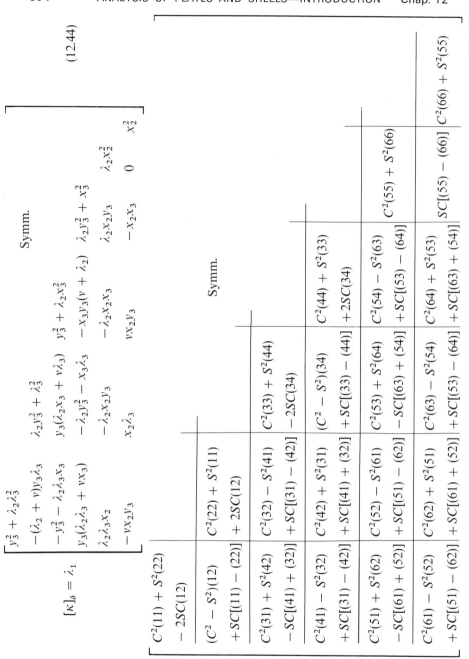

Suggested Exercises: Do problems 20, 21 and 22.

PROBLEMS

Problem 1: Compute the internal forces $\{P\}$ for $F_1^* = 200$ lb and $F_2^* = 300$ lb in the box beam of Figure 12.3. Compute u_1^* and u_2^* in terms of E.

Problem 2: Let the thickness of the panels for the box beam in Figures 12.3 and 12.4 be

$$t_1 = 0.05\ \text{in.}, \qquad t_2 = 0.05\ \text{in.}, \qquad t_3 = 0.05\ \text{in.}, \qquad t_4 = t_5 = 0.032\ \text{in.}$$

and let the area of each flange be $0.7147\ \text{in.}^2$ Compute the matrix $[a]^*$.

Problem 3: In Problem 2 set $F_1^* = 250$ lb, $F_2^* = 100$ lb. Compute the internal forces $\{P\}$ and displacements u_1^* and u_2^*.

Problem 4: Compute the shear flow in each panel in Problems 1 and 3.

Problem 5: Set $F_1^* = F_2^* = 300$ lb in the box beam of Figure 12.3. Compute the shear flow in each panel, the axial force in the flanges and the displacements u_1^* and u_2^*. How could you compute these quantities more directly for equal values of F_1^* and F_2^*?

Problem 6: Show why Equations (6.30) and (12.11) are equivalent.

Problem 7: Verify the results given for $[C]^{-1}$ and $[N]^{-1}$ in Equations (12.16) and (12.18), respectively.

Problem 8: Carry out the operations on the right-hand side of Equation (12.21) and compare with the results of Equation (12.22).

Problem 9: Write the stiffness matrix for the triangle of uniform thickness t and the coordinates shown.

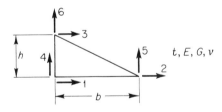

Problem 10: Repeat Problem 9 for the triangle shown.

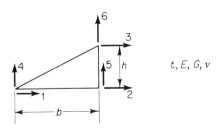

Problem 11: Show why Equations (6.32) and (12.24) are equivalent.

Problem 12: Verify the result given for $[D]$ and $[D]^{-1}$ in Equations (12.23) and (12.27) respectively.

Problem 13: Carry out the operations on the right-hand side of Equation (12.31) and compare with the results of Equation (12.32).

Problem 14: Verify that the product of $[\alpha]$ of Equation (12.32) and $[\kappa]$ of Equation (12.33) results in an identity matrix.

Problem 15: Write the stiffness and flexibility matrices for the three coordinates of the element shown. The triangle has uniform thickness t, elastic modulus E, and shear modulus G.

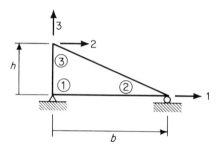

Problem 16: Repeat Problem 15 for the triangle and coordinates as shown in the figure.

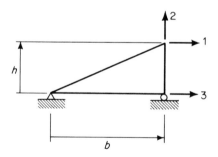

Problem 17: Verify the result given by Equation (12.41) and compute displacements u_i for the load as shown in Figure 12.10.

Problem 18: Use the results of Problem 12.17 to compute the stresses and strains in the elements.

Problem 19: Compute the displacements at the system coordinates for the structure of Figure 12.10 using the idealized model with four triangular plate elements and system coordinates as shown.

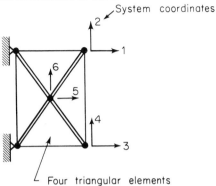

Four triangular elements

Problem 20: Using the code system approach transform the stiffness matrix of Equation (12.22) to matrix $[\kappa]_\delta$ for the coordinates numbered as in Figure 12.13(a) [The code is ⬜1 ⬜3 ⬜5 ⬜2 ⬜4 ⬜6 with the numbers in the boxes representing the coordinates in Figure 12.13(a) and the positions of the boxes representing the coordinates in Figure 12.7.] Check your results with Equation (12.44). Using $[\kappa]_\delta$, apply Equation (12.43) to generate $[\kappa]_q$ for the element of Figure 12.13(b). Check your results with Equation (12.45).

Problem 21: Using the result given by Equation (12.45) generate the stiffness matrix for the triangular element with coordinates numbered as shown.

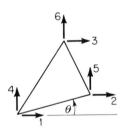

Problem 22: Compare the results obtained for displacements u_i in problems 17 and 19. Explain why $u_3 > u_1$ and $u_2 \neq -u_4$ in problem 17, whereas $u_3 = u_1$ and $u_2 = -u_4$ in problem 19. How can you compute u_1 or u_3 approximately by a quick crude computation?

REFERENCES

1. Karplus, W. J., *Analog Simulation*. New York: McGraw-Hill, 1958.

2. ———, and W. W. Soroka, *Analog Methods*, 2nd ed. New York: McGraw-Hill, 1959.

3. Arden, Bruce W., *An Introduction to Digital Computing*. Reading, Mass.: Addison-Wesley, 1962.

4. Desmonde, W. H., *Computers and Their Uses*. Englewood Cliffs, N.J.: Prentice-Hall, Inc., 1964.

5. Evans and Perry, *Programming and Coding for a Digital Computer*. New York: McGraw-Hill, 1961.

6. Wrubel, M. H., *A Primer of Programming for Digital Computers*. New York: McGraw-Hill, 1959.

7. Fisher, F. P., and G. F. Swindle, *Computer Programming Systems*. New York: Holt, Rinehart, and Winston, 1964.

8. McCracken, D. D., *Digital Computer Programming*. New York: Wiley, 1957.

9. ———, *A Guide to Fortran Programming*. New York: Wiley, 1961.

10. Germain, C. B., *Programming the IBM 1620*. Englewood Cliffs, N.J.: Prentice-Hall, Inc., 1962.

11. Shanley, F. R., *Strength of Materials*. New York: McGraw-Hill, 1957.

12. Norris, C. H., and J. B. Wilbur, *Elementary Structural Analysis*. New York: McGraw-Hill, 1960.

13. Parcel, J. I., and R. B. B. Moorman, *Analysis of Statically Indeterminate Structures*. New York: Wiley, 1955.

14. Gere, J. M., *Moment Distribution*. Princeton, N.J.: D. Van Nostrand, 1963.

15. Kinney, J. S., *Indeterminate Structural Analysis*. Reading, Mass.: Addison-Wesley, 1957.

16. Borg, S. F., and J. J. Gennaro, *Advanced Structural Analysis*. Princeton, N.J.: D. Van Nostrand 1959.

17. Maugh, L. C., *Statically Indeterminate Structures*, 2nd ed. New York: Wiley, 1964.

18. Hoff, N. J., *The Analysis of Structures*. New York: Wiley, 1956.

19. Au, Tung, *Elementary Structural Mechanics*. Englewood Cliffs, N.J.: Prentice-Hall, Inc., 1963.

20. Argyris, J. H., and S. Kelsey, *Energy Theorems and Structural Analysis*. London: Butterworth Scientific Publications, 1960.

21. Pestel, E. C., and F. A. Leckie, *Matrix Methods in Elasto-Mechanics*. New York: McGraw-Hill, 1963.

22. Timoshenko, S. P., and D. H. Young, *Theory of Structures*, 2nd ed. New York: McGraw-Hill, 1965.

23. ———, and J. N. Goodier, *Theory of Elasticity*. New York: McGraw-Hill, 1951.

24. Taylor, A. E., *Calculus*. Englewood Cliffs, N.J.: Prentice-Hall, Inc., 1959.

25. Morice, P. B., *Linear Structural Analysis*. New York: The Ronald Press, 1959.

26. Hall, A. S., and R. W. Woodhead, *Frame Analysis*. New York: Wiley, 1961.

27. Schwartz, J. T., *Introduction to Matrices and Vectors*. New York: McGraw-Hill, 1961.

28. Pipes, L. A., *Matrix Methods for Engineering*. Englewood Cliffs, N.J.: Prentice-Hall, Inc., 1963.

29. Ayres, F., Jr., *Theory and Problems of Matrices*. New York: Schaum Publishing Co., 1962.

30. Frazer, R. A., W. J. Duncan, and A. R. Collar, *Elementary Matrices*. New York: Macmillan, 1946.

31. Pipes, L. A., *Applied Mathematics for Engineers and Physicists*, 2nd ed. New York: McGraw-Hill, 1958.

32. Sokolnikoff, I. S., and R. M. Redheffer, *Mathematics of Physics and Modern Engineering*. New York: McGraw-Hill, 1958.

33. Salvadori, M. G., and M. L. Baron, *Numerical Methods in Engineering*. Englewood Cliffs, N.J.: Prentice-Hall, Inc., 1952.

34. Stanton, R. G., *Numerical Methods for Science and Engineering*. Englewood Cliffs, N.J.: Prentice-Hall, Inc., 1961.

35. Crandall, S. H., *Engineering Analysis*. New York: McGraw-Hill, 1956.

36. Lanczos, C., *Applied Analysis*. Englewood Cliffs, N.J.: Prentice-Hall, Inc., 1956.

37. Kreyszig, E., *Advanced Engineering Mathematics*. New York: Wiley, 1962.

38. Borg, S. F., *Matrix-Tensor Methods in Continuum Mechanics*. Princeton, N. J.: D. Van Nostrand, 1963.

39. Hurty, W. C., and M. F. Rubinstein, *Dynamics of Structures*. Englewood Cliffs, N.J.: Prentice-Hall, Inc., 1964.

40. Sylvester, R. J., and R. R. Foll, "Computer Solutions to Linear Buckling Problems," *2nd ASCE Conf. Electronic Computations* (1960), 429–41.

41. Timoshenko, S. P., and J. M. Gere, *Theory of Elastic Stability*, 2nd ed. New York: McGraw-Hill, 1961.

42. Livesley, R. K., *Matrix Methods of Structural Analysis*. New York: Pergamon Press, Macmillan, 1964.

43. Asplund, S. O., "Inversion of Band Matrices," *2nd ASCE Conf. Electronic Computations* (1960), 513–22.

44. Pei, L. M., "Stiffness Method of Rigid Frame Analysis," *Proc. 2nd ASCE Conf. Electronic Computations* (1960), 225–48.

45. Tezcan, S. S., discussion of "Simplified Formulation of Stiffness Matrices," P. M. Wright, *J. Structural Division*, ASCE, **89**, No. ST6 (December, 1963), 445–49.

46. Clough, R. W., E. L. Wilson, and I. P. King, "Large Capacity Multistory Frame Analysis Programs," *J. Structural Division*, ASCE, **89**, No. ST4, (August, 1963), 179–204.

47. Cross, H., "Analysis of Continuous Frames by Distributing Fixed-End Moments," *Trans.* ASCE, **96** (1932), 1–10.

48. Kani, G., *Die Berechnung Mehrstockiger Rahmen*, 5th ed. Konrad Wittwer Verlag, 1956. (English translation, New York: F. Ungar, 1957.)

49. Przemieniecki, J. S., "Matrix Structural Analysis of Substructures," *AIAA J.* **1**, No. 1 (January, 1963), 138–47.

50. Meissner, C. J., and R. S. Levy, "Flexibility Method of Coupling Redundant Complex Structures," *J. Structural Division*, ASCE, **89**, No. ST6 (December, 1963), 325–64.

51. Gatewood, B. E., and N. Ohanian, "Tri-Diagonal Matrix Method for Complex Structures," *J. Structural Division*, ASCE, **91**, No. ST2 (April, 1965), 27–41.

52. Rubinstein, M. F., "Multistory Frame Analysis by Digital Computers," *Proc. 2nd Conf. Electronic Computations*, ASCE (September, 1960), 261–81.

53. ——, "A Computer Program for the Analysis of Rigidly Connected Beams," *Proc. Symposium Use of Computers in Civil Engineering*, Paper No. 1, Lisbon, 1962.

54. ———, "Analysis of Large Complex Frames on a Small Computer," *J. Franklin Inst.*, Vol. 280, No. 2, pp. 101–119 (August, 1965).

55. Thadani, B. N., "Solution of Complex Multistoryed Structures," *Structural Engineer, J. Inst. Structural Engs.*, **XXXVII**, No. 6 (June, 1959).

56. Lustgarten, P., "Iterative Method in Frame Analysis," *J. Structural Division*, ASCE, **89**, No. ST2 (April, 1963), Part 1, 75–94.

57. Bondy, K. B., "Finite Element Plate Analysis Using Distributed Coordinates." M.S. Thesis, Univ. Calif. Los Angeles, June, 1964.

58. Archer, J. S., and C. H. Samson, Jr., "Structural Idealization for Digital-Computer Analysis," *Proc. 2nd Conf. Electronic Computations,* ASCE (September, 1960), 283–325.

59. Gallagher, R. H., *A Correlation Study of Methods of Matrix Structural Analysis*, New York: Macmillan, 1964.

60. Pian, T. H. H., "Derivation of Element Stiffness Matrices by Assumed Stress Distributions," *AIAA J.*, **2**, No. 7 (July, 1964), 1333–36.

61. ———, "Derivation of Element Stiffness Matrices," *AIAA J.*, **2**, No. 3 (March, 1964), 576–77.

62. de Veubeke, B. Fraeijs, *Matrix Methods of Structural Analysis*. New York: Pergamon Press, 1964.

63. Greene, B. E., D. R. Strome, and R. C. Weikel, "Application of the Stiffness Method to the Analysis of Shell Structures," *Amer. Soc. Mech. Engrs, Paper* 61-AV-58, 1961.

64. Grafton, P. E., and D. R. Strome, "Analysis of Axisymmetrical Shells by the Direct Stiffness Method," *AIAA J.*, **1**, No. 10 (October, 1963), 2342–47.

65. Turner, M. J., R. W. Clough, H. C. Martin, and L. J. Topp, "Stiffness and Deflection Analysis of Complex Structures," *J. Aeronaut. Sci.*, **23**, No. 9 (September, 1956), 805–823.

66. Hrennikoff, A., "Solution of Problems in Elasticity by the Frame Work Method," *J. Appl. Mech.*, **8**, No. 4 (December, 1941), A-169-A-175.

67. Clough, R. W., "The Finite Element Method in Plane Stress Analysis," *Proc. 2nd Conf. Electronic Computations, ASCE* (September, 1960), 345–78.

68. Wang, C. T., *Applied Elasticity*. New York: McGraw-Hill, 1953.

69. Bisplinghoff, R. L., Holt Ashley, and R. L. Halfman, *Aeroelasticity*. Reading, Mass.: Addison-Wesley, 1955.

70. Thadani, B. N., *Structural Mechanics*. London: Asia Publishing House, 1964.

71. Gillis, Peter P. and Kurt H. Gerstle, "Analysis of Structures by Combining Redundants," *Journal ASCE*, Vol. 87, No. ST1, Jan. 1961, pp. 41–56.

72. Argyris, J. H., "Matrix Analysis of Three-Dimensional Elastic Media Small and Large Displacements", *AIAA J.*, **3**, No. 1, (January, 1965), pp. 45–51.

73. Synge, J. L. and B. A. Griffith, *Principles of Mechanics*, 3rd Edition, New York: McGraw-Hill, 1959.

74. Gere, J. M. and W. Weaver Jr., *Analysis of Framed Structures*, Princeton, New Jersey; Van Nostrand, 1965.

75. White, Richard N. "Optimum Solution Techniques for Finite Difference Equations," *Journal of the Structural Division*, ASCE, Vol. 89, No. ST4, Aug. 1963, pp. 115–136.

Bibliography on Computers and Matrices in Structures

For an extensive bibliography on the Use of Digital Computers in Structural Engineering the reader is referred to the Journal of the Structural Division ASCE Vol. 89, ST6, Dec. 1963, pp. 461-491.

Additional papers may be found in the Proceedings of the 1st (1958), 2nd (1960), 3rd (1963), and 4th (1966) Conferences on Electronic Computations, American Society of Civil Engineers.

ANSWERS TO PROBLEMS

Chapter 1

1. No changes are required in Table 1.1. In Table 1.3 the content of address 6000 should be changed to 000003.
2. With two bit positions we have $2^2 =$ four distinguishable codes. If we add a third bit position then each of these four codes is expanded into two new distinguishable codes to give a total of $2^2 \cdot 2 = 2^3$ codes. Continuing this way we are led to 2^n codes for n bit positions.
3. Decimal numbers

    85.625
    88
     4.625
    11
    64.125

4. $11_{10} = 1011_2$
   $100_8 = 1000000_2$
   $1111_2 = 17_8$
   $1011_8 = 521_{10}$
   $13_8 = 11_{10}$

5. Binary numbers

    101111
    1000000
    1110
    1111101
    111001101010

6. Octal numbers

    57
    100
    16
    175
    7152

7. Binary numbers
    100111
    110100
    1100
    1010101
    011110111000

8. $167_{\boxed{10}}$ = 0001 0110 0111 bcd
    $893_{\boxed{10}}$ = 1000 1001 0011 bcd
    $245_{\boxed{10}}$ = 0010 0100 0101 bcd

9. Results of operations in decimal numbers
    62, 21, 4, 3

10. Binary numbers
    0.001
    0.111
    0.101101
    1101.011
    11101.0011
    1011111011.001101
    0.11110100110011....

                        repeat 0011
    0.100001

Chapter 2

1. 1,2; 1,3; 1,4; 2,3; 2,4

2. $F_3 = -3.232^k$

$$u_1 = 0.032 \frac{l^3}{EI}$$

$$u_2 = 0.0312 \frac{l^3}{EI}$$

3. $F_1 = \dfrac{EI}{l}\left(\dfrac{24}{l^2}u_1 - \dfrac{6}{l}u_2 - \dfrac{6}{l}u_3\right)$

$F_2 = \dfrac{EI}{l}\left(\dfrac{-6}{l}u_1 + 8u_2 + 2u_3\right)$

$F_3 = \dfrac{EI}{l}\left(\dfrac{-6}{l}u_1 + 2u_2 + 8u_3\right)$

4. $F_1 = \dfrac{EI}{l}\left(\dfrac{15}{l^2}u_1 - \dfrac{6}{l}u_2 - \dfrac{3}{l}u_3\right)$

$F_2 = \dfrac{EI}{l}\left(-\dfrac{6}{l}u_1 + 8u_2 + 2u_3\right)$

$F_3 = \dfrac{EI}{l}\left(-\dfrac{3}{l}u_1 + 2u_2 + 7u_3\right)$

5. $F_1 = \dfrac{EI}{l}(8u_1 + 2u_2 + 2u_3)$

$F_2 = \dfrac{EI}{l}(2u_1 + 8u_2 + 2u_4)$

$F_3 = \dfrac{EI}{l}(2u_1 + 8u_3 + 2u_4)$

$F_4 = \dfrac{EI}{l}(2u_2 + 2u_3 + 8u_4)$

6. Fixed end moment at left end $= \frac{2}{11}F_2$
Fixed end moment at right end $= \frac{3}{11}F_2$
7. Fixed end moment at left end $= -\frac{10}{33}F_1$
Fixed end moment at right end $= \frac{7}{33}F_1$
8. Fixed end moment at left end $= 0$

Chapter 3

1. (a) $\begin{Bmatrix} 5.0\ \text{kip} \\ -4.5\ \text{kip} \\ 1.5\ \text{kip} \end{Bmatrix}$ (b) $\begin{Bmatrix} 7.5 \\ 2.5 \\ 12.5 \end{Bmatrix}$

3. $\begin{bmatrix} 15 & -6 & -3 \\ -6 & 8 & 2 \\ -3 & 2 & 7 \end{bmatrix}$

4. $\begin{bmatrix} 24 & -6 & -6 & -6 \\ -6 & 8 & 2 & 0 \\ -6 & 2 & 8 & 2 \\ -6 & 0 & 2 & 4 \end{bmatrix}$

5. $\begin{bmatrix} 8 & 0 & 4 & 12 \\ 0 & 4 & 2 & -6 \\ 4 & 2 & 12 & 6 \\ 12 & -6 & 6 & 36 \end{bmatrix}$

6. $\dfrac{EI_1}{l_1}\begin{bmatrix} \dfrac{12}{l_1^2} & -\dfrac{6}{l_1} \\ -\dfrac{6}{l_1} & 4 + 3\left(\dfrac{I_2 l_1}{I_1 l_2}\right) \end{bmatrix}$

7.
$$2E \begin{bmatrix} 6\left(\dfrac{I_1}{l_1^3} + \dfrac{I_2}{l_2^3}\right) & 3\left(\dfrac{I_2}{l_2^2} - \dfrac{I_1}{l_1^2}\right) \\ 3\left(\dfrac{I_2}{l_2^2} - \dfrac{I_1}{l_1^2}\right) & 2\left(\dfrac{I_1}{l_1} + \dfrac{I_2}{l_2}\right) \end{bmatrix}$$

8.
$$\frac{EI}{l} \begin{bmatrix} 8 & 2 & 2 & 0 \\ 2 & 8 & 0 & 2 \\ 2 & 0 & 8 & 2 \\ 0 & 2 & 2 & 8 \end{bmatrix}$$

9.
$$a_{ij} = \frac{1}{\sqrt{2}EI_1} \int_0^{L_1} (L_1 - x_1)^2 \, dx_1 + \frac{1}{\sqrt{2}GA_1} \int_0^{L_1} dx_1$$
$$+ \frac{L_2 L_3}{\sqrt{2}GJ_1} \int_0^{L_1} dx_1 + \frac{1}{\sqrt{2}EA_2} \int_0^{L_2} dx_2 + \frac{L_3}{\sqrt{2}EI_2} \int_0^{L_2} (L_2 - x_2) \, dx_2$$

10.
$$\frac{l^3}{6EI} \begin{bmatrix} 2 & 5 & 8 \\ 5 & 16 & 28 \\ 8 & 28 & 54 \end{bmatrix}$$

11.
$$\begin{bmatrix} \frac{1}{3} & \frac{1}{2} & \frac{1}{2} \\ \frac{1}{2} & 1 & 1 \\ \frac{1}{2} & 1 & 2 \end{bmatrix}$$

12.
$$\frac{1}{24} \begin{bmatrix} 9 & -6 & 0 & -4 \\ -6 & 15 & -3 & 5 \\ 0 & -3 & 3 & -1 \\ -4 & 5 & -1 & 3 \end{bmatrix}$$

Chapter 4

1. $-131, 14$

2. $-29, 118, -45$

3.
$$\begin{bmatrix} 3u_{11} - u_{21} & 3u_{12} - u_{22} & 3u_{13} - u_{23} & 3u_{14} - u_{24} \\ -u_{11} + 2u_{21} - u_{31} & -u_{12} + 2u_{22} - u_{32} & -u_{13} + 2u_{23} - u_{33} & -u_{14} + 2u_{24} - u_{34} \\ -u_{21} + u_{31} & -u_{22} + u_{32} & -u_{23} + u_{33} & -u_{24} + u_{34} \end{bmatrix}$$

4. (1) 12

(2) $\begin{bmatrix} 8 & 8 & 2 & 0 \\ 4 & 4 & 1 & 0 \\ 0 & 0 & 0 & 0 \\ 4 & 4 & 1 & 0 \end{bmatrix}$

(3) $\begin{Bmatrix} 6 \\ 8 \end{Bmatrix}$

(4) Not compatible

(5) $\{4 \quad 7 \quad 32 \quad 9 \quad 4\}$

(6) Not compatible

(7) $\{13 \quad 13 \quad 12\}$

(8) $\begin{bmatrix} 8 & 3 & 28 & 10 & 3 \\ 7 & 4 & 31 & 11 & 3 \\ 3 & 13 & 43 & 11 & 5 \end{bmatrix}$

(9) Not compatible

(10) $\begin{bmatrix} 8 & 7 & 3 \\ 3 & 4 & 13 \\ 28 & 31 & 43 \\ 10 & 11 & 11 \\ 3 & 3 & 5 \end{bmatrix}$

5. Let $[a][b] = [c]$ and $[b][a] = [c^*]$. Then $c_{ij} = \sum_k a_{ik}b_{kj}$, and $c_{ij}^* = \sum_k b_{ik}a_{kj}$. Since $[a]$ and $[b]$ are diagonal matrices, then $a_{ik} = b_{ik} = 0$ for $i \neq k$, $a_{kj} = b_{kj} = 0$ for $j \neq k$. Hence, $c_{ij} = c_{ij}^* = 0$ for $i \neq j$, and $c_{ii} = a_{ii}b_{ii}$, $c_{ii}^* = b_{ii}a_{ii}$ or $c_{ij} = c_{ij}^*$ for all i and j; i.e. $[c] = [c^*]$.

7. (1) $\begin{bmatrix} -2 & 1 \\ 1.5 & -0.5 \end{bmatrix}$

(2) $\dfrac{1}{a_{11}a_{22} - a_{12}a_{21}} \begin{bmatrix} a_{22} & -a_{12} \\ -a_{21} & a_{11} \end{bmatrix}$

(3) $\dfrac{1}{k_{11}k_{22} - k_{12}k_{21}} \begin{bmatrix} k_{22} & -k_{12} \\ -k_{21} & k_{11} \end{bmatrix}$

(4) $-\dfrac{1}{7} \begin{bmatrix} 1 & 2 & 3 \\ 2 & 3 & 2 \\ 3 & 3 & 4 \end{bmatrix}$

(5)

$$-\tfrac{1}{2}\begin{bmatrix} 1 & 2 & 3 \\ 1 & 3 & 4 \\ 1 & 4 & 3 \end{bmatrix}$$

(6)

$$\tfrac{1}{4}\begin{bmatrix} 2 & 2 & 0 \\ 0 & 3 & 1 \\ 1 & 0 & 1 \end{bmatrix}$$

8.

$$\tfrac{1}{2}\begin{bmatrix} 1 & 1 & 1 \\ 1 & 3 & 3 \\ 1 & 3 & 5 \end{bmatrix}; \tfrac{1}{84}\begin{bmatrix} 5 & 3 & 3 \\ 3 & 13 & -1 \\ 3 & -1 & 13 \end{bmatrix}$$

These are the flexibility matrices of the structures in Figures 3.4 and 3.5 respectively.

9. Place a partitioning line between the first and second row of each matrix on the left of the equal sign, and between the fourth and fifth columns for the matrix on the right of the equal sign.

10. $k^* = 16.8$

11.

$$[k] = \begin{bmatrix} 12 & -6 & 0 & 0 \\ -6 & 8 & 2 & 6 \\ 0 & 2 & 4 & 6 \\ 0 & 6 & 6 & 12 \end{bmatrix}; [k]^* = \begin{bmatrix} 12 & -6 & 0 \\ -6 & 5 & -1 \\ 0 & -1 & 1 \end{bmatrix}$$

12.

$$\begin{bmatrix} \tfrac{1}{3} & \tfrac{1}{2} & \tfrac{1}{2} \\ \tfrac{1}{2} & 1 & 1 \\ \tfrac{1}{2} & 1 & 2 \end{bmatrix}; \tfrac{1}{19}\begin{bmatrix} 3 & 5 & 6 \\ -5 & -2 & 9 \\ 2 & -3 & 4 \end{bmatrix}; \tfrac{1}{5}\begin{bmatrix} -115 & 145 & -64 & -18 \\ 50 & -60 & 26 & 7 \\ 5 & -10 & 6 & 2 \\ 10 & -10 & 3 & 1 \end{bmatrix}$$

14. (1) 37

(2)

$$\begin{bmatrix} -6 & -13.5 & -25.5 \\ 4 & 9 & 17 \\ 8 & 18 & 34 \end{bmatrix}$$

(3)

$$\tfrac{1}{2}\begin{Bmatrix} 4 \\ 9 \\ 17 \end{Bmatrix}$$

(4)

$$\tfrac{1}{6}\begin{bmatrix} 7 & -9 & -6 & 4 \\ 12 & -15 & -15 & 6 \\ 12 & -45 & -15 & 6 \end{bmatrix}$$

(5) $\{2 \quad 4.5 \quad 8.5\}$
(6) 18.5
(7) $\{-3 \quad 2 \quad 4\}$
(8) 18.5
(9) 37
(10) 37

15. See answers to problems 2.6, 2.7 and 2.8.

Chapter 5

1. $\begin{Bmatrix} 0.5 \\ 1.0 \\ 1.5 \end{Bmatrix}$
2. $\begin{Bmatrix} 3 \\ -1 \\ 2 \end{Bmatrix}$
3. $\begin{Bmatrix} 1.0 \\ 1.5 \\ -0.5 \end{Bmatrix}$
4. $\frac{1}{12}\begin{Bmatrix} -39 \\ 82 \\ 61 \end{Bmatrix}$

5. Only trivial solution exists.

6. $u_1 = u_2 = u_3$

7. Only trivial solution exists.

8. $x_3 = 0 \quad x_2 = 2x_1$; for $x_3 \neq 0$ equations are inconsistent.

9.
$$\lambda_1 = 5.90, \begin{Bmatrix} 1.00 \\ 0.588 \end{Bmatrix}; \lambda_2 = 1.07, \begin{Bmatrix} 1.0 \\ -1.28 \end{Bmatrix}$$

10.
$$\lambda_1 = 17.5, \begin{Bmatrix} 1.0 \\ 1.8 \end{Bmatrix}; \lambda_2 = 4.66, \begin{Bmatrix} 1.00 \\ -1.505 \end{Bmatrix}$$

Chapter 6

2.
(a) $\{u\} = \dfrac{Q_1}{6EIl}\begin{Bmatrix} 2b^2 - 2ab - a^2 \\ -b^2 - 2ab + 2a^2 \end{Bmatrix}$

(b) $\{u\} = \dfrac{wl^3}{24EI}\begin{Bmatrix} 1 \\ -1 \end{Bmatrix}$

(c) $\{u\} = \dfrac{-Q_1a^2}{4EIl}\begin{Bmatrix} 0 \\ l - a \end{Bmatrix}$

(d)
$$u_1 = 0, u_2 = \frac{l}{4EI}\left[\frac{Q_1a_1}{l^2}(a_1 - 2b_1) - \frac{wl^2}{12} - \frac{Q_2a_2^2}{l^2}(l - a_2)\right]$$

3. $\begin{Bmatrix} u_1 \\ u_2 \end{Bmatrix} = \begin{bmatrix} 15 \times 10^4 & 6 \times 10^4 \\ 6 \times 10^4 & 4 \times 10^4 \end{bmatrix}^{-1}\left(\begin{Bmatrix} -12 \\ 0 \end{Bmatrix} - \begin{Bmatrix} 56 \\ 10 \end{Bmatrix}\right)$

$= \dfrac{10^{-4}}{24}\begin{bmatrix} 4 & -6 \\ -6 & 15 \end{bmatrix}\begin{Bmatrix} -68 \\ -10 \end{Bmatrix}$

$= 10^{-4}\begin{Bmatrix} -\frac{53}{6} \\ \frac{43}{4} \end{Bmatrix}$

Shear at fixed end 60.5^k
Moment at fixed end $35.5^{\prime k}$
Spring force 26.5^k (compression)

5. $F_1^0 = -\frac{1}{30}bl^2$, $\qquad F_2^0 = \frac{1}{20}bl^2$

7. $F_1^0 = -16.93$, $\qquad F_2^0 = 1.938$, $\qquad F_3^0 = 2.074$.

8.
$$
\begin{Bmatrix} u_1 \\ u_2 \\ u_3 \\ u_4 \end{Bmatrix} =
\begin{bmatrix}
8 & 2 & 0 & -3 \\
2 & 8 & 2 & -6 \\
0 & 2 & (4 + K_b) & -6 \\
-3 & -6 & -6 & 15
\end{bmatrix}^{-1}
\begin{Bmatrix} 1 \\ -7 \\ 2 \\ 24 \end{Bmatrix}
$$

9.
$$
[k] = 2 \cdot 10^3
\begin{bmatrix}
4 & 1 & -0.25 \\
1 & 4.1 & 0 \\
-0.25 & 0 & \frac{1}{6}
\end{bmatrix}, \qquad
\begin{Bmatrix} u_1 \\ u_2 \\ u_3 \end{Bmatrix} =
\begin{Bmatrix} 1.55 \times 10^{-2}\ \text{radians} \\ -8.67 \times 10^{-4}\ \text{radians} \\ 1.98 \times 10^{-1}\ \text{ft.} \end{Bmatrix}
$$

Torsion at E = torsion at F = -8.67×10^{-2} ft. kip.
Reactions at A: $M_A = 31^{\prime k}$ clockwise, $H_A = 7.75^k$ to the right.
Reactions at D: $M_D = 193.26^{\prime k}$ clockwise, $V_D = 56.1^k$ up.

10.
$$
\frac{EI}{2l^3}
\begin{bmatrix}
129 & & \text{Symm.} \\
3l & 16l^2 & \\
3l & 4l^2 & 16l^2
\end{bmatrix}
$$

11.
$$
[k] = \frac{EI}{l}
\begin{bmatrix}
37.5/l^2 & & \text{Symm.} \\
-3/l & 8 & \\
-1.5/l & 2 & 8
\end{bmatrix}
$$

$$l = 20\ \text{ft. 0 in.}$$

$$
\{u\} = [k]^{-1}
\begin{Bmatrix} 37.5 \\ 0 \\ 0 \end{Bmatrix} =
\frac{10^3}{EI}
\begin{Bmatrix} 8.264 \\ 0.1446 \\ 0.0413 \end{Bmatrix}
\begin{matrix} \text{ft.} \\ \text{radians} \\ \text{radians} \end{matrix}
\qquad (EI \text{ in units of k-ft}^2.)
$$

12.
$$
[\kappa]_q = \frac{EI}{l}
\begin{bmatrix} 4 & 6/l \\ 6/l & 12/l^2 \end{bmatrix}, \qquad
[\alpha]_q = \frac{l}{EI}
\begin{bmatrix} 1 & -l/2 \\ -l/2 & l^2/3 \end{bmatrix}
$$

$$
U_s = \frac{EI}{2l} \{q_1\ q_2\}
\begin{bmatrix} 4 & 6/l \\ 6/l & 12/l^2 \end{bmatrix}
\begin{Bmatrix} q_1 \\ q_2 \end{Bmatrix}
$$

$$
U_s = \frac{l}{2EI} \{Q_1\ Q_2\}
\begin{bmatrix} 1 & -l/2 \\ -l/2 & l^2/3 \end{bmatrix}
\begin{Bmatrix} Q_1 \\ Q_2 \end{Bmatrix}
$$

13.

$$[\alpha] = \begin{bmatrix} \begin{bmatrix} l/EI_y & -l^2/2EI_y \\ -l^2/2EI_y & l^3/3EI_y \end{bmatrix} & & & & \\ & [l/EA] & & & \\ & & \begin{bmatrix} l/EI_x & -l^2/2EI_x \\ -l^2/2EI_x & l^3/3EI_x \end{bmatrix} & \\ \text{elements not} & & & & \\ \text{shown are zero} & & & & [l/GI_z] \end{bmatrix}$$

14.

$$[\alpha] = \begin{bmatrix} \begin{bmatrix} l/3EI_y & -l/6EI_y \\ -l/6EI_y & l/3EI_y \end{bmatrix} & & & & \\ & [l/EA] & & & \\ & & \begin{bmatrix} l/3EI_x & -l/6EI_x \\ -l/6EI_x & l/3EI_x \end{bmatrix} & \\ \text{elements not} & & & & \\ \text{shown are zero} & & & & [l/GI_z] \end{bmatrix}$$

Chapter 7

2. Add 3 constraints by constraining rotation at three pins. Degree of indeterminacy of stable structure is 11.

3. (a) Indeterminate, 3; (b) indeterminate, 9; (c) unstable, 1.

4. (a) Indeterminate, 24; (b) indeterminate, 15; (c) unstable, 1.

6.

$$[b] = \begin{bmatrix} l_1 & 0 & 1 & 1 & -1 & l_2 & l_1 & -1 & l_2 & 0 \\ -1 & -1 & 0 & 0 & 0 & 0 & -1 & 0 & 0 & -1 \\ 0 & 0 & 0 & 0 & 0 & 0 & 0 & 1 & -l_2 & 0 \\ 0 & 0 & 0 & 0 & 0 & 0 & 0 & -1 & 0 & 0 \\ -l_1 & 0 & -1 & 0 & 1 & -l_2 & -l_1 & 0 & 0 & 0 \\ 0 & 0 & 1 & 0 & -1 & l_2 & 0 & 0 & 0 & 0 \\ 0 & 0 & 0 & 0 & 1 & -l_2 & 0 & 0 & 0 & 0 \\ 0 & 0 & 0 & 0 & -1 & 0 & 0 & 0 & 0 & 0 \end{bmatrix}$$

7.

$$\begin{Bmatrix} P_1 \\ P_2 \\ P_3 \\ P_4 \\ P_5 \\ P_6 \end{Bmatrix} = \begin{bmatrix} -0.2l & 1.75l & 0 & -1 \\ -0.6l & -1.75l & -l & 1 \\ 0.6l & 1.75l & l & -1 \\ 0 & -0.75l & -l & 1 \\ 0 & 0.75l & l & -1 \\ 0 & 0 & 0 & 1 \end{bmatrix} \begin{Bmatrix} F_1 \\ F_2 \\ F_3 \\ F_4 \end{Bmatrix}$$

8.

$$[a] = \tfrac{1}{6} \begin{bmatrix} 16 & & & & & & & & & \text{Symmetrical} \\ 5 & 2 & & & & & & & & \\ 12 & 3 & 12 & & & & & & & \\ 9 & 3 & 6 & 6 & & & & & & \\ -12 & -3 & -12 & -6 & 18 & & & & & \\ 12 & 3 & 12 & 6 & -15 & 14 & & & & \\ 16 & 5 & 12 & 9 & -12 & 12 & 16 & & & \\ -9 & -3 & -6 & -6 & 6 & -6 & -9 & 12 & & \\ 9 & 3 & 6 & 6 & -6 & 6 & 9 & -9 & 8 & \\ 5 & 2 & 3 & 3 & -3 & 3 & 5 & -3 & 3 & 2 \end{bmatrix}$$

9.

$$[a] = \frac{l}{6EI} \begin{bmatrix} \frac{32}{25}l^2 & & & \text{Symmetrical} \\ \frac{93}{20}l^2 & \frac{949}{32}l^2 & & \\ \frac{14}{5}l^2 & \frac{117}{8}l^2 & \frac{21}{2}l^2 & \\ -3l & -\frac{333}{16}l & -\frac{51}{4}l & \frac{39}{2} \end{bmatrix}$$

12.

$$[\beta] = \begin{bmatrix} -\frac{5}{4} & 0 & 0 \\ 0 & -1 & 0 \\ 0 & 1 & 0 \\ 0 & 0 & -1 \\ -\frac{3}{4} & 0 & 0 \\ \frac{3}{4} & 0 & 0 \\ 0 & 0 & 1 \\ \frac{5}{4} & 0 & 0 \end{bmatrix}$$

13.

$$[\beta] = \begin{bmatrix} 0 & 0 & 0 & 1 & 0 & 0 \\ 0 & 0 & 0 & 0 & 0 & 0 \\ \frac{4}{5} & -\frac{12}{25} & \frac{9}{25} & 0 & 0 & 0 \\ 0 & 0 & 0 & 0 & 0 & 0 \\ 0 & 0 & 0 & 1 & 0 & 0 \\ 0 & 0 & 0 & 0 & 1 & 0 \\ 0 & 0 & 0 & 0 & 0 & 0 \\ \frac{3}{5} & \frac{16}{25} & -\frac{12}{25} & 0 & 0 & 0 \\ 0 & 0 & 0 & 0 & 1 & 0 \\ 0 & 0 & 0 & 0 & 0 & 1 \\ 1 & 0 & 0 & 0 & 0 & 0 \\ 0 & \frac{3}{5} & \frac{4}{5} & 0 & 0 & 0 \end{bmatrix}$$

14. Answer is given by Equation (6.45), Section 6.9.

15.

$$[k] = \begin{bmatrix} 18.14 & & & & & \text{Symmetrical} \\ -3.686 & 9.892 \\ -4.915 & -2.811 & 8.252 \\ -1.2 & 6.72 & -5.04 & 8 \\ -0.24 & 6.144 & 0.192 & 2 & 7.2 \\ -3.84 & 2.304 & 3.072 & 0 & 1.6 & 3.2 \end{bmatrix}$$

18.

$$\{u\} = \begin{bmatrix} 1 & 0 & 0 \\ 0 & 1 & 1 \\ 0 & 1 & -1 \end{bmatrix} \{q\}$$

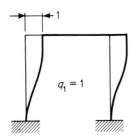

$q_1 = 1$

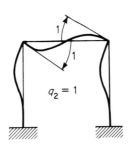

$q_2 = 1$

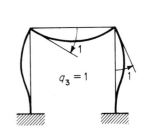

$q_3 = 1$

19.
$$[a]_q = [b]^T[a]_u[b] = \tfrac{1}{2}\begin{bmatrix} a_{11}^u - a_{12}^u & 0 \\ 0 & a_{11}^u + a_{12}^u \end{bmatrix}$$

(Note: $a_{11}^u = a_{22}^u$ from symmetry)

$$[b] = \tfrac{1}{2}\begin{bmatrix} 1 & 1 \\ -1 & 1 \end{bmatrix}$$

$$[k]_q = [\beta]^T[k]_u[\beta] = 2\begin{bmatrix} k_{11}^u - k_{12}^u & 0 \\ 0 & k_{11}^u + k_{12}^u \end{bmatrix}$$

(Note: $k_{11}^u = k_{22}^u$ from symmetry)

20.
$$[\beta] = \begin{bmatrix} -1/l & 1 & 0 \\ -1/l & 0 & 0 \\ 0 & 1 & 0 \\ 0 & 0 & 1 \\ -1/l & 0 & 1 \\ -1/l & 0 & 0 \end{bmatrix}$$

21.
$$[k] = \frac{EI}{l}\begin{bmatrix} 24/l^2 & \text{Symm.} & \\ -6/l & 8 & \\ -6/l & 2 & 8 \end{bmatrix}$$

22.
$$[\beta] = \begin{bmatrix} -\tfrac{5}{4} & 0 & 0 \\ 0 & -1 & 0 \\ 3/2l & 1 & 0 \\ -3/2l & 0 & -1 \\ 0 & 0 & 1 \\ \tfrac{5}{4} & 0 & 0 \end{bmatrix}$$

23. Answer is given by Eq. (6.45), Section 6.9.

Chapter 8

1.
$$[a]^* = \frac{l^3}{1920}\begin{bmatrix} 28 & -9 \\ -9 & 22 \end{bmatrix}$$

$$\{P\} = \frac{l}{80} \begin{bmatrix} 0 & 0 \\ -16 & 3 \\ 16 & -3 \\ 8 & 6 \\ -8 & -6 \\ 3 & -14 \\ -3 & 14 \\ -2 & 6 \\ 2 & -6 \\ 0 & 0 \end{bmatrix} \begin{Bmatrix} F_1^* \\ F_2^* \end{Bmatrix}$$

2. Answer same as in problem 1.

3. Good choice of redundants results by cutting all right-hand or left-hand columns. Poor choice of redundants results by cutting all girders. Reasons for good and poor choice are similar to reasons given for the choice of redundants in Figures 8.4(a) and 8.4(b).

4.

$$[a]^* = \frac{l}{230} \begin{bmatrix} 26 & -7 \\ -7 & 24 \end{bmatrix}$$

$$\{P\} = \frac{1}{115} \begin{bmatrix} -1 & -13 \\ 25 & -20 \\ 90 & 20 \\ 24 & 82 \\ -24 & 33 \end{bmatrix} \begin{Bmatrix} F_1^* \\ F_2^* \end{Bmatrix}$$

5.

$$[a]^* = \frac{l}{230} \begin{bmatrix} 26 & -7 \\ -7 & 24 \end{bmatrix}$$

$$\{P\} = \frac{1}{115} \begin{bmatrix} -24/l & 33/l \\ 25 & -20 \\ 90 & 20 \\ 24 & 82 \\ -24 & 33 \\ 0 & 0 \end{bmatrix} \begin{Bmatrix} F_1^* \\ F_2^* \end{Bmatrix}$$

6.

$$[a]^{II}_{22} = \frac{l}{12} \begin{bmatrix} 7l^2 & 0 & 0 \\ 0 & 8l^2 & 12l \\ 0 & 12l & 36 \end{bmatrix}$$

7.

$$[B] = \begin{bmatrix} 1 & 0 & 0 \\ 0 & 1 & 0 \\ l/2 & l & 1 \end{bmatrix}; \qquad [a]^{II}_{22} \text{ same as in problem 6.}$$

$$[a]^{II}_{22} = [B]^T[a]^{I}_{22}[B], \qquad [a]^{I}_{22} \text{ is given in Equation (8.17).}$$

8.

$$[B] = \frac{1}{l} \begin{bmatrix} 2 & -1 \\ -1 & 2 \end{bmatrix}$$

9.

$$[a]^{II}_{22} = \frac{l}{6} \begin{bmatrix} 4 & 1 \\ 1 & 4 \end{bmatrix}, \qquad [a]^{I}_{22} = \frac{l^3}{18} \begin{bmatrix} 8 & 7 \\ 7 & 8 \end{bmatrix}$$

10.

$$[B] = \begin{bmatrix} l & 0 \\ 0 & -1 \end{bmatrix}$$

11.

In problem 5 $[a]^{I}_{22} = \dfrac{l}{12} \begin{bmatrix} 14 & -9l \\ -9l & 14l^2 \end{bmatrix}$

$$[a]^{II}_{22} = [B]^T[a]^{I}_{22}[B] = \frac{l^3}{12} \begin{bmatrix} 14 & 9 \\ 9 & 14 \end{bmatrix}$$

12.

$$\{p\} = \begin{Bmatrix} -0.89'^k \\ -1.78'^k \\ 1.78'^k \\ 8.00'^k \end{Bmatrix}$$

13.

$$[B] = \begin{bmatrix} -1 & 0 \\ \frac{1}{2} & -\frac{1}{2} \end{bmatrix}$$

$$[a]^{I}_{22} = \begin{bmatrix} \frac{2}{5} & \frac{1}{3} \\ \frac{1}{3} & \frac{4}{9} \end{bmatrix}, \qquad [a]^{II}_{22} = \begin{bmatrix} \frac{8}{45} & \frac{1}{18} \\ \frac{1}{18} & \frac{1}{9} \end{bmatrix}$$

14. $\{F\}^0_I = [B]\{F\}^0_{II}$ from equilibrium [Eq. (8.26)]. Then from energy considerations (see Section 7.7) $\{u\}^0_{II} = [B]^T\{u\}^0_I$.

15.

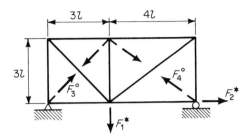

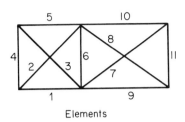

Elements

Primary structure with system coordinates

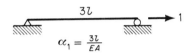

$$\alpha_1 = \frac{3l}{EA}$$

Typical element coordinate
(element 1 is shown)

$$
\begin{Bmatrix} P_1 \\ P_2 \\ P_3 \\ P_4 \\ P_5 \\ P_6 \\ P_7 \\ P_8 \\ P_9 \\ P_{10} \\ P_{11} \end{Bmatrix}
=
\begin{bmatrix}
0 & 1 & -1/\sqrt{2} & 0 \\
0 & 0 & 1 & 0 \\
4\sqrt{2}/7 & 0 & 1 & 0 \\
-\frac{4}{7} & 0 & -1/\sqrt{2} & 0 \\
-\frac{4}{7} & 0 & -1/\sqrt{2} & 0 \\
0 & 0 & -1/\sqrt{2} & -\frac{3}{5} \\
\frac{5}{7} & 0 & 0 & 1 \\
0 & 0 & 0 & 1 \\
0 & 1 & 0 & -\frac{4}{5} \\
-\frac{4}{7} & 0 & 0 & -\frac{4}{5} \\
-\frac{3}{7} & 0 & 0 & -\frac{3}{5}
\end{bmatrix}
\begin{Bmatrix} F_1^* \\ F_2^* \\ \hline F_3^0 \\ F_4^0 \end{Bmatrix}
$$

$$\underset{[b]^*}{\uparrow} \qquad \underset{[b]^0}{\uparrow}$$

$$[\alpha] = \frac{l}{EA} \begin{bmatrix} 3 & & & & & & & & & \\ & 3\sqrt{2} & & & & & & & & \\ & & 3\sqrt{2} & & & & & & & \\ & & & 3 & & & & & & \\ & & & & 3 & & & & & \\ & & & & & 3 & & & & \\ \text{elements} & & & & & & 5 & & & \\ \text{not shown} & & & & & & & 5 & & \\ \text{are zero} & & & & & & & & 4 & \\ & & & & & & & & & 4 & \\ & & & & & & & & & & 3 \end{bmatrix}$$

$$[a] = \frac{l}{EA} \begin{bmatrix} 9.129 & 0 & 5.851 & 6.168 \\ 0 & 7.000 & -2.121 & -3.200 \\ 5.851 & -2.121 & 14.49 & 1.273 \\ 6.168 & -3.200 & 1.273 & 17.28 \end{bmatrix},$$

$$[a]_{22}^{-1} = \frac{EA}{l} \begin{bmatrix} 0.0695 & -0.00512 \\ -0.00512 & 0.0583 \end{bmatrix}$$

$$[a]^* = \frac{l}{EA} \begin{bmatrix} 4.904 & 1.849 \\ 1.849 & 6.160 \end{bmatrix}$$

$$\{P\} = \begin{bmatrix} 0.2651 & 0.9074 \\ -0.3750 & 0.1310 \\ 0.4330 & 0.1310 \\ -0.3059 & -0.09265 \\ -0.3059 & -0.09265 \\ 0.4627 & -0.1980 \\ 0.3847 & 0.1755 \\ -0.3293 & 0.1755 \\ 0.2634 & 0.8596 \\ -0.3076 & -0.1404 \\ -0.2304 & -0.1053 \end{bmatrix} \begin{Bmatrix} F_1^* \\ F_2^* \end{Bmatrix}$$

17.

$$\text{Partial answer } [a]^* = \frac{1}{E} \begin{bmatrix} 806.67 & & \text{Symm.} \\ 3.55 & 0.07 & \\ -2.85 & -0.05 & 0.085 \end{bmatrix}$$

18. Partial intermediate answers and final answer:

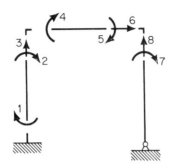

Element coordinates

$$[\alpha] = \frac{l}{12} \begin{bmatrix} \begin{bmatrix} 4 & -2 & 0 \\ -2 & 4 & 0 \\ 0 & 0 & 48 \end{bmatrix} & & \\ & \begin{bmatrix} 2 & -1 & 0 \\ -1 & 2 & 0 \\ 0 & 0 & 24 \end{bmatrix} & \\ & & \begin{bmatrix} 4 & 0 \\ 0 & 48 \end{bmatrix} \end{bmatrix},$$

$$[b] = \begin{bmatrix} -1 & -1 & l & 0 \\ 1 & 1 & -l & -l \\ 0 & 0 & 1 & 0 \\ 0 & -1 & l & l \\ 0 & 1 & 0 & -l \\ 0 & 0 & 0 & 1 \\ 0 & 0 & 0 & l \\ 0 & 0 & -1 & 0 \end{bmatrix}$$

$$[a] = \frac{l}{12}\begin{bmatrix} 12 & & & \text{Symm.} \\ 12. & 18 & & \\ -12l & -15l & 14l^2 + 96 & \\ -6l & -12l & 9l^2 & 14l^2 + 24 \end{bmatrix}$$

$$[a]^* = \frac{l}{12(115l^4 + 1680l^2 + 2304)}\begin{bmatrix} 156l^4 + 13248l^2 + 27648 & \text{Symm.} \\ -42l^4 + 8928l^2 + 27648 & 144l^4 + 11016l^2 + 41472 \end{bmatrix}$$

$$\{P\} = \frac{1}{115l^4 + 1680l^2 + 2304}\begin{bmatrix} -l^4 - 1392l^2 - 2304 & -13l^4 - 1320l^2 - 2304 \\ 25l^4 + 816l^2 + 2304 & -20l^4 + 168l^2 + 2304 \\ 114l^3 + 288l & 102l^3 + 360l \\ 90l^4 + 864l^2 & 20l^4 - 168l^2 - 2304 \\ 24l^4 - 576l^2 & 115l^4 - 33l^3 + 528l^2 + 2304 \\ -24l^3 + 576l & 33l^3 + 1152l \\ -24l^4 + 576l^2 & 33l^4 + 1152l^2 \\ -114l^3 - 288l & -102l^3 - 360l \end{bmatrix}\{F^*\}$$

19. System and element coordinates are taken the same as in the answer to problem 15.

$$\{P\} = -[b]^0[a]_{22}^{-1}[b]^{0T}\{\Delta\}$$

$[b]^0$ and $[a]_{22}^{-1}$ can be obtained from the solution to problem 15, and

$$\{\Delta\} = \begin{Bmatrix} 1 \\ \sqrt{2} \\ \sqrt{2} \\ 1 \\ 1 \\ 1 \\ \frac{5}{3} \\ \frac{5}{3} \\ \frac{4}{3} \\ \frac{4}{3} \\ 1 \end{Bmatrix} \times 3l \times 60°\text{F} \times 6 \times 10^{-6} \text{ in./in. }°\text{F}$$

21.

$$\{P\} = \begin{Bmatrix} 38.6 \\ -31.65 \\ 31.65 \\ -24.78 \\ 24.78 \\ 41.4 \\ -41.4 \\ 27.5 \end{Bmatrix}$$

(units of in.-lb)

22.

$$\{P\} = \begin{Bmatrix} -65.3 \\ -55.6 \\ 55.6 \\ 0 \end{Bmatrix}$$

(units of in.-lb)

Chapter 9

1. See answer to problem 3 Chapter 6.
2. Internal forces in the elements are shown in the figure.

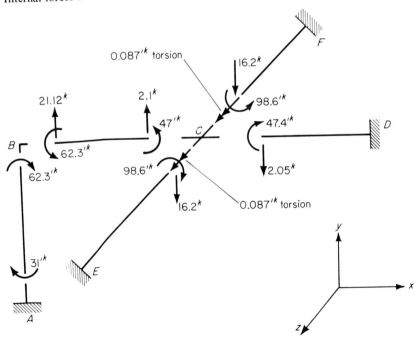

The moments and shears for members *AB*, *BC* and *CD* are in the *xy* plane. The moments and shears for members *EC* and *CF* are in the *yz* plane.

3.

$$\{P\}^f = \frac{1000}{8712} \begin{Bmatrix} -1224^{'k} \\ -1098 \\ 1098 \\ 1008 \\ -1008 \\ -1044 \end{Bmatrix}$$

4.

Element Coordinates

Element coordinates

$$\{P\}^f = \{P\}^0 + [\kappa][\beta][k]^{-1}(\{F\}^f - \{F\}^0)$$

$$= \begin{Bmatrix} -2 \\ 2 \\ -\frac{20}{3} \\ \frac{40}{3} \\ 0 \\ 0 \\ -2 \\ 2 \\ 12 \\ 12 \end{Bmatrix} + \begin{Bmatrix} 1.66 \\ 3.32 \\ 3.32 \\ 1.66 \\ 14.03 \\ 8.13 \\ 0.373 \\ 0.75 \\ 1.12 \\ 0.56 \end{Bmatrix} = \begin{Bmatrix} -0.34^{'k} \\ 5.32 \\ -3.35 \\ 15.00 \\ 14.03 \\ 8.13 \\ -1.63 \\ 2.75 \\ 13.12 \\ 12.56 \end{Bmatrix}$$

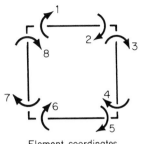

Element coordinates

$$\{P\}^f = \tfrac{1}{24}\begin{Bmatrix} 66 \\ 354 \\ 366 \\ 90 \\ 198 \\ 582 \\ 570 \\ 174 \end{Bmatrix}$$

16.

$$\{u\} = \begin{Bmatrix} 2.875 \\ -0.875 \\ -1.625 \\ 0.625 \end{Bmatrix}$$

9.75   5.25

9.75   5.25

$\{p\}^f$

2.25   0.75

2.25   0.75

17.

$$[k] = \begin{bmatrix} 36 \\ -6 & 8 \\ -6 & 2 & 12 \\ -6 & 0 & 2 & 8 \\ -36 & 6 & 6 & 6 & 72 \\ -6 & 2 & 0 & 0 & 0 & 12 \\ -6 & 0 & 2 & 0 & 0 & 2 & 16 \\ -6 & 0 & 0 & 2 & 0 & 0 & 2 & 12 \end{bmatrix}$$

18.

$$[\kappa]_\delta = \begin{bmatrix} EA/l & & & & & \text{Symm.} \\ 0 & 12EI/l^3 \\ 0 & -6EI/l^2 & 4EI/l \\ \hline -EA/l & 0 & 0 & EA/l \\ 0 & -12EI/l^3 & 6EI/l^2 & 0 & 12EI/l^3 \\ 0 & -6EI/l^2 & 2EI/l & 0 & 6EI/l^2 & 4EI/l \end{bmatrix}$$

$$[T]_\text{I} = [T]_\text{II} = \begin{bmatrix} \dfrac{\sqrt{3}}{2} & \tfrac{1}{2} & 0 \\ -\tfrac{1}{2} & \dfrac{\sqrt{3}}{2} & 0 \\ 0 & 0 & -1 \end{bmatrix}$$

$$[\kappa]_q = \begin{bmatrix} \dfrac{3}{4}\dfrac{EA}{l}+\dfrac{3EI}{l^3} & \dfrac{\sqrt{3}}{4}\dfrac{EA}{l}-\dfrac{3\sqrt{3}}{l^3}EI & -\dfrac{3EI}{l^2} & -\dfrac{3}{4}\dfrac{EA}{l}-\dfrac{3EI}{l^3} \\[2ex] & \dfrac{EA}{4l}+9\dfrac{EI}{l^3} & 3\sqrt{3}\,\dfrac{EI}{l^2} & -\dfrac{\sqrt{3}}{4}\dfrac{EA}{l}+\dfrac{3\sqrt{3}EI}{l^3} \\[2ex] & & 4EI/l & 3EI/l^2 \\[2ex] & \text{Symm.} & & \dfrac{3EA}{4l}+\dfrac{3EI}{l^3} \end{bmatrix}$$

$$\begin{bmatrix} -\dfrac{\sqrt{3}}{4}\dfrac{EA}{l}+\dfrac{3\sqrt{3}EI}{l^3} & -\dfrac{3EI}{l^2} \\[2ex] -\dfrac{EA}{4l}-9\dfrac{EI}{l^3} & 3\sqrt{3}\,\dfrac{EI}{l^2} \\[2ex] -3\sqrt{3}EI/l^2 & 2EI/l \\[2ex] \dfrac{\sqrt{3}EA}{4l}-3\sqrt{3}EI/l^3 & 3EI/l^2 \\[2ex] \dfrac{EA}{4l}+9\dfrac{EI}{l^3} & -3\sqrt{3}EI/l^2 \\[2ex] & 4EI/l \end{bmatrix}$$

19.
$$[k] = \begin{bmatrix} 28.35 & \text{Symm.} & \\ -0.3 & 7.2 & \\ -1.5 & 2 & 8 \end{bmatrix}$$

20.
$$\{u\} = \begin{Bmatrix} 1.033 \\ -0.0117 \\ 0.196 \end{Bmatrix}$$

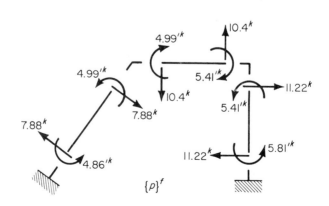

23. $\left\{\begin{matrix} u_e \\ u_f \end{matrix}\right\} = -\dfrac{1}{16{,}000} \left\{\begin{matrix} \frac{19}{6} \\ 3 \end{matrix}\right\}$

24.

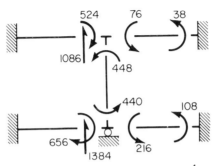

All numbers are to be multiplied by $\dfrac{1}{96{,}000}$

Chapter 10

1.

$$[k] = \begin{bmatrix} 5.454 & & \text{Symm.} \\ -1.909 & 6.821 & \\ -1.909 & -0.9346 & 6.821 \end{bmatrix}, \qquad [k]^{-1} = \begin{bmatrix} 0.2372 & & \text{Symm.} \\ 0.0769 & 0.1744 & \\ 0.0769 & 0.0454 & 0.1744 \end{bmatrix}$$

$$\{F\}^f = \left\{\begin{matrix} 8 \\ 0 \\ 3 \end{matrix}\right\}, \qquad \{F\}^0 = \left\{\begin{matrix} -10 \\ -1.0833 \\ -0.4167 \end{matrix}\right\}$$

$$\{u\} = [k]^{-1}(\{F\}^f - \{F\}^0) = \left\{\begin{matrix} 4.615 \\ 1.728 \\ 2.029 \end{matrix}\right\}$$

2.

$$[a]^* = \begin{bmatrix} 0.266 \\ 0.059 & 0.146 & & & & \text{Symm.} \\ 0.118 & 0.002 & 0.093 \\ 0.120 & 0.006 & 0.055 & 0.146 \\ 0.293 & 0.126 & 0.120 & 0.124 & 0.449 \\ 0.003 & 0.007 & \dfrac{0.5}{604 \times 12} & \dfrac{1.8}{604 \times 12} & 0.074 & 0.183 \end{bmatrix}$$

3. Answer is given in Figure 10.5(a) Section 10.3.

4.

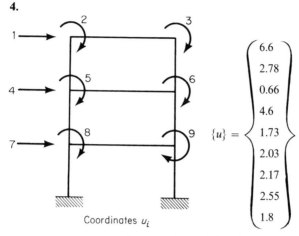

Coordinates u_i

$$\{u\} = \begin{Bmatrix} 6.6 \\ 2.78 \\ 0.66 \\ 4.6 \\ 1.73 \\ 2.03 \\ 2.17 \\ 2.55 \\ 1.8 \end{Bmatrix}$$

(answer within slide rule accuracy)

5. $\begin{bmatrix} 3.312 & -0.0312 \\ -0.0312 & 3.453 \end{bmatrix}$

6. $\begin{bmatrix} 3.58 & & & \text{Symm.} \\ 0.086 & 3.58 & & \\ 0.01 & 0.0055 & 3.6 & \\ 0.0055 & 0.01 & -0.06 & 3.6 \end{bmatrix}$

(answer within slide rule accuracy)

Chapter 11

1. Apply Betti's Law to Figures 11.1b and 11.1c and obtain relation 11.3.

2. $K_{ik} = \kappa_{ii}, \qquad C_{ik} = \dfrac{\kappa_{ki}}{\kappa_{ii}}$

$\overline{M}_{ik}$ and FES_{ik} are elements of $\{P\}^0$

M_{ik} and M_{ki} are elements of $\{P\}^f$

The relation $\kappa_{ik} = \kappa_{ki}$ is equivalent to relation 11.3.

3. Set $\overline{M}_{ik} = 0, \overline{M}_i = 0, FES_{ik} = 0, R_{ik} = 0$ in the equations summarized at the end of Section 11.2.

4. Answer is given at the end of Section 9.2.

5. See answer to problem 4 Chapter 9.

6. In problem 4 $\begin{Bmatrix} u_1 \\ u_2 \end{Bmatrix} = \frac{1}{32} \begin{Bmatrix} 35 \\ -49 \end{Bmatrix} = \begin{Bmatrix} 1.09 \\ -1.53 \end{Bmatrix}$

In problem 5 $\begin{Bmatrix} u_e \\ u_f \end{Bmatrix} = \begin{Bmatrix} 0.83 \\ 0.093 \end{Bmatrix}$ clockwise.

7. See answer to problem 16 Chapter 9.

8. See Figure 10.5, at the end of Section 10.3, for answers.

9. After four cycles of iteration:

$$M_{12} = 0, \; M_{21} = 88.20^{'k}, \quad M_{32} = 54.0^{'k}, \quad M_{43} = 46.78^{'k}, \; M_{54} = 156.6^{'k}$$
$$M_{23} = -88.20^{'k}, \; M_{34} = -53.8^{'k}, \; M_{45} = -46.78^{'k}.$$

10. (a) The results given are obtained by following the steps of Section 11.2 and using the newly defined quantities M'_{ik} and M''_{ik} for the columns of the first story.

(b) After two cycles of iteration: (sequence of iteration: story 1, joints 4, 5, 6, story 2, joints 7, 8, 9)

$$M_{14} = M_{25} = M_{36} = 0$$

$M_{41} = \quad 15^{'k}$	$M_{52} = \quad -72^{'k}$	$M_{63} = -31^{'k}$	$M_{74} = \quad 32^{'k}$
$M_{45} = -48^{'k}$	$M_{56} = \quad -45^{'k}$	$M_{65} = \quad 36^{'k}$	$M_{78} = -31^{'k}$
$M_{47} = \quad 36^{'k}$	$M_{58} = \quad -41^{'k}$	$M_{69} = -12^{'k}$	
	$M_{54} = \quad 145^{'k}$		

$$M_{85} = -41^{'k} \qquad M_{96} = -14^{'k}$$
$$M_{87} = \quad 68^{'k} \qquad M_{98} = \quad 14^{'k}$$
$$M_{89} = -26^{'k}$$

11. After four cycles of iteration: (same sequence of iteration as in Problem 10)

$$M_{14} = M_{25} = M_{36} = 0$$

$M_{41} = \quad 7^{'k}$	$M_{52} = \quad -76^{'k}$	$M_{63} = -32^{'k}$
$M_{45} = -41^{'k}$	$M_{56} = \quad -40^{'k}$	$M_{65} = \quad 43^{'k}$
$M_{47} = \quad 34^{'k}$	$M_{58} = \quad -40^{'k}$	$M_{69} = -12^{'k}$
	$M_{54} = \quad 156^{'k}$	

$M_{74} = \quad 30^{'k}$	$M_{85} = \quad -44^{'k}$	$M_{96} = -15^{'k}$
$M_{78} = -30^{'k}$	$M_{87} = \quad 70^{'k}$	$M_{98} = \quad 15^{'k}$
	$M_{89} = \quad -26^{'k}$	

$$\theta_4 = \frac{91.5}{E}, \; \theta_5 = -\frac{6.2}{E}, \; \theta_6 = \frac{9.6}{E}$$

$$\theta_7 = \frac{65}{E}, \quad \theta_8 = -\frac{16.4}{E}, \; \theta_9 = -\frac{10.9}{E}$$

θ's are in radians and $E = 30 \times 10^3$ ksi

First story displacement $= \dfrac{11,600}{E}$ inch to the right

Second story displacement $= \dfrac{15,365}{E}$ inch to the right

12. After six cycles of iteration:

$M_{12} = \quad 93^{'k}$	$M_{21} = \quad 93^{'k}$	$M_{31} = -107^{'k}$
$M_{13} = -93^{'k}$	$M_{24} = -93^{'k}$	$M_{34} = \quad 27^{'k}$
		$M_{35} = \quad 80^{'k}$

$$M_{42} = -107'^k \quad M_{53} = 20'^k$$
$$M_{43} = 27'^k \quad M_{56} = -64'^k$$
$$M_{46} = 80'^k \quad M_{57} = 44'^k$$

$$M_{64} = 20'^k \quad M_{75} = 55'^k \quad M_{86} = 55'^k$$
$$M_{65} = -64'^k \quad M_{78} = -55'^k \quad M_{87} = -55'^k$$
$$M_{68} = 44'^k$$

13. Approximate the distributed load by a series of concentrated loads, or use a numerical integration procedure in applying Betti's Law as discussed in Section 6.9.
14. $\overline{M}_{ik}$ values are given in Figure 11.12.
15. Answers are the same as in Figure 11.13 within slide rule accuracy.
16. See answer to problem 10.4.

Chapter 12

1.
$$\{P\} = \begin{Bmatrix} 214.3\,\text{lbs} \\ -14.3\,\text{lbs} \\ -285.7\,\text{lbs} \\ -28.6\,\text{lbs} \\ -28.6\,\text{lbs} \\ -457.2\,\text{lbs} \\ -542.8\,\text{lbs} \\ 457.2\,\text{lbs} \\ 542.8\,\text{lbs} \end{Bmatrix}$$
$$\{u\}^* = \frac{10^4}{7E} \begin{Bmatrix} 21.4 \\ 27.6 \end{Bmatrix}$$

2.
$$[a]^* = \frac{1}{E} \begin{bmatrix} 116.8 & 28 \\ 28 & 116.8 \end{bmatrix}$$

3.
$$\{P\} = \begin{Bmatrix} 227.9\,\text{lbs} \\ 22.1\,\text{lbs} \\ -122.1\,\text{lbs} \\ 44.2\,\text{lbs} \\ 44.2\,\text{lbs} \\ -411.6\,\text{lbs} \\ -288.4\,\text{lbs} \\ 411.6\,\text{lbs} \\ 288.4\,\text{lbs} \end{Bmatrix}$$
$$\{u\}^* = \frac{10^4}{E} \begin{Bmatrix} 3.2 \\ 1.868 \end{Bmatrix}$$

4.   In problem 1   In problem 3

$$q_1 = \quad 35.7 \text{ lbs/in.} \qquad\qquad q_1 = \quad 38 \text{ lbs/in.}$$
$$q_2 = q_4 = q_5 = \ -2.38 \text{ lbs/in.} \qquad q_2 = q_4 = q_5 = \quad 3.7 \text{ lbs/in.}$$
$$q_3 = -47.5 \text{ lbs/in.} \qquad\qquad q_3 = -20.4 \text{ lbs/in.}$$

5. $q_1 = 50 \text{ lbs/in.}$

$$q_2 = q_4 = q_5 = 0$$
$$q_3 = \ -50 \text{ lbs/in.}$$
$$P_6 = P_7 = -600 \text{ lbs} \qquad \{u\}^* = \frac{10^4}{E}\begin{Bmatrix} 4.2 \\ 4.2 \end{Bmatrix}$$
$$P_8 = P_9 = \quad 600 \text{ lbs}$$

For equal values of F_1^* and F_2^* each web and its two flanges can be analyzed as a separate beam with no coupling between the two beams.

9. Substitute $x_2 = b$, $x_3 = 0$, $y_3 = h$, $\lambda_3 = x_3 - x_2 = -b$ into Equation (12.22) and obtain

$$[\kappa] = \lambda_1 \begin{bmatrix} h^2 + \lambda_2 b^2 & & & & & \text{Symm.} \\ -h^2 & h^2 & & & & \\ -\lambda_2 b^2 & 0 & \lambda_2 b^2 & & & \\ (\lambda_2 + v)bh & -vbh & -\lambda_2 bh & \lambda_2 h^2 + b^2 & & \\ -\lambda_2 bh & 0 & \lambda_2 bh & -\lambda_2 h^2 & \lambda_2 h^2 & \\ -vbh & vbh & 0 & -b^2 & 0 & b^2 \end{bmatrix}$$

$$\lambda_1 = \frac{Et}{2bh(1-v^2)}, \qquad \lambda_2 = \frac{1-v}{2}$$

10. Substitute $x_2 = b$, $x_3 = b$, $y_3 = h$, $\lambda_3 = 0$ into Equation (12.22) and obtain

$$[\kappa] = \lambda_1 \begin{bmatrix} h^2 & & & & & \text{Symm.} \\ -h^2 & h^2 + \lambda_2 b^2 & & & & \\ 0 & -\lambda_2 b^2 & \lambda_2 b^2 & & & \\ 0 & \lambda_2 bh & -\lambda_2 bh & \lambda_2 h^2 & & \\ vbh & -bh(v + \lambda_2) & \lambda_2 bh & -\lambda_2 h^2 & \lambda_2 h^2 + b^2 & \\ -vbh & vbh & 0 & 0 & -b^2 & b^2 \end{bmatrix}$$

$$\lambda_1 = \frac{Et}{2bh(1-v^2)}, \qquad \lambda_2 = \frac{1-v}{2}$$

15.

$$[\alpha] = \frac{2bh}{Et} \begin{bmatrix} 1/h^2 & & \text{Symm.} \\ 0 & 2(1+v)/b^2 & \\ -v/bh & 0 & 1/b^2 \end{bmatrix}$$

$$[\kappa] = \frac{Et}{2bh(1 - v^2)}\begin{bmatrix} h^2 & & \text{Symm.} \\ 0 & (1 - v)b^2/2 & \\ vbh & 0 & b^2 \end{bmatrix}$$

16.

$$[\alpha] = \frac{2bh}{Et}\begin{bmatrix} 1/h^2 + 2(1 + v)/b^2 & & \text{Symm.} \\ -v/bh & 1/b^2 & \\ 1/h^2 & -v/bh & 1/h^2 \end{bmatrix}$$

$$[\kappa] = \lambda_1\begin{bmatrix} \lambda_2 b^2 & & \text{Symm.} \\ 0 & b^2 & \\ -\lambda_2 b^2 & vbh & h^2 + \lambda_2 b^2 \end{bmatrix}$$

$$\lambda_1 = \frac{Et}{2bh(1 - v^2)} \quad , \quad \lambda_2 = \frac{1 - v}{2}$$

17.

$$\{u\} = 10^{-4}\begin{Bmatrix} 10.08'' \\ -1.08'' \\ 11.25'' \\ 1.95'' \end{Bmatrix}$$

18.

$$\{\varepsilon\} = 10^{-6}\begin{Bmatrix} 0 \\ 8.41 \\ 0.9 \\ 9.4 \\ -1.88 \\ 0.89 \end{Bmatrix} \text{in./in.,} \quad \{\sigma\} = \begin{Bmatrix} 67 \\ 268 \\ 10.8 \\ 285 \\ 15 \\ 10 \end{Bmatrix} \text{lbs./in.}^2$$

19. The inverse of the 6 × 6 stiffness matrix was obtained with the aid of a computer.

$$\{u\} = 10^{-4}\begin{Bmatrix} 10.821'' \\ -2.157'' \\ 10.821'' \\ 2.157'' \\ 4.993'' \\ 0 \end{Bmatrix}$$

21. Use the following code to transform matrix $[\kappa]_q$ of Equation (12.45) to the stiffness matrix for the coordinates in the figure of problem 21

$$\boxed{1}\ \boxed{4}\ \boxed{2}\ \boxed{5}\ \boxed{3}\ \boxed{6}$$

The numbers in the boxes represent the coordinates in the figure of problem 21, and the positions of the boxes represent the corresponding coordinates in Figure 12.13b.

INDEX

M

Machine word, in computer, 5, 11
Matrices:
  addition of, 97–98
    program for, computer, 114
  conformable, for multiplication, 99
  equality of, 97
  introduction to, 87–90
  partitioned, 106
    addition and subtraction of, 107
    multiplication of, 107
  subtraction of, 98
    program for, computer, 114–115
Matrix:
  adjoint, 102, 103
  band (*see* Band matrix)
  column, 32
  definition, notation, 89, 95–97
  diagonal, 96
  flexibility (*see* Flexibility matrix)
  identity (unit), 96
  inverse of, definition, 102
    by cofactors, 102–104
    by Gauss-Jordan method, 111–113
    by partitioning, 110
  linearly dependent columns (or rows)
    of, 73, 74
  modal, 137
  nonsingular, 102
  null, 96
  positive definite, 149
  programming language, 116–117
    example, 118
  rank of, 102
  scalar multiplication of, 98
  singular, 102
  square, principal diagonal of, 96
  stiffness (*see* Stiffness matrix)
  symmetric, 96
  transposed, 96
  triangular, 125
Matrix algebra, 97, 98
Matrix of direction cosines, 253, 353
Matrix equations, 61, 104, 105
Matrix interpretive routine, computer program, 116, 117
Matrix multiplication, 98–100
  associative law in, 101
  commutative property in, 100

Matrix multiplication (*cont.*):
  continued products in, 101
  conformability check, 101
  distributive law in, 101
  geometric scheme for, 99, 100
  postmultiplication in, 100
  premultiplication in, 100
  program for, computer, 115
  properties connected with, 100, 101
  zero product in, 100
Maxwell-Betti theorem (*see* Betti's law)
Maxwell's reciprocity relationship, 143
Measurements, constrained (dependent), 34
  of displacement, 29, 30
  of force, 29, 30
  generalized (independent), 32, 33
Memory (*see* Computer, digital, memory)
Minor of a determinant, 90
Modal matrix, 137
Modulus of elasticity, 80
  shear, 81, 341
Moment area method, application of, 44, 45
Multistory frame, choice of redundants in, 219, 375

N

n-dimensional space, definition, 36
  vector in, 36
Newton, second law, 35
Nonlinear behavior, sources of, 41
Nonlinear structure, 38–41
Nonprismatic member, approximated by prismatic and tapered segments, 316–317
Nonsingular matrix, 102
Normal coordinates, 197–198
Null matrix, 96
Number system, 15–16
  base or radix in, 15
  binary, 16
  binary coded decimal, 18
  decimal, 15
    conversion to binary, 17, 27–28
  in general, 16
  octal, 15